CLUTCH & FLYW HANDBOOK

by Tom Monroe
Registered Professional Engineer;
Member, Society of Automotive Engineers

Contents

ANOTHER FACT-FILLED AUTOMOTIVE FROM HPBOOKS

PUBLISHER: Rick Bailey; EDITORIAL DIRECTOR: Tom Monroe, P.E., S.A.E.; SENIOR EDITOR: Ron Sessions, A.S.A.E.; ART DIRECTOR: Don Burton; BOOK DESIGN: Don Burton; TYPOGRAPHY: Cindy Coatsworth, Michelle Carter; DIRECTOR OF MANUFACTURING: Anthony B. Narducci: PHOTOS AND DRAWINGS: Tom Monroe, others as noted; COVER PHOTO: Don Winston.

Published by HPBooks, Inc.
P.O. Box 5367, Tucson, AZ 85703 602/299-4238
ISBN 0-912656-61-1 Library of Congress Catalog Number 77-20639
©1977 HPBooks, Inc. Printed in U.S.A.
5th Printing

Introduction

Slider clutches and super-sticky wrinkle-wall tires have been the biggest contributor toward putting Funny Cars into 230 MPH, 6 second E.T. brackets. Here's Dennis Fowler's car doing a burnout to heat up the tires for maximum adhesion. The clutch is a Crower-glide slider. *Slider photo courtesy Crower Cams & Equipment Co.*

To choose the right clutch and flywheel *system*, you first have to consider what it must do. That is, what your car is going to be used for: transportation, drag racing, road racing, oval-track racing or a combination of these? You must also know your car. How much power does your engine produce and at what RPM? You must know your car's weight, transmission and rear-axle ratios and the basic layout of the car. After these facts are clear in your mind, you can begin planning a clutch and flywheel *system.*

A lot of people go wrong by choosing the same set-up as the fastest car in their class. Now, this isn't the worst thing to do because it's hard to argue with success, but

when you do it on blind faith, you're the follower rather than the leader.

Your interest in this book indicates being the leader is your goal. Therefore, you must choose the best equipment available for your purpose.

This book will give you a complete understanding of clutches and flywheels, including the basic theory, how to install, adjust, service and use the equipment.

It's not always simple. There are three basic types of pressure plates with numerous combinations of static and centrifugal plate loads; multi-disc small-diameter clutch as-assemblies; various friction materials and sizes; clutch-linkage components and safety bellhousings.

The whole picture can become very confusing.

I am going to sort these things out, disect them, discuss the advantages and disadvantages of each type and make recommendations. I will describe each component right down to the rivets. When you've thoroughly digested this book, you'll have more working knowledge of the subject than has ever before been available to the public or even most racers. This book supplies information you'll need for designing some of your own components in addition to providing the "full-scoop" on things you will purchase. You will have all the information you'll need to design and install your own clutch and flywheel *system.*

One of 12 identically prepared IROC (International Race of Champions) Camaros. It is powered by a Traco 350 CID small-block Chevrolet which drives through an aluminum flywheel, organic-faced disc and a diaphragm pressure plate. *Clutch and flywheel photo courtesy Schiefer*

Willy T. Ribbs and Wally Dallenbach, Jr. dominated 1984 and '85 Trans-Am series in Roush-Protofab Capris. These and similar IMSA GTO cars must undergo many laps of being shifted without clutch failure or undue driver fatigue.

This is a Jeep? Actually it is a sand-drag racer. The object of this type of racing is to move as much sand in the shortest time possible—opposite from where you want to go.

Chapter One
CLUTCH BASICS

For these Funny Cars to accelerate, friction between the tires and the road surface is a must.

The clutch is a mechanical device placed in a power-transmission system to couple it together so it rotates as one unit. In an automobile or truck, the clutch couples the engine to the driveline. The clutch is usually located behind the engine. It has the basic function of connecting and disconnecting the engine to the driveline for the purposes of starting the engine while in gear, bringing the car to a stop while the engine is running, changing gears while the car is in motion and, what I consider the most important function, putting the car in motion from a dead stop. In this situation, the engine is rotating at relatively high RPM and the driveline is not turning. The clutch has to transmit sufficient engine torque to the driveline so the car is put in motion without stalling the engine. This little trick is done with *friction.*

What's bad for some is good for others—Friction is what we are told is bad for our engines. However without friction we wouldn't— couldn't go anywhere – clutches wouldn't engage and wheels would spin if they did. We could not even stand up or walk. Anyone who has slipped and fallen on his backside from stepping on a banana peel, wet grass, ice, snow or whatever, knows about a lack of friction. Generally defined, friction is the *resistance* to a relative motion between two bodies in contact. When you are walking, the force that

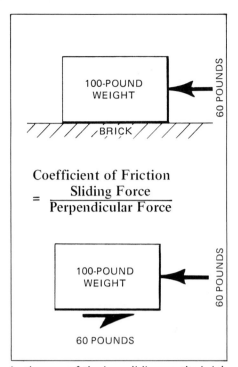

Coefficient of Friction

= $\dfrac{\text{Sliding Force}}{\text{Perpendicular Force}}$

In the case of the box sliding on the brick floor, the coefficient of friction is equal to the 60-pound sliding force divided by 100 pounds.

Coefficient of friction = $\dfrac{60}{100}$ = .60

For the box sliding on wood, the coefficient is .30, or $\dfrac{30}{100}$.

resists your foot from sliding out from under you is good old friction.

To dig into friction a little further, consider a box weighing 100 pounds. Say the box is wooden, it is sitting on a brick floor and once you start it moving, it takes 60 pounds to keep sliding it. If the same box were sitting on a wooden floor and it took 30 pounds to slide it after you started it moving, what determines the difference in the forces required to keep the same box sliding on the two surfaces? It is the *dynamic coefficient of friction*: The ratio of the force required to slide an object on a surface parallel to a surface and the force exerted perpendicular to the mating surfaces. The perpendicular force in this case is the weight of the box.

In the case of the box sliding on the brick floor, the dynamic coefficient of friction is equal to the sliding force of 60 pounds divided by 100 pounds, or 0.60. For the box sliding on wood, the dynamic coefficient is 30 pounds divided by 100 pounds, or 0.30.

Force required to begin relative motion is greater than the force needed to maintain motion when neglecting the effect of acceleration. In the example with the box, the 60- and 30-pound forces are required to keep the box sliding, however the force required to *start* sliding is greater. Called *breakaway force*, it is determined by the *static coefficient of friction*. These two forces or coefficients are directly related as described by the force-travel curve.

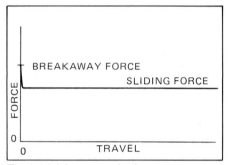

The initial force required to start an object sliding is more than the continued force required to keep it sliding. Called *breakaway force*, its magnitude is determined by the *static* coefficient of friction.

The static coefficient of friction is determined in the same manner as the dynamic coefficient:

STATIC COEFFICIENT OF FRICTION

= $\dfrac{\text{BREAKAWAY FORCE}}{\text{PERPENDICULAR FORCE}}$

The dynamic coefficient of friction is more important than the static coefficient of friction when applied to clutch peformance.

If there is sufficient friction, or clutch capacity available to engage the clutch when the engine is developing maximum torque, then there is enough static friction to resist slippage of the clutch. This means, if a car can accelerate when the clutch is slipping and the engine is developing peak torque, there is sufficient clutch capacity to keep the clutch engaged no matter what the engine power output after the clutch is once engaged.

As a result, static friction becomes secondary. Engaging and disengaging a clutch almost always involves sliding or *dynamic* friction. This is particularly true when a car is accelerated from rest. Therefore, when I refer to friction, or the coefficient of friction relative to clutches, I mean *dynamic friction*.

EARLY CLUTCHES

In the early stages of the automobile industry, engineers concerned themselves with engaging and disengaging the engine and the driveline. The cone clutch was one of the first used and it met this objective. This type of clutch has one very good characteristic—it has high torque capacity for a relatively small diameter. It does not require high pedal forces to operate it. A cone clutch has a high torque capacity because of the geometry of its design. The friction force it develops has a very large *moment arm*—the distance the force is applied from the center of rotation. However, you don't get something for nothing. The cone clutch has one very bad characteristic—it engages violently. If you have ever driven a car with a clutch that grabbed, you have an idea of how the cone clutch operates normally. As the clutch is engaged, the first indication of movement is a sudden lunge forward—or the engine dies.

Almost all early clutches used leather and cork as friction materials. They worked adequately in the days of low horsepower, but they would not be acceptable today.

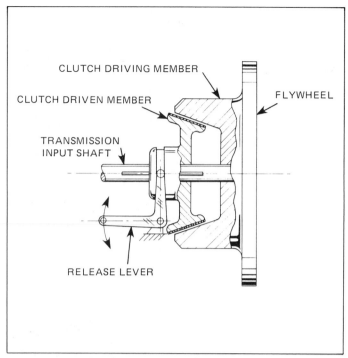

Early cone clutches fulfilled the primary objective of a clutch—transmit torque. They did this with a relatively small diameter and they featured violent engagement.

CLUTCH REQUIREMENTS

The head snapping caused by the cone clutch, the low heat-absorption capacity of leather as a friction material and other shortcomings of the early clutches provided the incentive that has gotten us where we are in present-day clutch design. The basic use of friction as the method of transmitting torque hasn't changed. What has changed is the efficiency of how torque is transmitted. Present-day clutches are assemblies of springs, pins, levers, rivets, stampings and castings. They are big and small and made of steel, aluminum, copper and numerous alloys. One thing you can be sure of—every part serves a definite purpose. Each part is joined together in an assembly to fulfill the requirements expected of a clutch. As with the cone clutch, transmitting torque is the primary function. The other requirements center around how torque is transmitted. For example, the clutch must provide smooth engagement and disengagement—not only for passenger comfort, but also to reduce shock loading on the driveline. The smoother clutch engagement is, the longer the driveline will last. Clutch durability is also important. The clutch must last a reasonable amount of time as related to the application. It is reasonable to expect a family-car clutch to last longer than one in a Pro-Stock drag-racing car. Clutch life related to the family car is in terms of miles driven—when applied to the Pro-Stocker, it is the number of 1/4-mile runs the clutch will withstand before it needs replacing.

No matter how smooth the clutch is, or if it lasts forever, it is no good if it won't fit into the confines of the particular automobile and driveline. For example, the larger the clutch is in

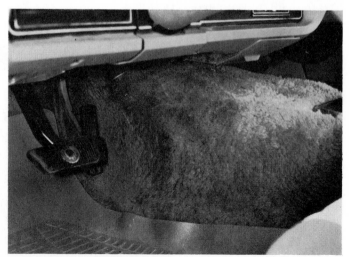

Transmission tunnels are for front-engined rear-drive cars. The largest portion of a tunnel is for clearance for the clutch or converter housing. Picture on the left is of a Toronado, a front-engined front-drive car with no transmission tunnel. A Mustang II is at right. If the Mustang clutch housing and transmission tunnel was much larger, there wouldn't be room for the passengers' feet.

your car, the larger the transmission tunnel must be because the largest part of the tunnel is for clutch-component clearance. Special small-diameter clutches are used in some racing applications to permit an engine to be set lower in a chassis for improved handling.

The final requirement has to do with how the clutch is operated. Because the clutch is manually operated, the force required to push on the pedal to operate the clutch must be held to a reasonable minimum—approximately 45 lbs. maximum is typical for a production *muscle-car.* Generally, increasing the capacity of a clutch also raises the pedal operating force. If the clutch capacity is high, there are ways to design the clutch or the clutch linkage to hold pedal forces to a minimum.

Depending on the application, compromises are made in some of the requirements—while additional stress is put on others. For example, if you want your engine to produce more power, you may have to give up something in the mileage or smoothness department. The same thing goes for clutches—if you want less pedal force you give up clutch capacity or just the opposite. The usual direction is toward increased capacity. I used to know a driver who had a short left leg because of high clutch-pedal forces in his truck. This sort of thing doesn't go over very well in the family hack, especially if the little lady drives it. So, when you are contemplating changing the clutch in your car, consider all the factors involved and how they affect one another . . . and who is going to drive the car.

"Grumpy" Jenkins isn't adjusting his carburetor for fuel economy just as his clutch isn't built for driver comfort. They are both set up for maximum acceleration in a quarter mile. Just the same, the driver must still be able to operate the clutch with ease.

Here's my wife trying to operate the clutch in my car. Her left leg isn't accustomed to a stiff clutch. Fortunately, we have the family wagon which keeps peace in the family.

TORQUE

Before talking about any mechanical device we need an explanation of *torque.* You hear about torque all the time in relation to engines. Well, what is it? Torque is a force which tends to twist something. It could be taffy, your arm or the crankshaft of an engine. It can be expressed in any number of ways so long as it involves a unit of force and of distance. For example, torque can be expressed in inch-ounces, inch-pounds, foot-pounds or meter-kilograms.

The best way to define torque is to explain what causes it. A force applied some distance from the center of rotation of something causes torque. Look at the sketch. A force **F** is applied some distance **D** from a center of rotation causing a torque **T** to occur. To find the value of the torque, multiply the force **F** by distance **D**, the lever arm. Now that we have the torque **T**, the lever arm and the force can be removed and replaced as shown on the other sketch. If the force is 50 pounds and the lever arm is two-feet long, torque is found this way:

Torque (T) = F X D
= 50 pounds X 2 feet
= 100 foot-pounds

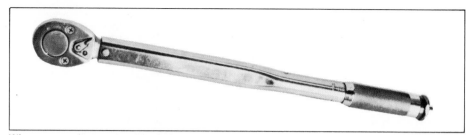

When torque is mentioned the first thing you probably think of is the output of an engine or a torque wrench like this one. Anyway, you know it has to do with a force trying to rotate something. Torque is usually expressed in inch-pounds or foot-pounds.

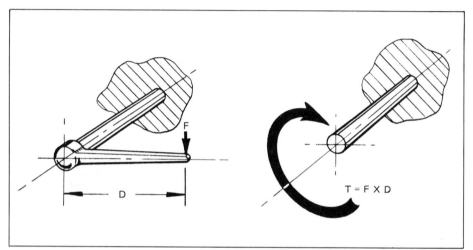

Torque is expressed as the multiple of a force applied to a lever arm a distance from a center of rotation where F is the force and D is the distance. Torque applied to the shaft is F X D which equals torque, T.

The clutch is merely a sophisticated clamp which transfers engine torque by squeezing a disc against the flywheel with a pressure plate. Organic-faced disc is shown with a Borg & Beck style pressure plate. *Photo courtesy Borg-Warner Corporation*

WHAT MAKES A CLUTCH?

Clutches are made up of two basic components—the *pressure plate* and *disc.* The disc is on the transmission input shaft and the pressure plate is attached to the flywheel. The clutch disc is between the pressure plate and flywheel. As the name infers, the pressure plate applies pressure or force to the disc as it clamps it against the flywheel. This force produces the friction to transfer engine torque to the driveline to propel the car. The pressure plate becomes the driving member and the disc becomes the driven member.

The clutch does not produce friction from weight as the box did in my first example. The principle is the same. Instead of using weight to obtain friction, the clutch uses force produced by a system of springs and levers in the pressure plate. The amount of friction produced is directly proportional to the amount of force applied perpendicular to the disc in direct proportion to the coefficient of friction between the disc and the pressure plate and flywheel.

We have run into something a little bit different with the disc and pressure plate than what I explained in the box example. A clutch disc has two friction surfaces. The box only had one. By modifying the example of the wooden box, the affect of two friction surfaces can be explained. Suppose two boxes are stacked on top of each other with a sheet of plywood in-between. The box on top weighs 100 pounds. What would be the force required to slide the sheet from between the two boxes if the boxes are restrained from moving?

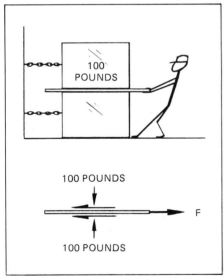

Force required to slide a sheet of plywood from between the boxes is twice the force required to slide the box on the plywood. This is because *two* friction forces are acting on the plywood sheet as opposed to *one* on the box. Illustration replaces objects with the forces acting on the plywood.

The previous example using the 100-pound box sliding on a wooden floor had one friction surface. The force required to slide the plywood sheet from between the two boxes, as shown in the sketch, is resisted by friction forces on both sides. The bottom drawing illustrates this. As the sheet is sliding, a force is developed on the top and the bottom and they are equal if we assume the weight of the plywood is zero. It isn't, but I have to make this kind of assumption to keep the example simple. The coefficient of friction for wood on wood is approximately .30 and the resulting force required to slide the plywood sheet is equal to this figure multiplied by the perpendicular force multiplied by the number of friction surfaces or:

F = 0.30 X 100 pounds X 2 = 60 pounds

When applied to the clutch, the pressure plate is sliding on the back side of the disc and the flywheel is sliding on the front side. The resulting forces are equal and resist relative motion between the engine and the driveline. The magnitude of these forces is determined by the amount of pressure or force exerted on the disc by the pressure plate.

T_e is the engine torque and T_r is the torque transmitted to the input shaft of the transmission as a result of friction at the clutch disc. The sketch omits the pressure plate and flywheel and replaces them with arrows simulating friction they exert on the disc. F_f is the friction at the flywheel and F_p is the friction at the pressure plate. If there is slippage between the disc and the pressure plate and flywheel, T_r and T_e will be equal, but the RPM of the two shafts will be different. Normally, the engine crankshaft will be turning faster. Because power or energy increases with torque and RPM, some of the engine's power is being lost between the output end of the crankshaft and the input shaft of the transmission.

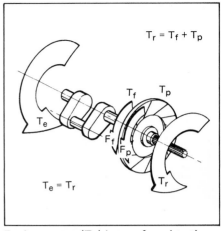

Engine torque (T_e) is transferred to the transmission input shaft by friction on the clutch facings (T_f and T_p) produced by clamping the disc to the flywheel with the pressure plate. When the clutch slips, torque produced by the engine is the same as that transferred to the transmission. However, power is lost in the form of heat due to the slipping.

This brings us to a very important law of physics, that of the Conservation of Energy. This law states, "Energy cannot be created or destroyed, although it can be changed from one form to another." Well, if the power/energy being produced by the engine is greater than that being transmitted to the transmission, where did the missing power/energy go? The clutch knows because it gets very hot when slipped and *heat is energy*. One of the biggest enemies of the clutch is heat and if slipped excessively, heat generated by friction cannot be dissipated fast enough, resulting in the disc losing effectiveness or being destroyed.

Chapter Two
CLUTCH DISCS

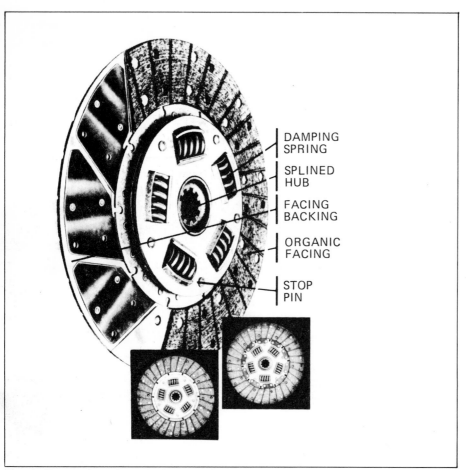

Clutch disc consists of two basic assemblies, the hub and the friction facing. The hub is made up of a forged center section with or without radially located springs and stampings. Stampings and rivets hold everything together. The facing assembly consists of the facing which is attached to a marcel and is then riveted to the hub assembly or is bonded or riveted directly to the hub. *Photo courtesy Zoom.*

DAMPING SPRING

SPLINED HUB

FACING BACKING

ORGANIC FACING

STOP PIN

Three basic types of clutches are available for passenger cars: Borg & Beck, Long and diaphragm styles. The major difference between these clutch types is in the design of the pressure plates. All-out high-performance clutches are modifications of these three basic styles. As for the discs themselves, they are basically the same except for the addition or deletion of parts and the use of different materials for different purposes. The basic clutch disc is made up of the hub, hub plates, torsional-damping springs, marcel and the friction facings, plus the rivets to hold it together.

The forged-steel hub is splined to match the transmission-input shaft. Splines permit the disc to float fore and aft on the transmission shaft so the clutch will engage and disengage properly. Also, the splines transfer engine torque to the transmission-input shaft, thus serving double duty. Splines range from one inch to 1-3/8 inches in diameter and have from 10 to 26 splines.

Depending on the manufacturer, the hub has five or eight rectangular slots located radially at the outer periphery of the hub. These slots contain coil springs. Coil springs in the hub provide a cushioning device. The springs compress to allow angular movement of the outer section of the disc relative to the hub or the inner portion of the disc. This causes a sliding motion and friction in the disc hub and, consequently helps damp engine and driveline vibrations. Because different engines and drivelines have varying characteristics, these springs must be suited to the particular automobile and application. You can see this by comparing several discs. The springs are usually different for different engines. They have varying diameters, number of coils and wire sizes. And still another coil spring usually resides inside the primary spring you can see. This provides additional damping and stiffness. The springs also soften clutch engagement. Damping is assisted by friction between the inner and outer portions of the sprung-hub assembly as they rotate relative to each other.

The forged-steel hub is located between two stampings which make up the driving portion of the hub—the driven portion is the splined forged hub. The two stampings making up the driving

THANKS

To cover the subject of clutches and flywheels, I had to go to the people in the industry to answer questions and to get updated on the latest "state of the art." Their help was limitless, and without it this book would not be complete. I especially thank: Earl Richey of Schiefer who reintroduced me to the world of clutches at the NHRA World Final drag races and supplied me with much information and a mountain of parts for many of the photos used throughout the book. Red Roberts and Dennis Bress of McLeod loaned more parts for the same purpose and answered question upon question over a period of several months. When it came to slider clutches, Frank Carstenson of Hays and Merv Scott of Scott Industries sorted me out by beginning and ending with the admonition that there is no one answer. Finally, Cliff Ridenour of Borg Warner supplied me with a wealth of engineering information and data and answered many detailed questions.

At the risk of leaving someone out, others who helped are Ken Nelson and Larry Hoofnagle of Borg-Warner, Rocky Bellino of Mr. Gasket, Ray Bickar of RAM, Dick Wells of SEMA, Jack Hart of NHRA, Jack Wells and Arnie Anderson of Ford Motor Company, Dick Sloan of S.K. Wellman, Kurt Waters of ARC Industries, Jim Culbert of CAE, Ed Stoffels of Quarter Master Industries, Tom Jakobowski of Chrysler, Dave Linderman of AMC, Gib Hufstader of Chevrolet, Warren Tihart of Direct Connection, Bob Jewell of Lucas Industries, Bill Neal of Neal Industries, Roman Kuzma and Carl Haas of Carl Haas Automotive Imports, Mike Dick of Weber, Wayne Evans of Perfection American, Dave Antel of Friction Products and Bob Molinari of Crower.

side have matching windows to locate and contain the coil springs. Assembling the complete hub is done by sandwiching the springs and the driven hub between the two stampings and riveting the stampings together.

The rivets holding the hub assembly together serve other purposes. They space the hub stampings apart preventing the forged hub from being clamped too tightly, but more importantly, they act as stops for the hub. Because of this they've acquired the name *stop pins*. As the hub is torqued approaching full compression of the coil springs, the forged hub is stopped by the stop pins. This prevents the springs or the hub assembly from being damaged.

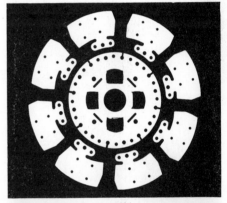

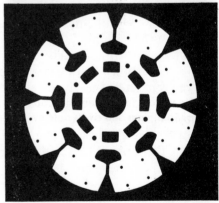

Two discs representing the conventional clutch disc styles. The top one has a separate hub disc with an approximate thickness of 0.050" with separate marcel cushion springs riveted to the disc. Marcel cushions range in thickness from 0.022" to 0.040" depending on the application. Bottom one has marcels integral with the hub. This is not as complex, however the marcels must be the same thickness as the hub. *Photos courtesy Borg-Warner Corporation*

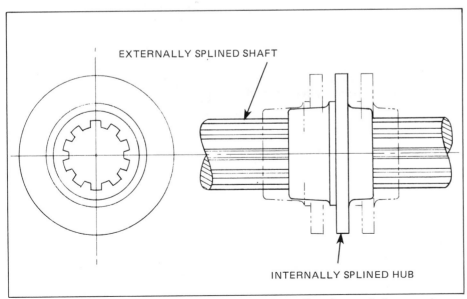

Internal splines in the disc hub permit the clutch disc to *float* fore and aft on mating external splines on the transmission input shaft. This is so the clutch will fully disengage and can transmit torque to the shaft when it is engaged.

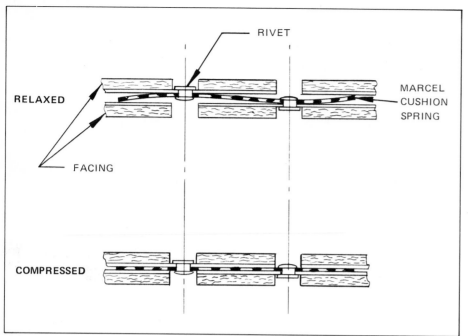

RIVET

RELAXED

MARCEL
CUSHION
SPRING

FACING

COMPRESSED

Marcel cushion compresses during engagement to soften clutch engagement and increase driveline life.

FRICTION MATERIAL ATTACHMENT

There are two basic ways to attach friction material (facing or lining) to the disc hub—bonding and/or riveting. When the bonding method is used, one of the hub discs is extended to the outside diameter of the clutch disc. The disc is flat and the friction material is bonded to the disc with resin as it is heated and compressed. Another method of bonding involves bonding the friction material to thin steel or aluminum backing plates matching the friction-material diameter. These facing assemblies are riveted to the disc or the *marcel*. Friction material may or may not have the metal backing for riveting. In either case, the friction facing is riveted to the marcel or disc through countersunk holes in the facings. Clearance holes are provided in the opposite facing for the rivets.

MARCELS

The *marcel* is a very large-diameter segmented-wave washer. It is made up of separate segments riveted to the hub assembly or is an extension of one of the discs which makes up one-half of the stamped portions of the hub. The marcel separates the flywheel and pressure-plate facings. This provides smooth clutch engagement. As the pressure plate contacts the disc, torque is transferred to the disc smoothly as the marcel becomes fully compressed—at which time the clutch approaches full engagement. Drive-line life and passenger comfort directly benefit from the marcel.

All-out competition drag-racing discs do not use marcels. Without it the time lag required to compress the marcel is eliminated, thus the jump off the starting line can be quicker. Driver or passenger comfort and driveline life are considered not important.

Friction facings are attached to the disc by riveting, bonding or a combination of riveting and bonding. Discs pictured represent these three methods. From top to bottom: bonded, riveted and bonded and riveted only.

ORGANIC FRICTION FACINGS

There are two basic types of friction materials—*organic* and *metallic*. Organic material is made up of several ingredients, all contributing to friction-material performance. Basic ingredients are asbestos, cotton, brass, rubber and phenolic resin. Although asbestos is the main friction-producing agent, the others do have an effect. The things holding everything together make up what is called the *binder*. They include the resin and the rubber. Cotton is included to hold the asbestos fibers together during manufacturing. After manufacturing, the cotton goes along for the ride.

Copper in the disc is in thin-wire form to serve three very important functions. First, it gives the disc the necessary strength to resist the centrifugal forces trying to burst the material. High-performance discs are tested to ensure burst capabilities up to 10,000 RPM. Next, copper acts as an abrasive to keep the metal friction surfaces free of glaze and foreign material that tend to form and reduce the performance of the clutch. Finally, the copper acts as a heat sink—it helps cool the disc by absorbing and dissipating heat.

Two types of organic facings are available. This may soon change to "were" available. The basic ingredients making up the two facings are about the same. The difference is in how they are manufactured. The first and most common facing is *molded* and is so called. The second is a woven lining sometimes refered to as a *pinwheel* lining. The woven lining is made up of continuous strands of cotton, asbestos and copper fibers. Woven linings are in jeopardy of being discontinued due to a problem with meeting government air-pollution standards. As the fibers are being woven, small fibers tend to break off and float in the air. Due to this problem manufacturers are discontinuing this method of manufacturing.

I broke this facing to show the thin copper-wire strands which increase facing burst strength, absorb heat and act as a scouring pad to keep the pressure plate and flywheel friction surfaces clean.

Friction facings for OEM—original equipment manufacturer—use are drilled and counterbored for riveting directly to the marcel springs. High-performance facings are bonded first to thin steel or aluminum backings prior to drilling and counterboring. This provides additional strength for the facing and a better method of mounting it to the disc. Clearance holes for the rivets are drilled, followed by counterboring. The counterbore is taken to the metal backing so the rivets will pull down on it. The counterbore also sets the installed height of the rivet lower than the friction surface of the disc plus the amount of wear that would

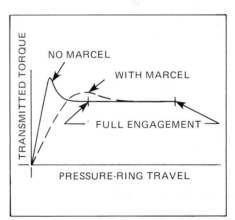

Marcel reduces driveline loading during engagement, increasing driveline service life as a result. Marcel limits the rate of torque build-up by progressively engaging the disc and substantially reducing shock loads transmitted to the driveline.

constitute a wornout disc. It is always risky to wait until the disc is worn down to the rivet heads—a ruined flywheel and pressure plate may result

When facings are bonded only, rather than bonding them to a backing and then bonding them to the disc, the facing is bonded directly to the disc. This method eliminates the weight of rivets and backing plates. The marcel cannot be used with bonded-only clutch discs, therefore engagement tends to be rather harsh and these disc types are prone to severe chatter during engagement.

Friction coefficients for organic linings vary from 0.24 to 0.38. The majority fall in the area of .30 and I'll use this average figure for calculations. Light-duty linings have a maximum operating temperature of 400°F (204°C) and heavy-duty linings go as high as 550°F (288°C).

These temperatures are known as *bulk temperatures*—the temperature of the *inside* of the material. The surface temperature of a facing—where it contacts the pressure plate and flywheel—can exceed 1000°F (538°C). This occurs when the clutch is being slipped. If such temperatures are maintained for a sustained period of time, the facing may fail to produce sufficient friction to transmit torque or may be destroyed completely.

Heat will reduce the strength of the lining so it will separate and tear apart. Organic facings tend to lose their friction-producing capability within a matter of a few degrees, say 5°F (1.8°C). The material may have a friction coefficient of .30 at a bulk temperature of 525°F (274°C) one second and a split second later, this may drop to .20 at 530°F (277°C). The disc heating rate will then increase dramatically because of increased slipping speeds.

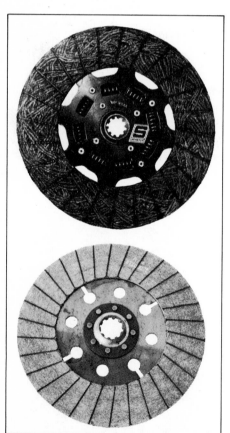

Two discs represent two types of facings. At top is a *pinwheel* lining made up of continuous strands of asbestos and cotton. At bottom is a *molded* facing. It uses shorter strands of asbestos and cotton. *Photo courtesy Schiefer*

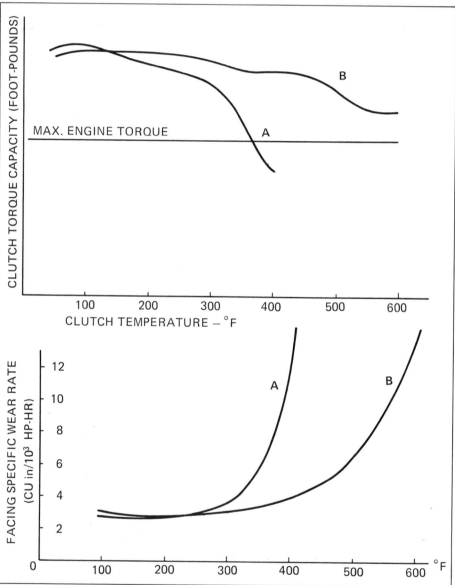

Two curves illustrate the effect of facing-material temperature on clutch torque capacity, or friction coefficient and facing wear rate. Facing A is a light-duty material as found in the typical passenger car and B is a heavy duty, high-performance facing. As facing temperatures increase, facing A's coefficient of friction degenerates to a point where it is incapable of transmitting maximum engine torque. Material B maintains sufficient friction to the point of destruction. Wear rates follow the same basic pattern. Accelerated wear of material A begins at a lower temperature than material B and at a much faster rate. *Curves courtesy Ford Motor Company.*

Here are two riveted organic facings failing due to high centrifugal loading while being tested under laboratory conditions. Discs are first heated to a temperature of 550°F (288°C) and then spun with an air-turbine until failure occurs—about 12,000 RPM. These photographs were taken with a high-speed camera tripped by wires surrounding each disc. Left photograph illustrates the classic high-RPM failure as the facing fails in tension between two rivet clearance holes. Another disc is shown as its facing is breaking up. *Photos courtesy Ford Motor Company*

CENTRIFUGAL FORCE

When a body rotates about any axis other than one at its center of mass, it exerts an outward force called *centrifugal force* upon anything which keeps it from going in a straight line. The heavier the weight or the faster it is rotated, the more the centrifugal force will be. To try this out for yourself, tie a rock or something weighing about a half a pound to a strong piece of string and swing it around in a circle. Make sure you are out in the open so if it lets go, you don't find out the damage centrifugal force can do. You'll notice, as the rock is rotated faster and faster, the greater the force becomes on the string. This is because centrifugal force becomes greater by the square of the speed at which it is rotated, shown by the equation:

$$\text{CENTRIFUGAL FORCE} = \frac{\text{MASS} \times \text{VELOCITY}^2}{\text{RADIUS}}$$

Where:

MASS is the weight of the object in pounds divided by the acceleration of gravity or 32.2 feet per second per second.

VELOCITY is in feet per second and the

RADIUS is the distance of the object from the center of rotation in feet. For a more usable equation:

$$\text{CENTRIFUGAL FORCE} = 0.0000284 \times \text{WEIGHT} \times \text{RADIUS} \times \text{RPM}^2$$

Where:

WEIGHT is in pounds.
RADIUS is in inches.
RPM is revolutions per minute.

To illustrate the effect of centrifugal force, consider an object weighing one pound located 6 inches from the center of rotation at 2000 RPM, the centrifugal force is:

$$\text{CENTRIFUGAL FORCE} = 0.0000284 \times 1 \text{ POUND} \times 6 \text{ INCHES} \times (2000)^2 = 682 \text{ POUNDS}$$

To get the real effect of centrifugal force, let's see what the increase is when the one-pound weight is rotated at 10,000 RPM.

$$\text{CENTRIFUGAL FORCE} = 0.0000284 \times 1 \text{ POUND} \times 6 \text{ INCHES} \times (10,000 \text{ RPM})^2 = 17,040 \text{ POUNDS}$$

By increasing the RPM five times, centrifugal force is increased to 25 times the original amount.

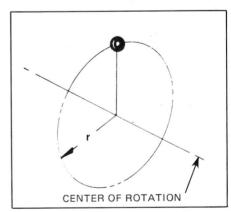

When a body rotates about any axis other than one at its center of mass, it exerts an outward force called *centrifugal force* upon anything which keeps it from going in a straight line.

15

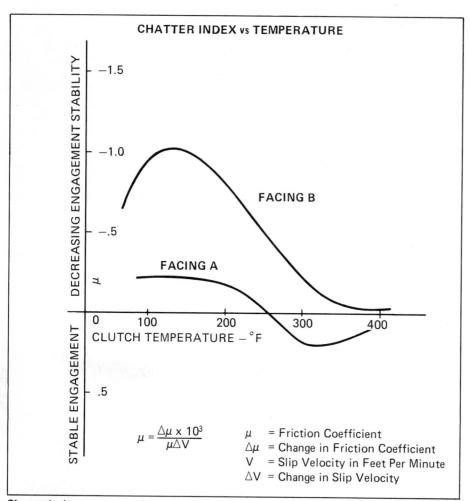

CHATTER INDEX vs TEMPERATURE

$$\mu = \frac{\Delta\mu \times 10^3}{\mu\Delta V}$$

μ = Friction Coefficient
$\Delta\mu$ = Change in Friction Coefficient
V = Slip Velocity in Feet Per Minute
ΔV = Change in Slip Velocity

Chatter Index represents the tendency of a clutch friction material to chatter or grab during engagement. Data used to generate these curves is obtained in laboratory testing by clamping the test material against a rotating surface at a given load and monitoring temperature, time, velocity and torque. The two materials shown are the same as graphed on page 14. As you can see, the high-performance facing B is more susceptible to chatter when relatively cold, but becomes more stable with an increase in temperature as does facing A. Stability is accompanied by a concurrent drop in the coefficient of friction. *Curve courtesy Ford Motor Company*

Radial grooves in friction facing act as *conduits* to let worn facing material escape from between the facings and the pressure plate and flywheel. They circulate air to help cool the clutch and force the disc away from the flywheel during disengagement.

Radial grooves in the friction material provides channels to let worn facings and foreign material escape from between the friction surfaces to reduce facing contamination. They also serve two other important functions. Air is channeled through the grooves for cooling the clutch and to assist in separating the facings from the flywheel and pressure-plate friction surfaces.

METALLIC FRICTION FACINGS

Two types of metallic friction materials are available—the full-circle sintered-iron type and the ceramic-copper pad type. Both are manufactured by sintering.

Sintered-iron and bronze facings— Sintered-iron facings are made from iron powder. Graphite powder is included to act as a dry lubricant to prevent clutch chatter and increase facing-wear resistance. Finally, silica sand, aluminum oxide, titanium oxide or iron oxide is added ·to keep the friction surfaces clean by a scouring action.

After the powder mixture is placed in a die, it is compressed at a pressure of 20 tons per square inch, reducing the volume of the powder approximately 75 percent. If the powder had a volume of four cubic inches prior to compressing, it ends up with one cubic inch afterwards. This process gives the part its shape.

The sintering process and assembly of the friction facings to the disc are done simultaneously. The facings are placed in a press with a copper-coated steel disc between them. The copper coating assists in the fusing process. A pressure of 250 to 300 pounds per square inch is applied to the stack of components while they are heated to a temperature ranging between 650°F—1800°F (343°C to 982°C). This combination sinters or fuses the powder particles together while fusing the friction facings to the steel disc. The friction surfaces on the disc are then surface ground to ensure parallelism, then they are grooved. The grooves have the same purpose as those in organic linings.

Pre-measured amount of powder is compressed under 40,000 pounds per square inch pressure to reduce its volume to 75 percent to make sintered facings like these.

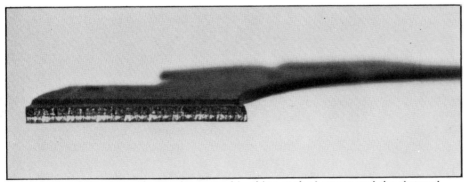

Section of a sintered-iron facing shows steel backing at the bottom and the sintered iron at the top.

thermal coefficients of expansion of the iron facing and the steel clutch disc.

Thermal coefficients of expansion indicate the amount materials grow when heated. There are a few odd ones which shrink when heated. In this case they both grow, but steel grows more than the iron facing. Because the two materials are rigidly fastened together, internal stresses build up, resulting in warped discs. To solve the problem, radial slots are cut through the discs every 60 degrees—fewer would not prevent warpage and any more are not required. Each slot ends in a hole near the center to prevent the disc from cracking, which could allow a section to break out. These slots are in addition to the grooves I mentioned earlier. Organic facings that do not use a marcel and are bonded directly to the steel disc do not require slots because the lining is flexible enough to comply to the expansion and contraction of the steel. Unlike organic discs, full-circle sintered discs are not available with sprung hubs. This is due to the type of application which will be discussed later on in the chapter.

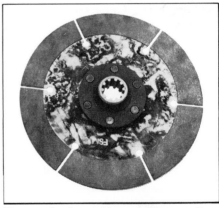

Slots cut in sintered-iron and bronze discs prevent warpage from occurring due to the difference between the *thermal coefficients* of expansion of the steel disc and the sintered facing. As the two materials are heated, one tries to grow faster than the other—like the bi-metal strip in a automatic choke. If the disc isn't relieved by slotting, it will warp.

The advantage of metallic friction linings over the organic type is the ability to handle very high temperatures, the number one enemy of clutches. The coefficient of friction of iron discs starts out at around .35 and remains fairly constant to about 400°F (204°C). The coefficient then starts to drop off slightly, getting down to .25 in the 1200° to 1300°F (649°C to 704°C) temperature range. Sintered-iron discs will continue to transmit torque right up to the melting point of iron, 2600°F (1427°C). Reaching this temperature is unlikely, however temperatures between the facings and the flywheel and pressure-plate surfaces reach 1200°F (649°C) easily. Flash temperatures of 2600°F (1427°C) are known to occur in slider applications.

Sintered-iron facings are mostly used full-circle the same as organic linings—they cover 360 degrees of the periphery of the disc. When the first discs of this type were used, they warped. The problem was caused by the differences in the

Here seven separate sintered-iron pucks are sintered directly to a steel backing. This keeps disc weight at a minimum and allows use of a conventional marcel. *Photo courtesy S. K. Wellman*

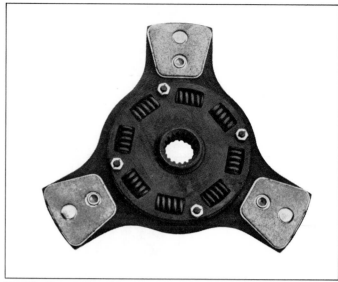

RAM's three-point disc uses six ceramic-copper buttons which give the high heat resistance of a metallic disc and the light weight of an organic disc. It is available as shown with a sprung hub but not with marcel cushion springs.

Sintered-iron discs are available in two other forms, both of which are sintered directly on backings or *substrates* similar to the backings used with bonded organic facings. After the facings are sintered and ground, they are attached to discs by riveting. One facing is full-circle just like the directly sintered disc, the only difference being the intermediate step of sintering on a backing and riveting to the disc. The only advantage here is that the facings can be replaced without having to replace the complete disc assembly.

One type of sintered-iron facing, introduced in 1976 by McLeod, is made up of a series of seven *pucks* evenly spaced around a backing to which they are sintered. The facings are assembled to the discs with or without marcels and sprung hubs are used exclusively, unlike the full-circle type.

Ceramic-Copper Pads—Ceramic-copper pads are basically the same as sintered iron except copper-based powder is used in place of iron. They are just as the name suggests, pads rather than a full circle. They are approximately five square inches in area and shaped like 2-1/4-inch segments of a circular disc. The ceramic copper is sintered directly to copper-coated plates which are drilled and counterbored for riveting to a disc. They can be arranged in any number of patterns, however, only three are commonly used. The first, and most common, is a three-pointed-star pattern. Three pads per side are riveted directly on a disc which has the area removed between the pads to lighten the disc assembly. These discs are available with or without sprung hubs. The other type uses six pads per side with a solid hub. These discs are available from RAM Automotive. Schieffer offers solid-hub discs with four pads per side.

The number of pads used depends on the application. The ceramic-copper material likes heat just like the sintered iron and can operate effectively up to 1400° F (760° C).

It is interesting to note that metallic linings have been used for years in the heavy-equipment industry and have just been recently put to use in high-performance applications.

Chapter Three
PRESSURE PLATES

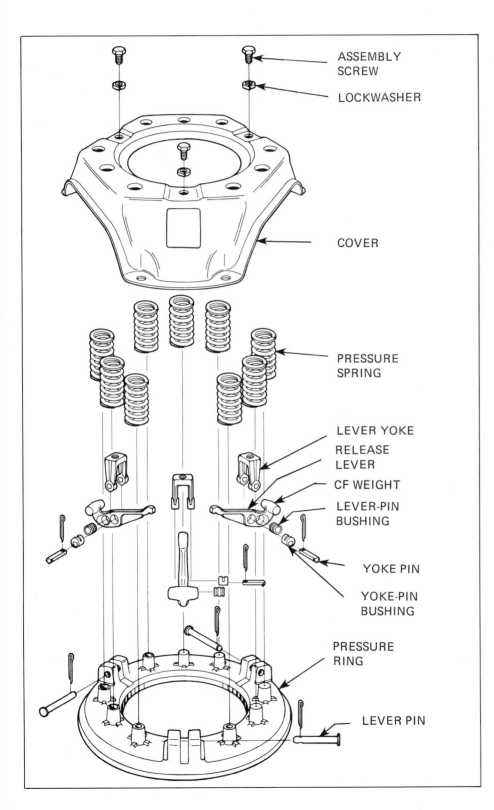

ASSEMBLY SCREW

LOCKWASHER

COVER

PRESSURE SPRING

LEVER YOKE

RELEASE LEVER

CF WEIGHT

LEVER-PIN BUSHING

YOKE PIN

YOKE-PIN BUSHING

PRESSURE RING

LEVER PIN

Having dissected the driven portion of the clutch, let's do the same thing to the driving part—the pressure plate. The pressure plate supplies sufficient force or pressure to the disc so enough friction is developed to transmit engine torque to the driveline. As I said earlier, the clutch has to: Transmit torque positively and smoothly, engage and disengage fully, be durable, fit the space, be reasonably easy to operate and be cost-effective.

The three basic clutch designs—Borg & Beck, Long and the diaphragm—are all capable of operating within these parameters. If they weren't, they wouldn't have survived the requirements of the automobile manufacturers even though each company seems to have its preference. For example, Ford has historically used the Long-style clutch, but is switching over to the diaphragm, Chrysler and American Motors use the Borg & Beck style. General Motors uses the diaphragm. When considering high-performance applications, certain concessions have to be made in clutch design and performance, however the three basic styles are all used.

Generally, all pressure plates have the same component design and the parts are assembled similarly.

Long pressure plate is distinguished by nine pressure springs and three forged-steel release levers with integral centrifugal weights extending outside the cover. When the release levers are depressed for disengagement, they pivot at the pressure-ring and at yokes attached to the cover. *Drawing Courtesy ACE Jameson.*

High-performance Long pressure plate with the cover removed. It has a 0.156"-thick steel cover, a ductile cast-iron pressure ring and insulators between the springs and pressure ring.

You can spot a Long pressure plate intended for high-RPM use by the absence of centrifugal weights at the ends of the release levers (arrow). *Photo courtesy RAM Automotive.*

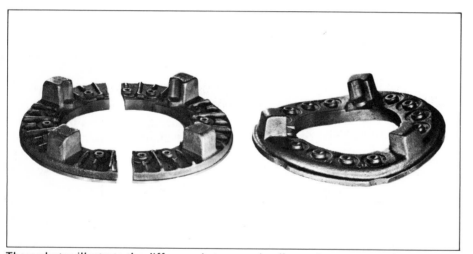

These photos illustrate the difference between a ductile cast-iron pressure ring and one made of grey cast iron. The grey-cast-iron breaks before it bends—and with a lot less force. Ductile pressure-ring bent at 20,000 pounds. Only 4,000 pounds broke the grey cast-iron one. *Photos courtesy Zoom.*

LONG PRESSURE PLATE

To keep things from getting all tangled up, let's look at one style of pressure plate at a time. In my estimation, the Long style is the easiest to understand so I'll start with it.

The pressure plate is made up of the cover, pressure ring, springs, linkages and levers. The cover is attached to the flywheel and transmits torque and pressure to the pressure ring through springs, levers and linkages. The cover is a steel stamping made from 0.125- to 0.156-inch-thick material. High-performance clutches use the thicker material. From the flywheel-mounting surface to the top of the cover, Long covers measure about 3.0 inches. The covers are shaped to make them stronger. Shape is a much more effective way to get strength than increasing material thicknesses because it does it without adding weight or material cost. Six mounting holes are unevenly spaced on a bolt circle diameter of

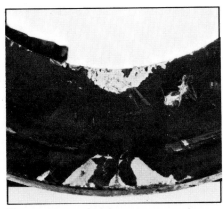

To prevent an aluminum pressure-ring friction surface from galling, a heat shield must be added. The dark area on this pressure ring is a plasma-sprayed heat shield which was damaged when the slider it was a part of exited the car at high RPM. Plasma-sprayed heat shields are ground to approximately 0.015" thickness after molten steel is applied by a spraying process.

Springs made from high-nickle silicon-steel alloy wire have a higher resistance to heat than conventional spring material. This permits a pressure plate to be operated at higher temperatures without damage to the springs. Using an asbestos spacer between the springs and pressure ring allows even higher temperatures.

11-3/8, 11-5/8, 12-5/8 or 12-7/8-inches. The outside diameter of the covers is approximately one inch larger than the bolt-circle diameter.

Pressure Rings—Production pressure rings are generally made from grey cast iron. This material does not have sufficient strength for high-performance use. Don't dismay—other materials do offer the needed strength. Ductile cast iron is probably the most common and widely used. High-strength forged aluminum is also available—6061 T-6 or 7075 T-6. Aluminum cannot act as its own friction surface, so one has to be added. This friction surface is called a *heat shield.* The most common method of doing this is to rivet a slotted-steel plate on the ring or to spray hot steel or bronze on the friction surface. This process is called *plasma spraying.* Spray hits the pressure-ring surface and bonds to the aluminum. It is built up to about 0.080". Then it is ground flat to about 0.015" thickness.

Spring Load—is applied to the

Flywheel, disc and pressure ring are useless without a way to clamp the pressure-ring to the disc and flywheel. This is the job of the pressure springs and cover.

pressure ring by coil springs—Long-style pressure plates usually use nine springs. Pressure is applied by compressing the springs between the pressure ring and the cover. The more the springs are compressed and the stiffer they are, the higher the load will be. A wide range of pressure-plate loads is offered. The majority fall between 2500 and 3500 pounds. The load you choose should relate to the amount of torque being developed by the engine.

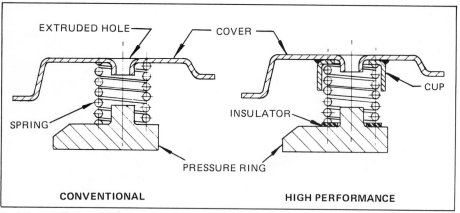

At left is a section of a typical Long-style pressure plate spring setup. At right is a high-performance clutch with cups welded to the underside of the cover to provide additional stability for the springs at high RPM.

Pressure ring of a pressure plate conducts heat just like this metal spoon in a cup of boiling soup. One burned hand coming up. Metal-to-metal contact between the springs and the pressure ring allows the springs to conduct heat from the pressure ring. This reduces spring load and will shorten the life of the clutch if excess slippage results.

On the left is the spring cup prior to being welded into the cover. Also shown are the spring, insulator and another guide which slips over the spring boss at the pressure ring. Eight more spring assemblies just like the one on the right and the cover is ready for the pressure ring.

To locate the springs, "bosses" are cast or forged on the pressure ring. These bosses fit the inside diameter of each coil spring. At the cover, extruded "holes" also fit the inside diameter of the springs. These not only assist during assembly, they also hold the springs in place during clutch operation. At high RPM the springs tend to bow outward due to centrifugal force. Locating devices prevent this from happening. For ultra-high-performance uses, cups welded to the cover fit around the outside diameter of each spring. This further restrains the spring from moving at high revs.

Pressure rings can become hot enough to destroy the disc when the clutch is slipped excessively. And, the pressure ring can warp to a concave shape. If this happens, the pressure plate should be replaced or the pressure ring re-machined flat. As the pressure ring is being heated, so are all the other parts of the clutch. It is just like leaving a metal spoon in a pot of boiling soup on the stove. It doesn't take long to drop it if you try to pick it up with your bare hands. Clutch parts absorb heat in the same manner. Most of them can survive—except the springs. When they are heated much over 375°F (190°C), they will lose temper. They don't get mad, they get soft. The resiliency—springiness—is lost and the pressure plate gradually loses its torque-transmitting capacity because it can't clamp the disc as hard. To alleviate this, high-performance pressure plates use silicon-alloy springs which can withstand higher temperatures. To help further, asbestos pads are placed between the pressure ring and the springs. These insulate the springs from the ring so they stay cooler when the clutch is slipped.

Now that we have the springs to load the pressure ring against the disc, we need something to release it so the car can be shifted, started or idled.

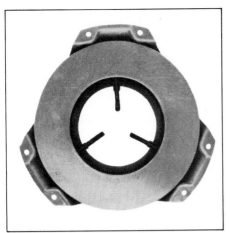

Long pressure plate from a disc's-eye view. You can recognize a Long-style pressure plate by looking into the center of the cover. If it has three forged-steel release levers, it is a Long pressure plate.

The Long pressure plate accomplishes this by means of a simple lever arrangement. If you consider the friction surface of the pressure ring as the front of the pressure plate—it will simplify things quite a bit.

Release Levers—As you look at the back of a pressure plate through the center opening in the cover, you see three forged-steel fingers pointing toward the center. These are the *release levers* or *fingers*. When depressed, they withdraw the pressure ring, moving it rearward. This releases the disc so the engine and driveline can rotate independently. The levers are pivoted at a mounting point on the cover and farther out from the center at mounting points on the pressure ring. As the levers are depressed, they try to pull the cover forward and the pressure ring backward. Because the cover is mounted to the back of the flywheel, it cannot move. The pressure ring is forced back, compressing the nine pressure-plate springs.

The levers are attached to the cover by forged-steel yokes. Each lever has one yoke attached to the cover by a drilled and tapped hole

for a bolt. At the other end, the yoke straddles the lever. A pin goes through the yoke and the lever to create a pivot. To keep wear at a minimum, the pin is surrounded by a bushing in the lever. A cotter key is installed in the end of the pin to hold the assembly together.

The same basic setup is used at the pressure ring except the yoke is an integral part of the ring. It is forged or cast into the pressure ring, depending on the ring type. It also straddles the lever and uses a pin and bushing for the pivot and a cotter key for retention. In some cases, these bushings are offset to let the manufacturer offer pressure plates with different installed lever heights by just using bushings with different offsets. "D" shaped holes in the bushings and yokes prevent the bushings from rotating.

One characteristic of the Long release-lever arrangement is, as the levers operate, they rotate through an arc. This tries to pull the pressure ring toward the center of the pressure plate or the yokes away from the center. To compensate for this, the cover flexes at the yoke mounting points. This only becomes a problem if the levers operate through a large angle. This problem is discussed in the slider chapter.

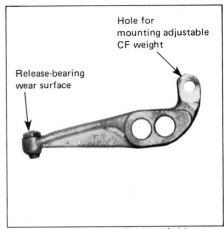

Round-headed bolt at the tip of this Long-style release lever is not for adjustment. It's a release-bearing wear surface which can be replaced without having to replace the complete lever. Lever has been modified so it can be used with adjustable weights in a slider clutch.

The relationship between the distance from the inner ends of the lever where the release bearing contacts it—I'll talk about this later—and cover pivots and the distance between the cover pivots and pressure-ring pivots determines the lever ratio of the release levers. For example, if A = 2.5 and B = .49, the lever ratio is equal to

$$\frac{A}{B} \text{ or } \frac{2.5}{.49} = 5.1:1,$$

a common ratio for a Long-style pressure plate. This is considered

Shim on top of the release-lever yoke is for lowering the lever height. Enlarged release-lever tip is the contact point for the release bearing.

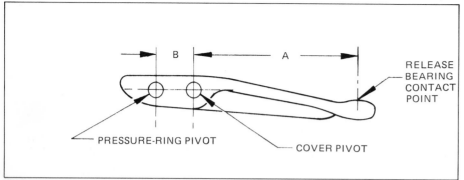

The ratio A/B is the release-lever ratio. It determines release-bearing travel for a given amount of pressure-ring lift. It also determines the force required to do this. Small ratios require less travel and more force. These are considered *fast ratios*.

to be a "slow ratio." A fast ratio for a Long pressure plate would be 4.7:1. This means for a given travel of the release bearing, which is directly related to pedal travel, there would be more pressure-ring lift. Because *fast* refers to speed, the pressure ring pulls away from the clutch disc at a faster rate for a given speed at the clutch pedal. With fast ratios, pedal forces go up in the same proportion as speed and travel.

Assume we have a pressure plate with a 5.1:1 lever ratio. If the plate exerts a force of 3000 pounds on the disc, the load required to begin lifting the pressure ring is equal to pressure-plate load divided by lever ratio—

FORCE REQUIRED TO BEGIN PLATE LIFT

$$= \frac{\text{PRESSURE PLATE LOAD}}{\text{LEVER RATIO}}$$

$$= \frac{3000}{5.1} = 588 \text{ pounds.}$$

If the pressure ring must withdraw 0.125 inch to release the disc, the amount of travel the release bearing will have to move the fingers is equal to

LEVER RATIO X PRESSURE PLATE TRAVEL = 5.1 X .125 = .6375 inch.

Therefore, the release-lever load is inversely proportional to the lever ratio. Lever travel required for clutch disengagement is directly proportional to the lever ratio. To simplify this: The bigger the lever ratio, the more travel required and the less load for a given pressure plate. It works the other way too: The smaller the ratio, the less travel but the load is higher.

CENTRIFUGAL ASSIST

Now that we're into the head-scratchin' stuff, let's not stop. Release levers can do more than release the clutch—they can be designed to do just the opposite.

Practically all Long-style pressure plates are *centrifugally assisted*. To explain this, let's get into the different types of forces producing pressure-plate loads. The most obvious is *static load*. Independent of engine speed, static load is the same when an engine is shut off as when it is turning. Static load is produced by the pressure-plate springs. Next is *centrifugal load* which is produced by a mass spinning around an axis. I talked about centrifugal force previously—about its bad effects on clutch discs. It tries to tear them apart. Well, some ingenious guy decided to let centrifugal force work *for* him and here's how.

Weights added as an integral part of each release lever are called *centrifugal weights* or CF *weights.* Amount of weight, location on a lever and how the fingers are positioned in the pressure-plate assembly determine the amount of centrifugal assist.

As was discussed on page 15, centrifugal force is directly proportional to weight, radius about which the weight is rotated and speed of rotation. To repeat the definition of centrifugal force: When a body rotates about any axis other than one at its center

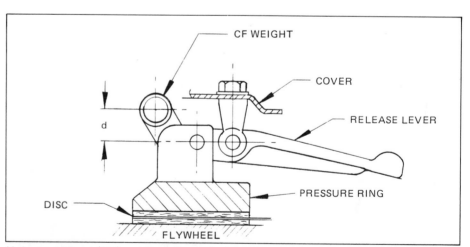

If the centrifugal (CF) weight at the end of the release lever is increased in weight or dimension d is increased, centrifugal assist at the pressure-ring will also increase. Two ways of varying centrifugal assist are varying the weight or rotating the lever in the pressure-plate assembly.

of mass, it exerts an outward force called *centrifugal force* upon anything which keeps it from going in a straight line. This is how the pressure ring is loaded centrifugally, the disc is clamped between the pressure ring and flywheel, preventing the CF weight on the release levers from going in a straight line perpendicular to the center of rotation. Picture spinning a ball over your head at the end of a string. The force preventing the string from becoming parallel to the ground is gravity. Because gravity doesn't get larger, the faster the ball is spun the closer string approaches parallel. The same effect is experienced with CF weights. The higher the engine RPM the more the levers try to rotate. Rotation is prevented because the levers are restrained by the pressure-plate cover and the pressure ring. The result becomes increased pressure-plate loading.

Why go to all the trouble fooling around with such things as CF weights when all one would have to do is stiffen the pressure-plate springs to get the desired plate load? True enough except for one thing. CF weights are designed to load the pressure plate progressively as engine RPM builds. Torque output also increases with RPM to a certain point. Well you say, "So what?" Pedal force is the reason. At the lower RPM, pedal force will be less with a clutch using weights than one without weights which merely relies on static spring pressure to develop the same pressure. For example, a typical pressure plate having a 2750-pound static load which is centrifugally loaded may have a total load of 3500 pounds at 4000 RPM, an increase of 750 pounds due to centrifugal-force. To have the same plate load, a pressure plate without centrifugal weights will have a plate load of 3500 pounds at any RPM with the higher pedal forces accompanying higher plate loads. This makes CF weights sound like "the best thing since

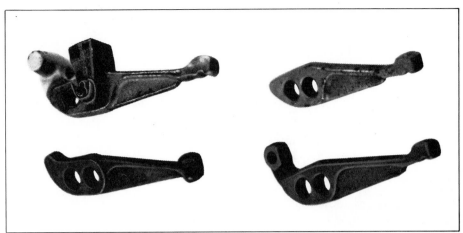

These levers illustrate the differences in Long CF weights. Lever with the yoke has a *full* CF weight. Lever immediately below it has a 3/8 weight and the one at the top right has no weight at all. The one at the bottom right has a hole drilled in what is left of its CF weight so bolt-and-washer weights can be added or deleted to vary centrifugal assist.

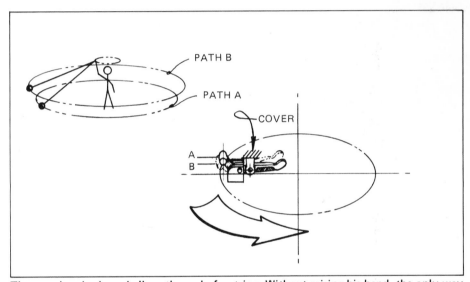

The man is spinning a ball on the end of a string. Without raising his hand, the only way to raise the ball's path from A to B is to spin it faster. The same effect applies to the clutch. The CF weight on a release-lever starts from point A when not rotating. As the engine RPM is increased, the weight tries to move to point B but cannot because it is restrained by the pressure ring, thereby increasing pressure-plate load.

sliced bread"—not exactly, but I'll come back to CF weights again when we look into applications.

The release-lever yoke on the pressure ring serves double duty. It acts as a drive lug for the pressure ring. The three lugs extend through "windows" in the cover and as the cover is rotated by the flywheel, the edges of the windows bear against the lugs to drive the pressure ring and subsequently, the disc. The window edges also act as

Two pressure-plate-cover styles. Both use the Long method of driving the pressure ring with the combination release-lever yoke and drive lugs extending through windows in the covers. Conventional one at left has rectangularly blanked holes (windows). At right is a competition version with reinforced windows.

wear surfaces as the pressure ring moves back and forth during engagement and disengagement. High-performance Long pressure plates are available with reinforced windows. This is done by turning down flanges in the windows to give additional bearing surface for the drive lugs. This prevents the windows from becoming enlarged or "beat-out" during severe use.

BORG & BECK PRESSURE PLATE

The major difference between the Long and the Borg & Beck pressure plates is in the release-lever design and the method of providing centrifugal load. Subtle differences in other areas are of no major consequence when it comes to a performance comparison between the two designs.

Borg & Beck cover-material thicknesses are similar to Long-style plates, 0.125" to 0.156" with high-performance models using the heavier material. The flywheel-to-pressure-plate mounting holes are evenly spaced on circle diameters of 11-5/8" or 12-5/8", depending on pressure ring diameter. Long clutches have unevenly spaced mounting holes. Later on you'll see how this affects swapping to a different clutch style.

Cover-window reinforcing is done by turning down flanges at the pressure-ring drive lugs. This gives the drive lugs more bearing surface and prevents windows from enlarging during severe usage.

A replaceable wear shim (arrow) fits between the drive window and the aluminum pressure-ring drive lug on this slider pressure plate.

Springs—Borg & Beck pressure plates commonly use 12 springs, as compared with nine in the Long. This permits less overall pressure-plate depth—the distance from the flywheel-mounting surface to the back of the cover. The maximum height of the Borg & Beck pressure plate is 2.72", over 1/4" less than a Long. This is possible because the three additional springs reduce the load per spring. Consequently, smaller springs can be used for equivalent plate loads.

For example, 2400 pounds is a typical load for a pressure plate. The Long uses nine springs so each spring supports 2400 pounds divided by the number of springs, or 267 pounds. Assume the springs are compressed 0.75" from *free height*—the springs' unloaded height—to obtain this load. Spring rate becomes 356 pounds per inch: 267 pounds divided by 0.75". Now, the Borg & Beck pressure plate uses 12 springs. The pressure plate load is distributed over three more springs yielding a lower spring load—2400 pounds divided by 12 springs equals 200 pounds for each spring. The spring rate for these springs is 267 pounds per inch. Rate and load are 33 percent lower than required for the equivalent Long pressure plate. The Borg & Beck style pressure plate can be designed more compactly because of the additional springs.

Another advantage, mostly theoretical, is evenly distributed load on the pressure ring. Supposedly, this

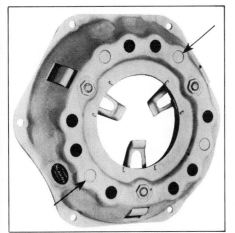

Borg & Beck pressure plate is easily recognized by its three stamped-steel release levers, 12 springs and evenly spaced cover-to-flywheel mounting holes. Plugged holes (arrows) at the center of some of the springs are balance weights. *Photo courtesy Schiefer*

Borg & Beck pressure plate ready to be assembled to the pressure ring, springs and levers.

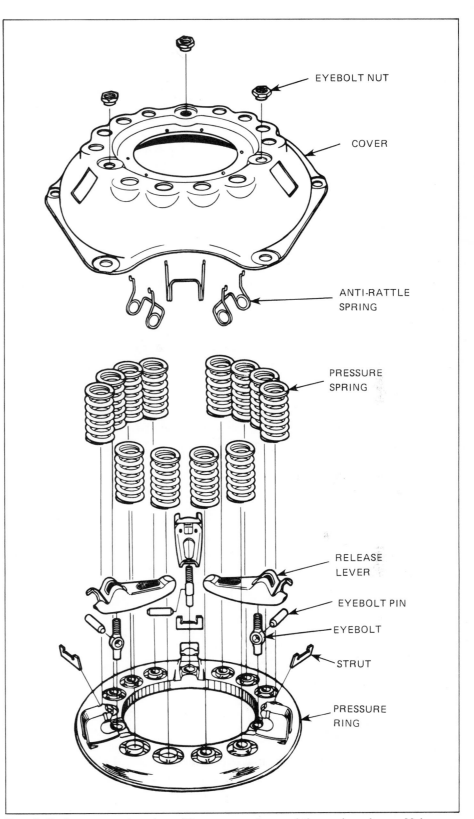

Borg & Beck pressure plates have 12 pressure springs and three release levers. Major distinguishing features of this style pressure plate are the stamped-steel release levers, how they operate and the centrifugal-assist method. Centrifugal assist devices are not shown in this drawing. *Drawing courtesy ACE Jameson*

Spring on left is from a Long-style pressure plate and the one on the right from a Borg & Beck. Because the Borg & Beck style has three more springs, each spring carries less load for a given amount of pressure-ring load. You can see this by the obvious differences in the spring wire sizes.

COIL SPRINGS

I'll just go far enough to point out the "hows-and-whys" of how coil springs operate without trying to design them. Starting with the "spring-rate," the amount of force required to compress a spring with a given amount of force a given distance is usually expressed in pounds per inch. If you have a spring lying around the house and want to find its rate, just stand on it and measure how much it compresses 1.5", the rate can be found by dividing your weight—180 pounds—by the spring deflection—1.5 or

$$\text{SPRING RATE} = \frac{\text{LOAD}}{\text{DEFLECTION}}$$

$$= \frac{180 \text{ pounds}}{1.5 \text{ inches}}$$

$$= 120 \text{ pounds per inch}$$

If this spring was compressed two inches, the load required to do it is equal to the rate of the spring multiplied by the deflection, or

SPRING LOAD
= SPRING RATE
  X DEFLECTION
= 120 pounds X 2.0 inches
= 240 pounds.

The formula for calculating spring rate is:

SPRING RATE (K)

$$= \frac{G \times d^4}{8 \times D^3 \times n}$$

Where:

K is the spring rate in pounds per inch.

G is the torsional modulus of elasticity of the material. For steel,

G equals 11,500,000 pounds per square inch.

d is the wire diameter in inches.

D is the mean diameter of the spring, measured from the center of the wire on each side. One easy way to measure this is to measure the outside diameter of the spring and subtract wire diameter from this figure.

n is the number of active coils—number of coils which bend or do the work as the spring is compressed. For the type of springs used in pressure plates, this is equal to the total number of coils, minus two.

What this formulas says is, if you want to increase the rate of a spring, the wire diameter must be increased or the mean diameter of the active coils must be reduced. **G** remains relatively constant for steel springs.

When we look at the springs in terms of the clutch, they should be as small and light as possible. This means they should be designed so they are fully stressed or loaded to the limit—as the load is reduced so is the wire size. Also, as load is increased, so must the wire size to prevent overloading the springs. Therefore, for two springs loaded or *stressed* to their maximum, the one with the larger wire size will weigh more and will have a higher *compressed height*—the height at which all the coils in the spring touch each other. Consequently, if a spring is not used efficiently, or stressed to its maximum, it will be bigger and "taller" than need be.

reduces the tendency of the cover to flex and the pressure ring to warp when subjected to high heat during severe usage. I have yet to see this occur because when pressure rings warp, they do so in a concave manner—the outside periphery of the pressure ring friction surface pulls ahead of the inside diameter.

One final comment about the Borg & Beck spring arrangement, the springs are located at the pressure ring by bosses loosely fitting the inside diameter of each spring. Rather than an extruded hole fitting the inside diameter of each spring for retention, as with the Long, the cover is formed around them. For high-performance models, an aluminum guide fits inside each spring. These guides fit through holes in the cover and are staked in place for retention. They prevent the springs from bowing and distorting at high RPM.

Release Levers—The mechanics of the Borg & Beck and Long release levers are based on the same principle. The geometry of both of the levers are very nearly the same: Both have two pivot points and similar ratios. The similarity comes to a halt when the components are compared. Borg & Beck levers are stamped instead of forged. Inboard pivots at the cover are made up of a threaded eyebolt and eyebolt pin. Each eyebolt extends through a lever and then through the cover to which it is attached by a special nut.

The forward ends of the eyebolts extend into holes in the back of the pressure ring which act as guides during engagement and disengagement. Each lever has a pocket stamped in it to locate it and to provide a bearing surface. At the release-bearing-contact points on the inner end of each lever, a cylindrical radius provides a rolling contact point for the release bearing as the levers are actuated.

A compression strut is placed between the lever and pressure ring. This is in place of the pin used in Long-style plates. It eliminates any binding between the cover, ring and

Rather than having extruded holes in the cover to retain the springs, the Borg & Beck cover fits around the outside diameters of the springs. For additional spring retention, hollow aluminum guides which fit inside the spring are installed in the cover in the same manner as the balance weights shown. Riveted plate is for the centrifugal roller to bear against.

Release-lever assembly of a Borg & Beck style pressure plate consists of a stamped-steel release lever, an eyebolt, eyebolt pin and a strut. The eyebolt supports the release levers. Each eyebolt fits into a drilled hole in the back of the pressure ring, centering it in the pressure-plate assembly. The pressure ring is free to move back and forth as the clutch is operated. When a release lever is depressed by the release bearing, it rotates about the eyebolt-pin and forces the pressure ring away from the clutch disc by a strut which fits between a boss on the pressure ring and the lever.

pressure plate as occurs with solid pivots. Visualize the Long-style lever arm. As it pivots on the inner pivot, the outer pivot moves back and forth—also moving in and out slightly through an arc. Therefore, there has to be some "fight" between the two pivots. If the cover was as rigid as a forged or cast pressure ring, the Long style would bind and wear, however the stamped cover flexes enough to comply with the small amount of

The strut is seated in a depression in the release lever and is located laterally by straddling the pressure-ring lug. As the Borg & Beck release levers are operated they travel though an arc, however the strut automatically compensates for in-and-out movement.

travel required. The strut does the same thing for the Borg & Beck system by compensating for the lateral movement at the outboard end of the release lever. The link is free to pivot on the release lever and the pressure ring, relieving any binding which may occur between the pressure ring and cover during lever movement.

To locate the strut positively, a flat depression is stamped in the outer end of the lever. The strut sits in this depression. The other end of the strut bears against the drive lug on the release lever and the strut fits between the lever and lug. Lugs are grooved on each side to locate the struts. Tabs extend from the strut into these grooves, preventing the struts from moving inboard, outboard or sideways. The only thing left in the release-lever department is a method to keep the struts from falling out when the levers aren't loaded. This is done with mouse-trap-type springs. These bear against the cover and the inboard ends of the release levers, keeping a slight preload on the struts and holding them in place when they are unloaded.

One more note about the lever system. The drive lugs extend through windows in the cover in the same manner as on the Long style. The lugs play the same dual role: They provide a pivot point for the release levers and transfer engine torque from the cover to the pressure ring.

Centrifugal Rollers—The Borg & Beck pressure plate obtains centrifugal assist in a completely different manner than the Long pressure plate. The basic theory is still the same, weights are introduced into the assembly and the heavier the weights, the more the assist. The difference lies in the manner in which the assist is provided. Rather than locating the weights on the levers, they are separate parts which sit in grooves in the pressure ring and wedge behind the cover.

These centrifugal weights are termed *rollers*. Either three or six

Because the Borg & Beck style release levers are not retained from traveling rearward, some provision must be made to hold them in place during full engagement. This is accomplished with a mouse-trap-type *anti-rattle spring* for each lever as shown installed in this cover.

Borg & Beck pressure-rings are driven in the same manner as Longs, with drive lugs extending through windows in the cover. Windows cannot be reinforced because the flanges would interfere with the release-lever struts.

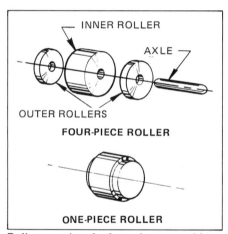

Rollers consist of a four-piece assembly, or are of a one-piece construction. Outer rollers are retained to the inner roller by a pin or axle which press-fits into the outer rollers leaving the inner to rotate as it moves against the inside of the pressure plate cover. The outer rollers seat in machined bosses on the back of the pressure ring. Single-piece rollers are machined from bar stock and rather than "rolling," they are heavily lubricated so they will slide against the cover—hopefully.

rollers are used for each pressure plate—or none at all. A four-piece roller includes one inner roller, two smaller outer rollers and a pin to hold the rollers together and act as axle for the inner roller. Outer rollers are supported by the grooves in the pressure ring and the pin supports the inner roller as it wedges against the side of the cover. The side of the cover slopes at the point of contact with the roller, causing

the roller to want to move forward against the back of the pressure ring as it is forced out by centrifugal force. This causes a wedging action to occur between the pressure ring and the cover, loading the pressure ring against the disc and flywheel. A subsequent increase in clutch capacity occurs as pressure-plate load increases. Single-piece rollers are also used.

When a Borg & Beck pressure

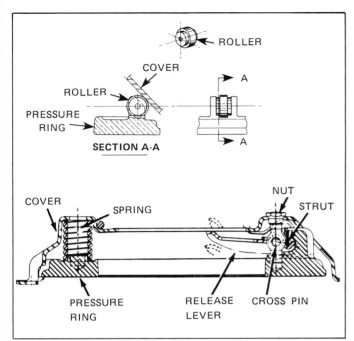

Each roller sits in a groove in the pressure ring and is forced against the cover by centrifugal force, causing a wedging action. This loads the pressure ring against the disc and increases pressure-plate load as the square of engine RPM.

plate is used without rollers it seems obvious there is no change in plate load with RPM. I say "seems to be" because there can actually be a reduction in load at high engine RPM if the springs distort because they are not retained adequately. This points out the need for proper spring retention—guides are an absolute must for high-RPM applications, whether rollers are used or not. There is also some effect from the positioning of the release levers but it is minimal.

DIAPHRAGM PRESSURE PLATE

What characterizes the diaphragm pressure plate from the Borg & Beck and Long styles is the spring it uses to load the pressure ring. The basic pressure ring and cover are retained but designed to accommodate the spring. The word *diaphragm* indicates the type of spring used—a diaphragm or *Belleville* spring. The Belleville spring is shaped like a coolie's hat, or a shallow cone with the center cut out. For clutch applications the

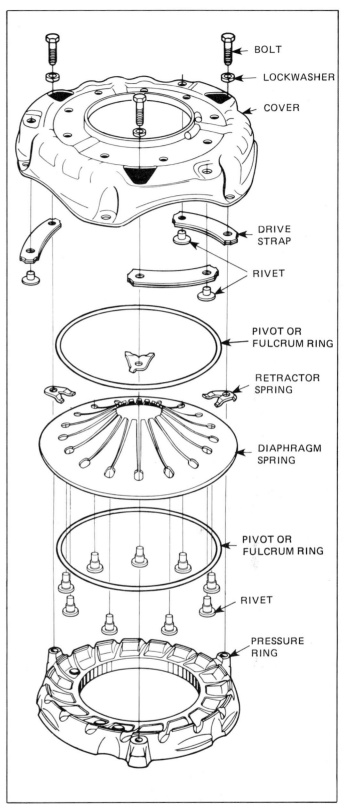

Diaphragm pressure plates are relatively new as automotive clutches go. They are unique because the conventional coil pressure springs and release levers are replaced by a single diaphragm or Belleville spring. You can recognize this type of pressure plate by the 18 flat-steel fingers in the center rather than the usual three release levers. *Drawing courtesy ACE Jameson*

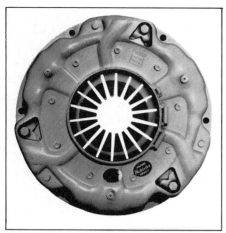

There's no doubt about what kind of pressure plate this is—it's a diaphragm! This is Schiefer's Super Rev-Lok.® *Photo courtesy Schiefer*

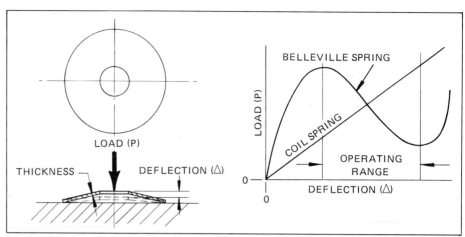

Section drawing of a Belleville spring. As load P is applied, the spring tends to flatten. Graph shows load/deflection of a coil-spring pressure plate compared to a diaphragm pressure plate. Load for a coil-spring is directly proportional to deflection, whereas the load for the Belleville spring drops off after passing a certain point.

The simplicity of a diaphragm pressure plate is illustrated here. Compare this photo to the Long and Borg & Beck pressure plates on pages 20 and 27.

spring is slotted from the inside out, making a series of release levers—usually 18. The difference is the levers and spring are one piece rather than over 30 for the other two pressure plates. One thing that becomes apparent is the diaphragm pressure plate is lighter and more compact, a distinct advantage.

Explaining how a Belleville spring operates is a little more difficult than a coil spring. The force required to compress a coil spring is directly proportional to the amount it is compressed, providing the distance between the coils is constant and the wire diameter is constant. If the spring is properly designed, force increases at a constant rate until the spring goes "solid"—it is compressed to the maximum with each coil touching the one next to it. This does not occur with a Belleville spring.

As it is compressed, the load drops off. You have probably experienced this yourself with *oil-canning*. This is where one end of a can pops in and out from pushing on it or filling with liquid. It doesn't have to be a can. It can be an area of sheet metal or a Halloween noise maker. When pushed on, it requires less force as it goes "over-center." This is a situation where force would be required in the other direction to keep the noise maker or whatever from continuing to deflect. The Belleville spring should never reach this point because of the danger of spring damage, however it is an exaggerated example of how this type of spring works. The Belleville spring as applied to the clutch has the main advantage of providing a high plate load in a relatively short amount of travel and with less force at the release bearing. The release-bearing force is directly re-

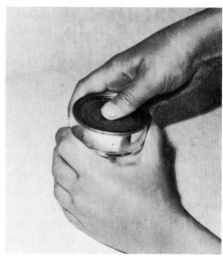

Diaphragm spring is a sophisticated tin-can bottom. As you push on the bottom of a tin can, you can feel the Belleville-spring effect. It pushes hard at first and then pops "over center" with little effort. It does the opposite when you release it.

lated to the amount of force required to operate the clutch pedal.

Another advantage can be illustrated from the force-deflection curve. A coil-spring pressure plate—Borg & Beck and Long—*loses plate load as the disc wears* because the springs extend. In other words, the springs aren't compressed as much as when the disc was new. The diaphragm pressure plate has *increased plate load as the disc wears*. Look at the Load-Deflection curve. As

Early flat-spring diaphragm pressure plate with high-RPM engagement problems. Diaphragm fingers extend rearward in their engaged position, assume a flat position when disengaged. Consequently, centrifugal force on the fingers tries to hold the pressure plate in the released position and is successful if engine RPM is high enough.

CAUTION—Do not attempt to modify your diaphragm pressure plate to increase its plate load. The result will be pressure-plate or related-component failure. For example, one horrible example I have seen is "stacking" one Belleville spring on top of another to double plate load—pedal forces are also doubled. The springs weren't damaged, however in one case the pressure-plate cover was permanently deformed and in another the clutch linkage was quickly destroyed. A readily available high-performance diaphragm pressure plate would've done the job without the resulting grief.

So you thought all diaphragm pressure plates were the same? One thing is the same with these pressure plates. None of them experience high-RPM engagement problems. Small-diameter flat-diaphragm pressure plates don't have the problem in the first place and the larger 11" unit has bent fingers to ensure high-RPM engagement.

the spring deflection line moves to the left on the curve, the plate load drops off proportionally with coil springs. The diaphragm plate has an "S" curve and when the plate is loaded correctly when new, load increases substantially with wear. Therefore, the diaphragm clutch is superior in this respect.

One of the diaphragm clutch's limitations is the narrow deflection band it has to work in. If the spring is not compressed enough when new, plate load drops off rapidly as the disc wears. If the spring is compressed too much, permanent damage may result dur-

ing disengagement—or the clutch may not engage at high RPM due to centrifugal forces on the fingers. In the early stages of diaphragm-clutch development, the spring was shaped like a very flat cone. Racers soon discovered disengagement of the clutch at high RPM forced the spring into a reverse cone and the clutch remained disengaged—the

clutch pedal would stay on the floor! In many cases the result was an over-revved or blown engine. This gave diaphragm clutches a bad name, to say the least. It was soon discovered the cause was centrifugal force acting on the spring and holding it in the released position. As engine RPM dropped, the clutch would engage. To cure the problem, the release fingers were bent rearward toward the release bearing. Now, as a spring is compressed for disengagement, the fingers do not reach the "flat" or over-center position. At high RPM, centrifugal force on the fingers returns them to their original position and the clutch is immediately engaged.

The problem becomes one of proper matching of the disc to the pressure plate. Disc thickness must fall in the range shown by the Load-Deflection curve. This is critical and I'll discuss it more later.

Another limitation of the diaphragm pressure plate is the lack of a centrifugal-assist device. I am sure this can be done by using rollers between the cover and spring or pressure ring as in the Borg & Beck. However, nothing like this is currently available. When the demand gets great enough, this is sure to happen.

Let's look at how the Belleville spring fits into and operates in a pressure plate. I haven't explained how the spring lifts the pressure ring, only the load and deflection characteristics. The first question I had when I saw my first diaphragm pressure plate was, "How can a big round dishpan lift a pressure plate?" The secret is how it is clamped into the cover. This is done with a couple of steel rings which fit on both sides of the diaphragm, one on the cover side and the other on the pressure-ring side. These are called *pivot rings* or *fulcrum rings,* depending on who is talking. The diaphragm is trapped between the two rings. The whole assembly is held in place by a series of shoulder rivets or bolts which go through clearance holes in the spring and shoulder against the front side of the cover with the small ends protruding through the cover to which they are riveted or attached with nuts. The pivot ring on the front side of the spring is held in place by the rivet heads which also fit against the inside diameter of the ring. The other ring is trapped between the cover and the spring.

A subtle difference here distinguishes another type of diaphragm pressure plate. Instead of using a fulcrum ring between the cover and the spring, a ring is formed or stamped into the cover, getting rid of still another part. You can see this by looking at the backside of the pressure plate. It appears as a circular depression in the cover interrupted only by the attaching rivets or bolts. This type is called

There are two diaphragm-pressure-plate styles: the Rockford type which uses two fulcrum rings and the Belleville style shown here. This one eliminates the fulcrum ring between the cover and the spring by using a series of depressions in the cover (arrow).

the *Belleville style* and the one using two rings is called the *Rockford style.*

The spring is approximately ten inches in diameter and the pivot-ring 8.40 inches. Because the outside diameter of the spring extends beyond the pivot ring, the outside perimeter of the spring moves rearward as the release fingers move forward. The pressure ring is machined on the back side to

To pull the pressure ring back with the diaphragm, the Rockford style uses a retractor spring at the bolt which attaches the pressure ring. This spring hooks over the back of the diaphragm and as the spring is depressed, it pulls the pressure ring with it.

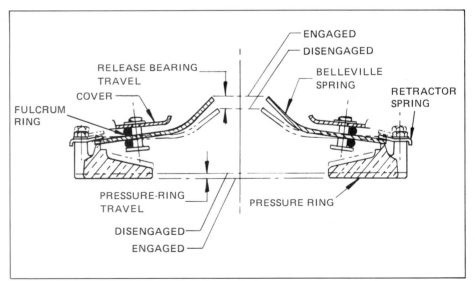

The Belleville spring plays the role of the release levers and provides the loading force for the pressure plate. As the center of the spring is depressed, the outer edge of the spring pulls the pressure ring away from the disc for disengagement. This is a Rockford type as shown by the two fulcrum rings.

match the outer diameter of the spring it seats against. Three clips or retractor springs clamp the pressure ring to the spring. These are bolted to the pressure ring and pull down on the backside of the spring, forcing it against the ring. As the release fingers are depressed, the outer edge of the diaphragm pulls the pressure ring back from the disc with the retractor springs, disengaging the clutch.

The lever ratio of the diaphragm clutch is determined in a different manner than on Long or Borg & Beck styles. It is the ratio between the release-lever load and plate load and more appropriately called *spring ratio*. It is calculated as follows:

SPRING RATIO = PRESSURE-PLATE LOAD / RELEASE-FINGER LOAD

This is because the release fingers of the diaphragm spring deflect when they are loaded by the release bearing. For example, if the ratio is 3.5:1 and the plate load is 3000 pounds, then the force at the fingers required to begin the plate to lift is 857 pounds. By dividing the pressure plate load by the spring ratio we get:

RELEASE-BEARING LOAD = PRESSURE-PLATE LOAD / SPRING RATIO

As the clutch is disengaged, the force required at the release bearing gets smaller. This is important because it directly relates to pedal force. Pedal force reduces as the pedal is depressed. Not so with the coil-spring designs—as they are disengaged the pedal force increases because the coil springs are compressed more. The assumption is there are no other springs in the clutch linkage. This accounts for the gradual conversion of the auto industry to the diaphragm clutch— to give the lowest possible pedal forces, making the car or truck easier and more comfortable to operate. The total clutch system becomes less expensive when the

diaphragm clutch is used, even though the clutch itself is more expensive than the other pressure-plate types.

Formulas used to calculate loads, rates and stresses for diaphragm springs are so involved and complicated that it would take an extra book to explain them. The formulas are only a close approximation based on prior test data and to use them involves the use of no less than six graphs. The final determination is made in the laboratory after a spring is designed and built. Because I am only concerned with explaining the springs, not designing them, I will generalize the explanation.

Only two things can be done to change a spring once a pressure plate has been designed—material thickness of the spring and width of the radial slots. It is only natural that as the thickness is increased,

the rate will increase, thus increasing the load the spring exerts for a given deflection. Also, by reducing the slot width the load will increase because there will be additional material to bend. The opposite effects occur when material thickness is reduced and the slots are widened. Areas which cannot be changed due to the critical nature of the spring are the outside diameter and the location of the pivot ring. The amount of lift required to disengage the disc is fixed. Therefore, the two items the manufacturers play with to give different pressure-plate loads are the material thickness and the radial-slot thickness.

One of the excellent features of the diaphragm pressure plate is the distributed load the spring applies to the pressure ring. Instead of applying loads locally in nine or 12 places as with the Long and Borg &

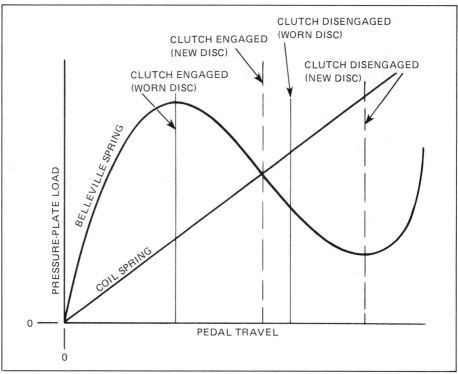

Converting the curve shown on page 32 to show pedal travel versus pressure-plate load, you can see pressure-plate load with the diaphragm drops off as the pedal is depressed and the pressure ring is withdrawn. It increases with coil-spring pressure plates. As the disc wears, the engagement/disengagement band is transposed to the left and plate load increases with a diaphragm pressure plate, but is reduced with the coil-spring type.

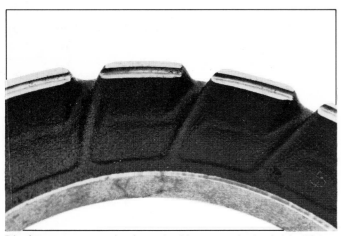
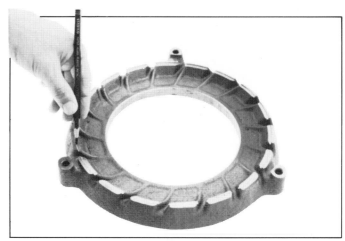

Diaphragm pressure ring has raised bosses on its backside. They are machined as seats for the diaphragm spring. The inside diameter is clearanced to clear the spring when the pressure plate is released. The swirl pattern and notches through the spring seat aren't just for looks, they assist in cooling the clutch by pumping air through the pressure plate.

Beck styles, the load is applied "full-circle." More importantly, the spring itself pulls the pressure ring back for disengagement instead of three levers pulling the pressure ring back against the resisting force of the coil springs. The significance with this is there is no load on the pressure ring during disengagement.

Finally, the pressure ring has to be driven. This is accomplished with three spring-steel *drive-straps,* shaped like circle segments. They are flat and have holes in each end— one for riveting or bolting to the cover and the other for bolting to the pressure ring. The straps flex during engagement and disengagement and are under tension while transmitting engine torque from the cover to the pressure ring. The straps are strong enough to withstand compression loads when the engine is used for braking during deceleration.or for push starts.

LONG/BORG & BECK PRESSURE PLATE

The only remaining "conventional" pressure plate to discuss is the Long/Borg & Beck style. This pressure plate uses the best of both in one assembly. It uses the release lever and centrifugal-assist components of the Long and the 12 springs and bolt pattern of the Borg & Beck. This provides flexibility for anyone having a GM,

Chrysler or American Motors product. Remember, GM products use the diaphragm pressure plates and Ford is in the process of converting to the diaphragm. Chrysler and AMC use the Borg & Beck. Keeping in mind that these two pressure plates have the same bolt patterns, the need to buy a new flywheel or redrill the one you have can be avoided by using the Long/Borg & Beck pressure plate if you want to convert to the Long style and have room for it in your bell-housing.

SPECIAL APPLICATION CLUTCHES

Nearly all the special-application clutches used today are derivatives of the types I have covered. They are made up of several types of multi-disc clutches, combinations of various discs and pressure plates and the dog clutch.

DOG CLUTCHES

The dog clutch is a unique animal. It does two things—connects and disconnects the engine and driveline—no in-between. Once engaged there can be no slippage between the engine and the driveline. Engagement is done inside an "in & out box" by one of two methods. Halibrand uses a "dog plate" which bolts directly to the engine crankshaft flange and transfers engine torque to the mating dog

Another difference between the Rockford and Belleville styles of pressure plates are the drive-strap arrangements. Belleville drive straps are set low in the cover and are riveted to ears which are an integral part of the pressure-ring. Drive-straps are used to retract the pressure ring instead of separate retractor springs. Rockford drive straps are set higher in the cover above the spring as pointed out in the top photo. *Rockford photo courtesy Schiefer*

The advantage of a Long/Borg & Beck combination pressure plate is you can replace your diaphragm or Borg & Beck pressure plate with one which has the best features of a Long without the necessity of replacing your flywheel. It will also fit into small bellhousings due to its low Borg & Beck profile.

Here's a pressure plate I threw in to confuse you. You might think it's another combination Long/Borg & Beck because of the number of springs—12 instead of nine. Look again and you'll see the cover has a Long bolt pattern. About the only advantages this type of pressure plate has over the Long is its lower profile for getting into tighter bellhousings and more even pressure-ring load distribution. It also installs onto a flywheel drilled with the Long bolt pattern.

which slides back and forth on the in & out box shaft to which it is splined. CAE uses a different method by permanently engaging the in & out box input shaft to the engine crank with a splined crank flange. This input shaft is comparable to the input shaft of a standard transmission and is engaged in the same manner as you would the top gear of a three- or four-speed manual transmission. A blocking ring, or dog in this case, is splined to the input shaft leaving it free to move back and forth. For engagement, a lever moves the dog forward into engagement with dogs on the input shaft.

The dog clutch is unique because it is used in one type of racing—quarter, three-eights, and an occasional mile oval track. Cars that use them — sprinters, super-modifieds and midgets—do not have "on-board" starters and must be push-started with the dog engaged.

Because push vehicles sometimes can't develop enough traction to get a big sprinter underway on dirt or clay with the dog engaged, the car is rolled first. After the car has gained sufficient momentum, the wheels are locked up for rapid engagement of the dog clutch. Right after the dog is engaged, the brakes are released, turning the engine over and firing it.

Because simplicity is the number-two objective behind performance when designing and building a

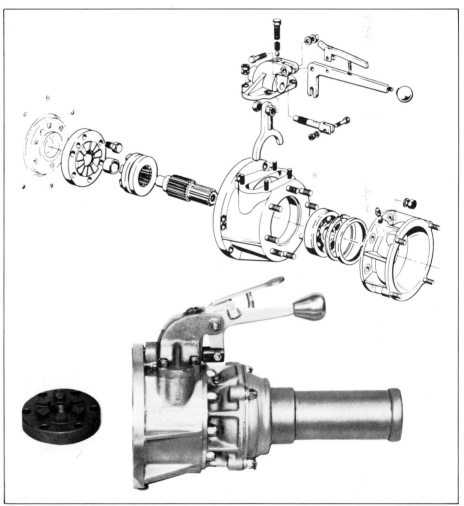

The in-and-out box is used exclusively in midget, sprint cars and Super-Modified race-cars. It is a dog clutch which is engaged by sliding a dog on the main shaft into engagement with a companion dog on the back of the engine crank. A lever locks the dogs into place. *Photo and drawing courtesy Halibrand Engineering*

sprint car, the conventional clutch is discarded in favor of the dog type because all have flying starts. No shifting is required and the races are so short that pit stops are not required. Considering these conditions, who needs a conventional clutch? One could be used for starting but the cars have only one gear and excessive slippage would be required to get a car rolling. Instead of using a clutch, the old pickup truck with a big wooden bumper is used. The cars are pushed off and ready to race and when one comes to a stop, the race is over for that car.

MULTIPLE-DISC CLUTCHES

A multiple-disc clutch is just what the name suggests, a clutch using more than one disc. The number of discs commonly ranges from two to four. Added torque capacity is the reason for their use. The three most-common methods used to increase the capacity of a clutch are to increase pressure-plate-clamping load, increase clutch diameter or increase the number of friction surfaces. Many times, all three methods are taken advantage of in the same clutch. Other times, a reduction in one of the three makes it necessary to increase one or both of the others.

Take for example road-racing cars such as Can-Am or Formula 5000. One of the major contributing factors to the cornering ability of one of these cars is the center of gravity height from the ground. The center of gravity is a point where all the weight of the car could be theoretically concentrated and weight transfer due to braking, cornering and accelerating would not change. The major factor in determining where the center of gravity will be is the location of the engine in the car—the lower the engine, the lower the C.G. The first limiting factor in lowering an engine is the clutch and flywheel diameter once all the trick stuff is done to the oil pan. If a 10-1/2-inch clutch using a 14-3/32-inch ring gear is reduced to a 7-1/4-inch

With the dog engaged, this sprinter is being pushed off to fire the engine in preparation for a race at Phoenix International Raceway, a one-mile paved oval. The Jeep comes in handy when the sprints are run on clay or dirt. Extra traction is needed to get the cars rolling.

Ayrton Senna in JPS Lotus on short downhill straight at Detroit Grand Prix: Positioning engine low in chassis is vital to handling of this type car. Small-diameter clutch and flywheel allow this.

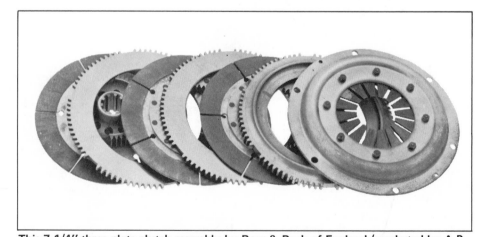

This 7-1/4'' three-plate clutch assembly by Borg & Beck of England (marketed by A.P. Racing in the U.S.) has an overall diameter of 8-1/2''. It can transmit up to 700 foot-pounds of torque. Splines on the floater plates mesh with the pressure-plate spacer ring. One disc is splined to the transmission input shaft while the others are splined to the first disc.

An example of what a multi-disc clutch can do is illustrated by these two pressure plates. The 11" diaphragm unit on the left used with a single disc transmits approximately 100 foot-pounds less torque than the 7-1/4" pressure plate with 1000 pounds less plate load and three discs.

Borg-Warner's Double Coupler dual-disc clutch was a production option for use behind the Chevrolet big-block in the Corvette. It has a very high torque capacity and excellent durability. *Photo courtesy Borg-Warner Corporation*

clutch and 12-13/32-inch ring gear, the engine can be lowered over 1-1/2 inches—a very substantial figure. The crunch comes in the form of lost clutch capacity from the reduced diameter. It can all be gained back through the use of more discs without increasing pressure-plate load. In fact, A.P. Racing markets a "Borg & Beck of England" four-plate 7-1/4-inch-diameter clutch which they say transmits 925 foot-pounds of torque.

Four types are available, ranging from the single-plate to the four-plate. Torque capacities are 160, 340, 700, and 925 foot-pounds, respectively. The single-plate, 160-foot-pound clutch is intended for small engines and the four-plate, 925-foot-pounder is for Can-Am and Championship car use. It is interesting to note the pressure plates for all four units are basically the same. Torque capacity is increased by the addition of discs.

The single-disc clutch has two driving surfaces, the flywheel and the pressure ring. As discs are added, driving surfaces must also be added and the distance between the flywheel and the pressure plate must be increased to make room for the added pieces. A *floater plate* is added between each disc that doesn't already have a driving surface. Floater plates are driven by *stands* which space the pressure plate away from the flywheel whatever distance it takes to make room for the additional plates and

This 8-1/2", three-disc clutch from McLeod has the floater-plate drive stands separate from the pressure-plate stands. To keep weight at a minimum, floater plates are the same diameter as the disc except for the ears which fit around the drive stands.

Pressure-ring and floater plates of the three-disc 7-1/4" Borg and Beck clutch are driven by very large diameter splines on the inside of the spacer ring. Holes are strategically placed in the spacer ring to let worn friction material escape.

discs. When engaged and disengaged the floater plates can move freely back and forth much in the same way as clutch discs on the transmission-input shaft—and they transmit torque.

The number of floater plates required is one less than the number of discs. For example, a single-disc clutch does not require a floater plate—one minus one is zero. A two-disc clutch requires one plate—two minus one is one.

Floater-plate designs vary. One thing they all have in common is the inside and outside diameters match the diameters of the clutch-disc friction-material surfaces. Anymore would be wasted material and excessive weight. Floater plates are made from ductile cast iron or steel—usually not over 1/2-inch thick. Spacers and drive stands are either round or square and number six or three. Mating ears on the floater plates fit around the stands which drive them.

Borg & Beck's small-diameter clutch uses a unique method of supporting the floater plates. An aluminum ring is used much in the same way as the stands. It fits around the outside diameter of the plates and is splined on its inside diameter. The plates have mating splines on their outside diameters, permitting them to float and be driven like the discs on the transmission-input shaft.

This clutch uses three solid-hub, sintered-bronze discs with a diaphragm pressure plate and can transmit 700 foot-pounds of torque. The complete unit, including the pressure plate, the three discs, two floater plates and the drive ring, weighs only 12 pounds-3-1/2 ounces! Throw in the tiny flywheel with its starter ring gear and it is still under 21 pounds. This clutch is available from Carl A. Haas Automobile Imports, Quarter Master Industries, RRS Engineering and Tilton Engineering.

A 10-inch double-disc clutch offered by Borg Warner called the *Double Coupler* is different because

Floater-plate of the Borg-Warner Double Coupler does not float like the majority of multi-disc clutches. The intermediate/floater plate is attached to the diaphragm-pressure-plate drive straps mid-point between the cover and the pressure ring. When the clutch is disengaged, the plate is pulled back from the flywheel to ensure that the clutch disengages positively.

it uses an intermediate plate which does not float. A diaphragm pressure plate uses long drive straps located on the outside diameter of the cover and pressure ring to mount and drive the plate. Plate-mounting ears are attached to the drive straps and for clutch disengagement, the drive straps pull the intermediate plate away from the disc rather than letting it "float" away. This clutch was developed in conjunction with Chevrolet and was a Corvette option for 454-CID engines.

SLIDER CLUTCHES

One very specialized clutch is the slider. It is unique due to the fact that it was designed to slide or slip —something which is completely foreign to the conventional clutch. The duration of time it must slip— approximately 2 to 3 seconds—is long considering the torque it must transmit. Sliders come in two styles and with varying number of discs. The most common is 11.00" with three discs for the Top Fuelers and Funny Cars, however, there are single and dual-disc units available.

Why have a clutch that slips in the first place? The reason goes back to the coefficient of friction. If you'll remember, static friction is higher than dynamic. Therefore, the maximum force a tire can develop is higher right before it spins—or slips. Now, the term *coefficient of friction* is not completely correct because a tire *grips* as it conforms to the road surface. The maximum theoretical coefficient of friction is 1.00. This means if an object weighs 1000 pounds, it can't take over 1000 pounds to start it moving on a level surface. An oversimplification, but you get the idea. Based on a coefficient of friction of 1.00, some slide-rule boys were saying an E.T. (elapsed time) of under 9.05 seconds at a top speed of 198 MPH was the absolute maximum for the quarter mile, excluding the effect of aerodynamics.

This is grip. I snapped this photo at the instant Jim Liberman opened the throttle. Note the parachute line still hanging limp.

This photo series shows what is involved in one run of a Top-Fuel dragster. The engine is fired with a remote starter while the clutch is disengaged. The car then pulls up to the burnout area stopping with the rear tires in water. Engine revs are brought up and the clutch is engaged. The car accelerates with the tires spinning and the clutch locked up. The transmission is shifted into high gear. After the burnout, the car is pushed back behind the starting line by the car's crew and the car is staged. After staging, the lights on the Christmas tree head for the green and engine revs are brought up to about 6000 RPM. On the green, the clutch is engaged. It slips for about 400 feet from the starting line before fully engaging. The clutch may slip a slight amount as the transmission is shifted and the engine RPM drops below the clutch stall speed.

During burnouts, the slider clutch is fully engaged and the tires spin to heat up the tires for maximum traction. During the run the clutch slips and the tires are kept on the verge of breaking loose for maximum acceleration.

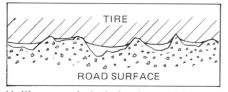

Unlike two relatively hard materials sliding on each other, the tire is a soft material against a hard one, the road surface. Because roads have irregular surfaces the tire interlocks with it. The softer the tire, the more it interlocks to create additional grip. Grip and how to set up your car for maximum traction are explained in "How To Make Your Car Handle," another H.P.Book.

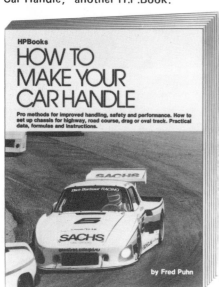

Therefore, to keep tires at their peak force-producing capability, they should be right on the edge of breaking loose. At the same time, the engine revs should be kept up for maximum torque and to prevent it from *bogging*. You can spot a good run by watching the tires of a car. If they are just on the verge of *hazing* the length of the quarter mile, it'll be a good run. This means just a fraction more power applied to the tires and they will spin, they'll "go up in smoke" and lose traction. This usually results in a lost race as acceleration drops off substantially.

Slider clutches are used with the Lenco-type transmissions which do not require the clutch to be disengaged while the transmission is shifted. Once the clutch is engaged, it remains so for the duration of a run. Therefore, due to the highly specialized nature of the slider clutch and the severe usage it is subjected to, special tailoring of the components is required.

Slider-clutch discs use sintered-iron facings due to the extremely high temperatures encountered during a typical run. Organic facings would be destroyed in a matter of

However, as a result of the *grip* developed by wrinkle-wall tires and super-sticky rubber compounds, Top Fuel dragsters are now capable of a 5.5-second, 250-MPH-plus quarter mile. For a car to do this, tire *grip* must exceed 1.50 when put in terms of the coefficient of friction. For a complete explanation on *grip* and how a tire reacts to forces such as braking, accelerating and cornering, see the HPBook, *How To Make Your Car Handle*.

Planetary gears used in transmissions such as the Lenco do not require clutch disengagement for shifting. Full power can be maintained without any interruption for shifting.
Photo courtesy Lenco Equipment Co.

The driving force from a Top Fuel or Funny Car is so high that axle housings bend if they are not strong enough or properly reinforced. This Ford axle housing is reinforced across the back.

For a given engine, the amount of CF weight used governs the RPM at which a slider will lock up. More weight results in sooner lock up—less gives later lock up. Every Fueler and Funny-car mechanic carries a weight assortment for his clutch.

seconds if subjected to the same treatment. To eliminate any unnecessary parts, slider-clutch discs don't use marcel cushioning springs or damping springs in the hub. I say unnecessary because there is sufficient damping from the slipping clutch and the "wrinkle-wall" drag-race tires to keep impact loading of the driveline to a minimum. Also, the additional parts would mean lower clutch durability and slower response. It is not uncommon to see the rear axle of a Fueler or Funny car last longer than a typical Modified, Super Stock or Gasser using manual transmissions, even though the driving loads are much higher. For example, axle housings must be reinforced to prevent them from bending due to the very high traction loads—the axle housings bend which causes the rear tires to toe-in if not reinforced properly.

The major distinguishing feature of the slider clutch is the pressure plate. Practically all slider clutches use Long-style pressure plates modified for this special purpose. The major reason for using the Long is its release-lever/CF-weight design. The slider clutch depends on centrifugal assist for plate load rather than the static load from the springs. Sometimes static pressure-

plate load can be as low as 300 lb. where the total load required for lock-up will be 2500 lbs.—the CF weights must make up the difference. As you know, the CF weights of the Long pressure plate are at the end of the levers outside of the cover. For adjustment purposes, the levers are cross-drilled at the end of the levers where the CF weights are located. Most of the weight is removed from each lever. To increase CF assist, weights are

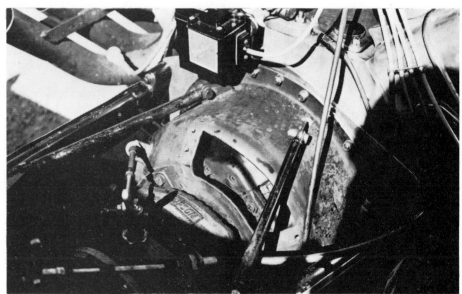

This bellhousing has its access cover removed so the lever heights, CF weights or static spring loads can be adjusted between runs. The smart guy changes only one thing at a time.

Minus the pressure plate, this is what a three-disc slider clutch looks like. The aluminum flywheel uses 6 to 12 drive stands to space the pressure plate to make room for the three discs and two floater plates. They also drive the floater plates. Discs use sintered-iron facings and solid hubs.

This is Hays' Tork-Loc slider clutch and flywheel assembly. It uses the basic Long pressure-plate design with externally adjustable CF weights, release-lever heights and static spring load. Six extra pressure-plate-cover bolts are used for additional rigidity.

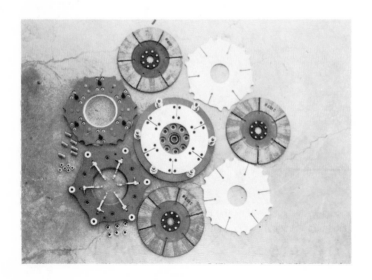

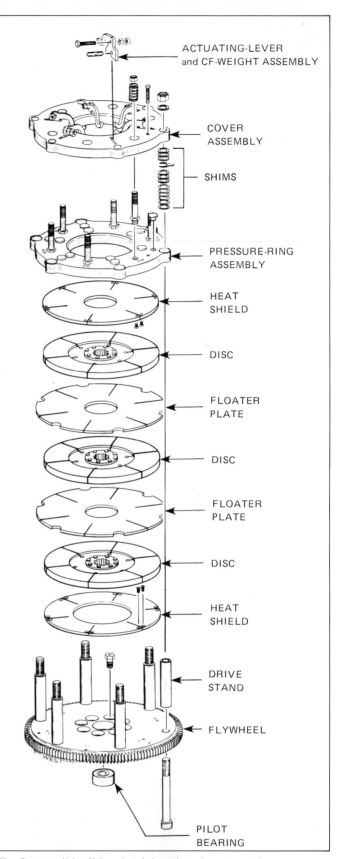

The Crowerglide slider clutch is unique in automotive competition. What makes it unique is the pressure plate. Load is derived solely from the centrifugal action of the levers.
Drawing courtesy Crower Cams and Equipment

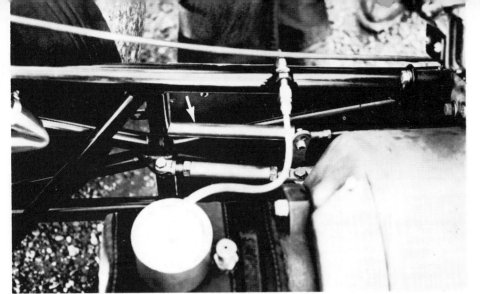

Because transmissions used in Top-Fuel dragsters don't have neutral, the clutch must be disengaged for towing or moving a car with the engine off. For convenience, a tube (arrow) has been placed between a vertical frame member and the clutch release lever to hold the clutch in its released position so the car can be moved.

added in the form of bolts, nuts and small washer-like weights, depending on the desired affect. The ends of the levers protrude outside the cover and are accessible through an access hole in the clutch housing, making adjustment an easy operation. Static plate load can be adjusted also.

Let's go through what happens with a typical slider clutch during a run. First, the car does a "burn-out" whether it is a Fueler or a Funny car. The rear tires are stopped in a puddle of water or traction compound, engine RPM is brought up to about 6000 RPM and the clutch is engaged. Because the tires can't develop much traction, they spin and the transmission is shifted into top gear. As the car moves out of the water and the engine picks up revs–up to 11,000 RPM–the tires heat up to a temperature where they develop maximum grip. The clutch remains locked-up during the burnout as the car moves down the track approximately 150 feet. The car is now pushed back past the starting line and "staged"–brought up to the line and stopped when the staging line is tripped on. The car is now ready for a start.

Engine RPM is brought up to the 6000 RPM area again and the clutch is engaged along with full

throttle being applied just as the green light comes on. Rather than the clutch locking up as it did during the burnout, the tires develop much more traction and the clutch begins to slip instead of the tires. The RPM at which this happens has been predetermined through testing and development–usually about 4000 RPM. Approximately 400 feet out from the starting line the engine and clutch discs approach the same RPM and the clutch becomes fully engaged and remains so as engine RPM increases, the transmission is shifted once and the car goes through the lights at the finish line. The chute is now popped, and because the Lenco *freewheels* when coasting, the clutch disengages and the engine is shut down. The run is over. If the clutch hadn't slipped one of two things would have happened, engine RPM would have been pulled down to a point causing it to "bog" and lose power or the tires would have "gone up in smoke" and maximum traction would have been lost– the result of both being a slow time or lost race.

The Crowerglide–A slider clutch which does the same thing by a different method is the Crowerglide. It is unique because it is a dry-disc clutch which uses only centrifugal force to load the pressure ring. The only springs used

withdraw the pressure ring from the discs, so additional centrifugal assist is required to overcome this "negative" load.

The major difference between how a conventional slider and a Crowerglide operate occurs at launch. With the conventional slider, engine RPM is increased to 5000 or 6000 RPM and the clutch is engaged on the green light. This is done by releasing the clutch pedal and simultaneously opening the throttle. Cars using a "glide" start with the throttle pedal *only*. Because revs much over 2000 RPM would cause premature clutch engagement, a Crowerglide-equipped car must sit with its engine at idle until the instant the green light flashes on. The throttle is then opened up. Because of the Crowerglide's dependance on centrifugally induced pressure-plate load, torque transferred to the driving tires builds at a slower rate than with the conventional slider. After launch, the Crowerglide and Long slider act about the same. They both slip until the centrifugally assisted plate load is enough to transmit full engine torque.

Before I get into the particulars of how this clutch works, you should realize that even though it looks complicated, it is really very simple. It is something like being scared to death of an instructor or teacher because of what others have said and being relieved to find out otherwise. Once you pick it up you will see what I mean.

Another point to mention is, the Crowerglide is not only used for drag-racing applications, it is also used in oval-track applications. The object is nearly the same as with drag cars, keep engine revs up so the engine won't bog. The principle and adjustments procedures are still the same. To complete the kit, Crower offers a bellhousing, release bearing, input shaft and operating mechanism.

The Crowerglide is a multi-disc clutch just as the conventional "slider." It normally uses three

The slider clutch isn't confined to only drag racing. This two-disc 8-inch Crowerglide is intended for oval-track racing—specifically super-modifieds and sprint cars.

Here's where a sprint car can benefit from a slider—exiting a turn with the engine "off the cam." The slider lets you gear your car with a lower numerical ratio so the engine won't be over-revved on the fast portion of the track. The clutch will let the engine operate in a power band so you won't lose any acceleration coming off the corners.

discs but is available with fewer, if less torque is to be transmitted. The drag clutch is 11 inches in diameter and the oval-track clutch is eight inches in diameter. Sintered-iron discs and steel floater plates are used as in Long sliders. The pressure plate is unique.

As I said, the pressure plate uses no static load—all the driving torque of the Crowerglide is derived purely from centrifugal force. There are springs in the pressure plate. However, their purpose is opposite to those in the conventional pressure plate. They are used to pull the pressure ring away from the clutch discs, whereas the springs in other clutch types are used to clamp the clutch discs between the pressure ring and flywheel. The drag type uses six springs and the oval-track type uses five. These are used to adjust clutch *stall speed*. This is the point at which an engine coupled to the clutch will cease to gain RPM when at full throttle—providing the transmission input shaft is turning slower than the engine. To do this there are studs attached to the pressure ring which project back through the cover—one for each spring—through counterbored holes which act as spring seats.

After the cover is set over the pressure ring, the five or six springs are placed concentrically around the studs and retained by locknuts. The more the springs are tightened down, the higher the stall speed of the pressure plate becomes. The higher the loads exerted by the springs, the more centrifugal force is required to overcome this negative static force. Because centrifugal force increases with RPM, the stall speed will be higher.

Crowerglide Actuating Levers—The Crowerglide clutch has *actuating levers*, not just *release levers*. This is the difficult thing to understand. Once you understand how the levers operate, you've got it.

First, the levers serve the purpose of manual engagement or disengagement and centrifugal engagement of the clutch. They are pivoted on the pressure-plate cover however, are not attached to the pressure ring as in the Long and Borg & Beck styles.

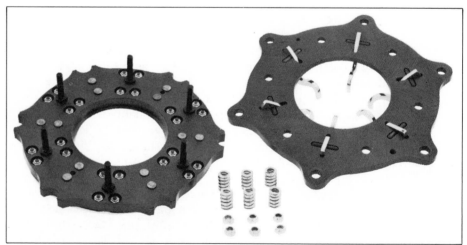

Rather than loading the pressure-ring against the clutch discs, springs in the Crowerglide pressure plate retract the pressure ring. As the springs are compressed by the adjusting nuts the stall speed, or RPM at which the clutch locks up, is increased. Six springs and nuts are shown with the cover and pressure-ring assemblies.

Here is a starter in place on the blower-drive pulley of a Funny car. A shot of fuel in the injector intake, the ignition switched on and it's ready to go. Starting in this manner is necessary because of the absence of an on-board starter.

The arm of each lever protrudes out the back of the cover then inboard like the conventional type. Directly behind the lever pivots is a hole in each lever for the addition of a bolt, nut and washers for counter-weighting. Because the levers load the pressure ring, they must be in contact with it at some point. This contact occurs between the cover and pressure ring however, the levers are not connected to the pressure ring.

The lever pivots are set in grooves in the cover and the lever and pivot assemblies are held in place by the stall springs loading the pressure ring against the levers. Each corner of the lever contacts hardened steel-button-wear surfaces set into the pressure ring.

As the clutch pedal is depressed, the release bearing pushes against the lever. In this instance, the bearing should be called an *engagement bearing* because as the bearing moves the levers forward, the inboard corners of the levers move the pressure ring forward to overcome the stall springs and engage the clutch discs. This is for starting a car's engine by pushing or with rolls. However, most Crowerglide-equipped cars are started with remote starters, so a clutch linkage is not used anyway.

A Funny Car burnout and run is just about the same as a Top-Fuel dragster, but because Crowerglides are normally used rather than the Long-style sliders, the process is a little different. One minor difference is a Funny Car can back up because they incorporate reverse—Fuelers do in rare instances. The major difference is a Crowerglide equipped car accelerates by bringing the engine from idle to full throttle on the start rather than having the tach sitting on six-grand to begin with.

No, this isn't a Funny Car doing a burnout—it's making a run at the sand drags. Replace the wrinkle walls with paddle tires and you have the wildest dune buggy ever. How does 100 yards in 2.5 seconds at 140 MPH sound?

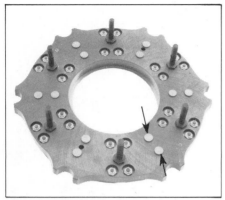

Crowerglide clutch engages when there is sufficient force from the levers bearing against the hardened-steel buttons set into the back of the pressure-ring to overcome the stall-speed springs.

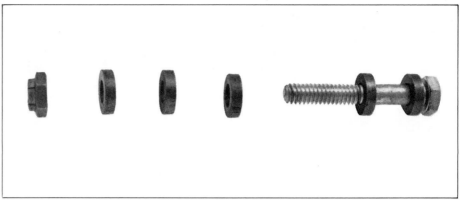

Just as with the Long slider, more or less weight on the levers and you get a corresponding change in centrifugal assist. Note the lock nut is the "hug-lock" type because just one run would melt a nylon insert in a nylon-lock nut.

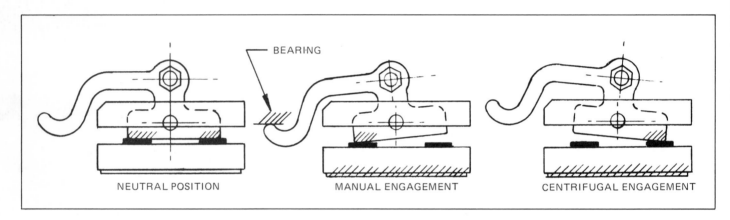

NEUTRAL POSITION   MANUAL ENGAGEMENT   CENTRIFUGAL ENGAGEMENT

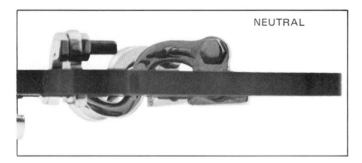

NEUTRAL

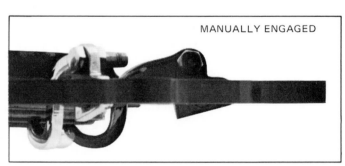

MANUALLY ENGAGED

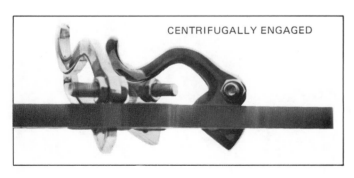

CENTRIFUGALLY ENGAGED

With the levers in the neutral position, the stall-speed springs pull the pressure ring back against the lever, holding them in the neutral position. As the lever is depressed, the inboard heel of the lever bears against a hardened steel button in the pressure-ring, pushing the ring into engagement with the discs for staging the car or moving it slowly. As engine revs increase, centrifugal force begins to act on the levers, rotating them in the opposite direction so the outboard heel of the levers bear against another pressure-ring button. The amount of pressure-plate load varies as the square of engine RPM. Cross-hatched areas in the sketches indicate points being loaded.

Everybody gets into the act. Here's Joe Smith on his dual-engined Harley doing a burnout. It is equipped with a scaled-down version of the Crowerglide.

Now for engaging the clutch for burnouts, staging and launching the car, the fingers are rotated in the other direction loading the outboard corners of the levers as the centrifugal loads increase with the RPM of the engine. The pressure plate is again forced into the discs, clamping them at a force which varies as the square of engine RPM. As engine RPM increases, so does the clamping force of the pressure plate until this force is sufficient to engage the clutch fully.

One point to recall is the difference between the static and dynamic coefficients of friction. As the clutch is slipping, it sees the *dynamic* coefficient of friction. When it locks up this changes to *static* because there is no relative motion between the driving and driven portions of the clutch. Because static friction is higher than dynamic, slippage will not occur when a transmission is shifted into high gear and engine RPM drops below what it was when lockup occurred in low gear—unless this drop is substantial. Less clamping force is required to keep the clutch from slipping than for initial lockup.

Oval-Track Crowerglide—As I mentioned earlier, the Crowerglide is used in some oval-track applications as well drag racing. It is best used for short-track applications with relatively slow corner speeds. For instance, a Super Modified on a 1/4-mile dirt or asphalt circle track will have engine RPM drop considerably when the car is in the turns. To keep the engine speed at the best peak-torque output, the stall springs can be adjusted to keep revs above a desired minimum RPM. Therefore, the car can come off the corners quicker because of more available power.

For convenience, a car with a clutch can be fitted with a starter. This eliminates the need for push starts. Also, when a spin-out occurs, the clutch will automatically disengage as engine revs drop to idle. Once the car is straightened out, it can continue the race.

Chapter Four
CLUTCH DESIGN

With all the available clutch components, you can literally design your own clutch system to fit your application exactly. You have a choice of friction materials, diameters, pressure-plate styles, how the plate load is derived and any number of choices to make.

Now that we've gone over the different types of clutches and the parts which make up these clutches, let's look at the "hows and whys." Pressure-plate loads, disc diameters, number of discs and other factors determine how a clutch will perform and they all relate to overall clutch performance.

Torque capacity is what the clutch is all about—the transfer of engine torque to the driveline. Engine torque must be transferred with maximum efficiency. It would be useless to go to all the trouble and expense of building a super engine just to hook it up to a clutch that can't handle it. Nothing is more frustrating than to be accelerating under full power and see the tach needle take off as the clutch slips and acceleration ceases.

When the clutch is engaged, it is at full efficiency. For all practical purposes, it is 100 percent even though a negligible amount of power is lost to aerodynamic drag. This is essential for proper cooling and the loss is so low that it need not be considered. As a result, the clutch is the most efficient mechanical device in the driveline when functioning properly. When it slips it is a power robber, a percentage is lost in the form of heat and what is left over is transmitted to the transmission on the way to the rear wheels. As you know, the amount of torque a clutch can transmit is directly related to pressure-plate load, all other things being equal. As explained at the beginning of the book, slipping the clutch is necessary to get a car in

Both of these cars require clutch slippage to get them moving. The difference in the initial slip rates of the two cars may be as high as 5000 RPM.

motion when powered by an inter-anl-combustion engine. Cars powered by electric motors or steam engines don't need a clutch or torque converter because they do not require RPM to develop torque. On the other hand, the internal-combustion engine requires between 1000–2000 RPM to get a car away smoothly under normal street-driving conditions. Under full-race conditions where maximum acceleration is the main objective, starting RPM must be much higher. How high? This depends on the car and the engine.

First, let's look at the basic formula which describes clutch capacity, or how much torque a given clutch can transmit. This formula is:

$$T = \frac{PNrC_f}{12}$$

Where:

T = Capacity in foot-pounds of torque.
P = Pressure-plate load in pounds.
N = Number of friction facings: Two for a single-plate clutch, four for a two-plate clutch, six for a three-plate and so on.
r = Mean effective radius in inches.
C_f = Coefficient of friction.

As can be seen from the formula, an increase in any of the factors on the right side of the equal sign will increase clutch capacity. This is

all well and good, however there is a limit to how much any of them can be increased. For example, pressure-plate load is directly proportional to the pedal force required to operate the clutch. There is a practical limit to what a human can do comfortably. On the other hand, a certain amount of force is required for proper control. Also, as the pressure-plate loads are increased, so are the loads on engine thrust bearings during clutch release. As the clutch-release bearing applies a load to the release fingers, it is also loading the end of the engine crankshaft the same amount. This re-

sults in accelerated wear of the crank thrust bearings as the plate loads exceed 3000 pounds. Also, organic clutch facings should not be loaded over 40 pounds per square inch. Metallic facings as used on today's clutch discs can work with almost any load.

As the number of friction facings or clutch discs is increased, clutch capacity increases dramatically. For every clutch disc there are two friction facings. This means if you start with a single-disc clutch and add another while maintaining the same plate load, clutch capacity will double. One of the limiting factors

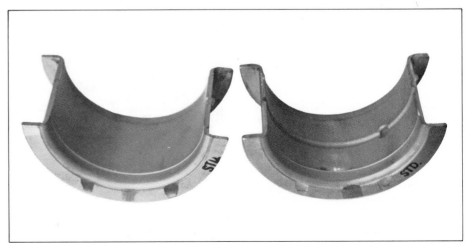

Pressure-plate release-bearing load is transmitted directly to the flanged portion of these engine crankshaft bearings. As pressure-plate load is increased, so is the thrust load on the bearings. Excessive clutch load drastically reduces thrust-bearing life.

McLeod's 8-1/2" triple-disc clutch uses a modified diaphragm pressure plate from a 2.3-liter Pinto. Its capacity is well over 600 foot-pounds.

is cost. If you are one of the lucky individuals to whom cost is no object, then great things can be done in this area. This doesn't mean to say that just adding more and more discs will solve all the clutch problems, it is not that simple. Other things can happen, mostly bad, if careful thought is not given. The formula used here tells you what a clutch can transmit, but it does not replace experience. For example, if you have an A-Modified production drag car and want to increase clutch capacity without going up in plate load, you may just install a double-disc clutch. If you do this without any thought, and use the wrong double-disc clutch, trouble may result. First, the inertia or rotating mass of the transmission-input shaft has just been increased considerably. As the transmission is shifted, synchros or dogs in the transmission must match the speeds of the input shaft to the driveline before engagement can occur. As weight is added to the input shaft, higher loads are on the transmission during shifting. The result may be broken transmissions or missed shifts or both. Other problems can occur if the wrong clutch is used, even though

the formula gives you the *right* numbers—if other factors aren't considered. For instance, some multi-disc clutches have less resistance to heat. The floater/s can't absorb and reject heat as efficiently as a pressure plate and flywheel. This is particularly true in the case of small-diameter units, particularly those with organic facings. I interject this information now to prevent someone from dropping the book and running out to buy the first multi-disc clutch he can find.

Mean Effective Radius, r, depends on the diameter of the clutch. An 11-inch clutch with the same plate load and facing width as a 10-inch clutch has more capacity. This radius describes a point at which the total friction force could be applied to produce the same torque as the distributed friction force. To find this radius, the following formula is used:

$$r = \frac{1.02 \, (r_o + r_i)}{2}$$

Where:

r = Mean effective radius in inches.

r_o = Outside disc radius in inches.

r_i = Inside disc radius in inches.

The limiting factor is the space

available to install a larger diameter clutch. At the design stage, clutch diameter is restricted by the amount of room available after considering all the other factors that must go into the package of an automobile. Take a look at the transmission tunnel in your car. The largest part of this tunnel is at the firewall— around the clutch. If it were much larger, there wouldn't be room left for your feet. Because we are not concerned with the initial design so much as improving on a design, we have to work with what we've got. This restricts us to an 11-inch-diameter clutch when we consider most domestic-built eights and sixes.

Again, *bigger is not necessarily better.* In fact, there are some special applications which may require a reduction in clutch diameter while the capacity must be increased at the same time!

The final factor in the capacity equation is the coefficient of friction of the disc facing. I'll use the number 0.30 as this is a good average for both organic and metallic facings. Organic friction materials vary somewhere between 0.24 and 0.38. At full fade, this figure drops off to about 0.20. In the case of metallic linings, the friction coefficient remains about the same as the

Increasing friction with heat in a clutch is not always a good thing. If this were the case with the sliders in these Funny Cars, they wouldn't slide. These cars were clicking off about 200 mph at this point. Note distorted rear tires.

temperature increases. In the case of sintered bronze, friction actually increases with temperature up to a point slightly higher than where an organic facing would fade. This is an advantage in some cases but not in others.

Let's see how the numbers work now. Starting out with a 10-inch-diameter single-disc clutch using a two-inch-wide organic facing and a plate load of 2500 pounds, find the capacity by plugging the numbers into the formula. First, the Mean Effective Radius must be solved for using the inside and outside radius of the disc facings. Ten divided by two equals five inches. The inside radius is this number minus the facing width, or five inches minus two inches equals three inches. Plugging these numbers in, we get:

$$r = \frac{1.02\,(5+3)}{2} = 4.08 \text{ inches}$$

Now, using this number in the capacity formula, we get:

$$T = \frac{PNrC_f}{12}$$
$$= \frac{2500 \times 2 \times 4.08 \times 0.30}{12}$$
$$= \frac{6120}{12}$$

$$= 510 \text{ ft-lb.}$$

If the clutch has overheated to the point of fade, capacity drops considerably as the coefficient of friction drops to 0.20. The resulting capacity becomes:

$$T \text{ (faded)}$$
$$= \frac{2500 \times 2 \times 4.08 \times 0.20}{12}$$

$$= 340 \text{ ft.-lb.}$$

The 0.10 reduction in the coefficient of friction gives a corresponding 33-percent reduction in torque-transmitting capacity. A good example of why a clutch should not be slipped excessively.

The capacity formula lets you determine clutch capacity. It can also be used to determine the minimum required pressure-plate load,

Mark Donohue accelerating hard in his 917 Turbo-Porsche as he exits a left-hander at Mosport Park. The success of this car was largely due to the engine's reported output of 1500 HP and the car's excellent handling. A small-diameter, multi-disc clutch transmits this power while permitting the engine to be set low in the chassis for minimum c.g. height. *Photo by Larry Griffin*

number of discs and clutch diameter required to transmit the torque of a given engine. Facing-material friction coefficients don't vary that much, so choosing the proper material is more a matter of the application rather than the small variances in the coefficient of friction. How heat affects the friction coefficient *is* a factor. Being able to do this is important because we are trying to find a clutch to transmit the torque of a given engine under specific conditions, not an engine to fit a clutch. Also, because we are living in the real world, a clutch must be able to withstand a variety of bad conditions such as disc wear, weakening springs, contamination from oil, dirt and grease and other detracting influences. To compensate for these, a 20-percent service

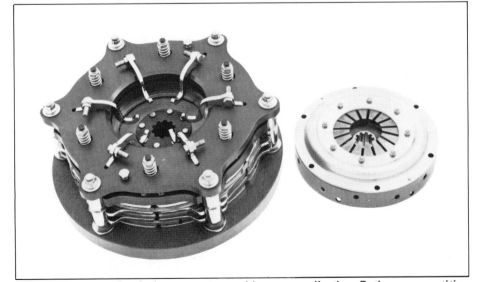

An excellent example of why you must consider your application. Both are competition clutches. Both have three metallic-faced discs and are used in cars which weigh approximately the same and reach a maximum speed of approximately 250 MPH. The 11" Crowerglide is used mostly in Funny Cars and the 7-1/4" Borg and Beck is used in Indy cars.

margin is added to the formula by multiplying T by 1.2, or:

$$(1.2)T = \frac{PNrC_f}{12}$$

and

$$T = \frac{PNrC_f}{14.4}$$

Now, if we have an engine which produces 500 foot-pounds of torque at 4000 RPM and we want to find the minimum pressure-plate load required to transmit this torque using the same clutch, we can do so by transposing the equation to give:

$$P = \frac{(14.4)\,T}{NrC_f}$$

or

$$P = \frac{14.4 \times 500 \text{ foot-pounds}}{2 \text{ surfaces} \times 4.08 \text{ inches} \times .30}$$
$$= 2941 \text{ pounds}$$

If this were a Long or Borg & Beck style pressure plate using centrifugal assist, the static pressure plate load could be held to 2500 pounds with a centrifugal assist of 440 pounds at the rated RPM.

By going to a multi-disc clutch, the torque-producing capability of a clutch goes up dramatically. For example, if a double-disc clutch is used in the above application, let's see what the resulting pressure-plate load would be. Remember, the number of friction surfaces would be four, or twice the number of discs.

$$P = \frac{14.4 \times 500 \text{ foot-pounds}}{4 \text{ surfaces} \times 4.08 \text{ inches} \times .30}$$
$$= 1470 \text{ pounds}$$

This is half of the previous pressure-plate load. With this type of improvement, one would have to take a second look at the multi-disc clutch. A lot of people have and as a result the multi-disc clutch is finding its way into virtually all types of racing applications. Chevrolet even offered a 10-inch double-disc unit as an option for the 454-CID-equipped Corvette. This equipment is available under the following part numbers, but unless you have a Chevrolet which can use the flywheel, you may have to modify your flywheel.

Borg-Warner's Double Coupler can be used with engines other than big-block Chevrolets if the flywheel is drilled to match and you have a 1-1/8''-10- or 26-spline transmission input shaft. Borg-Warner part numbers are 360132 for the pressure plate, 300141 for the floater/center plate and 380259 and 380327 for the 1-1/8'' 10- and 1-1/8'' 26-spline discs, respectively.

Let's run through a practical application using the formulas. Given an engine which develops 500 foot-pounds maximum torque, using a clutch diameter of 10.5 inches, find the required pressure-plate load. Using the formula on page 51, we have:

$$T = \frac{PNrC_f}{12}$$

and transposing to solve for pressure plate load,

$$P = \frac{12T}{NrC_f}$$

To solve for **r**, the inside diameter of the disc must be known. Without having a disc in front of you to measure, it is handy to know that friction-facing widths are usually 20 percent of the outside diameter of the clutch. Therefore, the facing width for a 10.5-inch clutch is .20 multiplied by 10.5 inches, or 2.1 inches. To solve directly for the inside diameter, subtract twice the facing width—**w**—from the outside diameter:

$$ID = OD - 2w$$
$$= 10.5 \text{ inches} - 2 \times 2.1 \text{ inches}$$
$$= 6.3 \text{ inches}$$

Now you have all the numbers necessary to solve for the mean effective radius. Keeping in mind that the radius is half the diameter and inserting the numbers into the formula:

$$r = \frac{1.02\,(r_o + r_i)}{2}$$
$$= \frac{1.02\,(5.25 + 3.13)}{2}$$
$$= 4.184 \text{ inches}$$

Now, solve for minimum pressure-plate load:

$$P = \frac{12 \times 500 \text{ foot-pounds}}{2 \text{ facings} \times 4.184 \text{ inches} \times .30}$$
$$= 2390 \text{ pounds}$$

Using the graph, start at the torque capacity of 500 foot-pounds and read across until hitting the correct clutch-diameter curve. In this case, 10.5 inches. Then read straight down to pressure-plate load. 2400 pounds is close enough. Now add 20 percent to this figure for the service margin. So, 0.20 multiplied by 2400 pounds then added to 2400 pounds equals 2880 pounds, more than enough plate load to handle 500 foot-pounds of engine torque.

Static load versus centrifugal assist— Now we have the proper pressure-plate load. It must be distributed between static and centrifugal load. This decision is based on the RPM of the engine at maximum torque and the maximum RPM at which the transmission will be shifted. Therefore, it will be a trade-off between pedal effort at high and at low revs. The first is encountered while shifting during a race and the other while driving on the street.

If too much centrifugal load causes shifting to be difficult while racing, then the centrifugal load must be reduced and static load increased to make up for the reduced centrifugal load at peak torque RPM. This situation causes increased pedal effort at lower RPM, making street driving more uncomfortable. That's the problem: To get sufficient plate load without making the car impossible to drive on the street—and keep the high-rev pedal

efforts low enough so you can operate the clutch pedal satisfactorily for shifting.

Sifting this can of worms is an impossible task without a few ground rules. For practical purposes, don't use a pressure plate with less than a 2000-pound static load. On the other hand, don't use a pressure plate with a static load exceeding 3600 pounds at any RPM. The reason for this is the normal ratio between pressure-plate load and pedal forces is 60:1. Therefore, a 2000-pound pressure plate will yield pedal-operation forces in the area of 30—35 pounds. A pressure-plate load of 3600 pounds will result in efforts averaging 60 pounds. A 35-pound pedal effort is considered to be *optimum* by automotive engineers; 45 pounds is considered *stiff*. When we get to the 60-pound class, it is considered *excessive*, but nothing the dedicated racer can't handle if absolutely necessary. Now, it's easy to make sure you get a performance pressure plate with more than 2000 pounds of static load because few are available with less. Big things can happen on the other end of the scale, however. For example, if some poor unsuspecting guy happened to choose an 11-inch, six-roller, 2700-pound static-loaded Borg & Beck clutch for his car which he planned to shift at 8500 RPM, the pressure-plate load would be 6200 pounds at this RPM. Pedal effort would be over 100 pounds. Impossible for fast shifting and extremely uncomfortable. A guy would end up with a short left leg. A full-weighted Long would yield the same basic results. A clutch with this kind of plate load would have enough capacity to handle nearly 900 foot-pounds of torque at 5000 RPM. It's very unlikely that a street/competition car would ever need this much clutch.

As for choosing a pressure plate for your car, I recommend if you find the maximum plate load required for the peak torque of your engine to be less than 2800

CENTRIFUGAL ASSIST vs ENGINE RPM
LONG STYLE PRESSURE PLATE

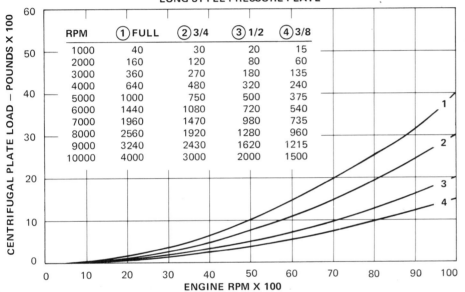

RPM	① FULL	② 3/4	③ 1/2	④ 3/8
1000	40	30	20	15
2000	160	120	80	60
3000	360	270	180	135
4000	640	480	320	240
5000	1000	750	500	375
6000	1440	1080	720	540
7000	1960	1470	980	735
8000	2560	1920	1280	960
9000	3240	2430	1620	1215
10000	4000	3000	2000	1500

3 & 6-ROLLER 10.95-INCH-DIAMETER BORG & BECK PRESSURE PLATE
CENTRIFUGAL PLATE LOAD vs ENGINE RPM

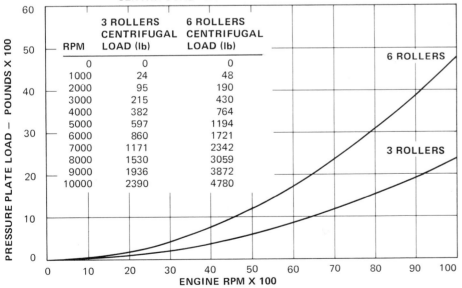

RPM	3 ROLLERS CENTRIFUGAL LOAD (lb)	6 ROLLERS CENTRIFUGAL LOAD (lb)
0	0	0
1000	24	48
2000	95	190
3000	215	430
4000	382	764
5000	597	1194
6000	860	1721
7000	1171	2342
8000	1530	3059
9000	1936	3872
10000	2390	4780

Use these curves for determining centrifugal assist of Long or Borg & Beck pressure plates. To use them, move up from the RPM you are interested in to the proper assist curve, then go left and read centrifugal load.

For a drag car such as this Mustang, a 100-percent statically loaded pressure plate should be used. If too much assist is used, pedal forces will be too high to shift consistently at high revs.

pounds, don't bother with centrifugal devices. If the load is over this figure, look at the possibility of going to a larger-diameter clutch. If this doesn't work out, start the process of elimination using the pressure-plate load to torque capacity curves on page 71 and the centrifugal-assist curves on the preceding page. When choosing centrifugal assist, keep in mind you are trying to do two things, keep pedal forces low for high-RPM shifting *and* for street driving.

Remember, you can't have both. It turns into a real balancing act. With no CF assist, the pedal forces will be the same at all RPM. With maximum assist, pedal forces will be low at low engine revs and high at high revs. As centrifugal assist is reduced, the forces get closer. The best way of explaining how to choose the correct amount of CF assist is to go through two extreme examples:

First Example: Given a big-block engine producing 650 foot-pounds of torque at 4000 RPM. It is intended for drag racing, therefore, high-RPM-fast shifts are to be made—7500 RPM for this car. The

car originally had a 10.5-inch clutch. First the plate load must be determined. Going to the load-capacity curve and reading over from 650 foot-pounds, the minimum plate load for a 10.5-inch clutch is 3050 pounds. Adding the 20-percent service factor to this load will only move it farther from 3050 pounds. Therefore, go to the 11-inch clutch. Just so happens the load is 2800 pounds, but 20 percent must still be added. Providing this is the largest-diameter clutch that can be used for this car, it will have to do. Adding 20 percent to the plate load:

Plate load = 2800 pounds + .20 X 2800 pounds = 3360 pounds

In an attempt to get street pedal forces down, centrifugal assist should be tried. Because the car is to be shifted at over 6000 RPM, I recommend you not consider the three-roller Borg & Beck because of its tendency to hang up when fast shifts are made at high RPM. The rollers, which are wedged between the cover and the pressure ring, must be "unwedged." This

leaves the Long style. If the flywheel has a diaphragm or Borg & Beck bolt pattern, use the combination Long/Borg & Beck. Looking at the Long pressure-plate centrifugal-assist curves on page 55, try the full assist just to see what happens. Assist at 4000 RPM is 640 pounds, reading up from 4000 RPM to the full-assist curve and across to centrifugal load. To get minimum static load:

3360 − 640 = 2720 pounds.

Not too bad for street driving because the plate load would be about 3000 pounds at 3000 RPM. or approximately 50 pounds pedal force.

Now look at the high-RPM shifting force. At 7500 RPM, the centrifugal assist is 2200 pounds. Add this to 2720 static plate load, the plate load is nearly 5000 pounds, pedal force 83 pounds! Too much for quick operation of the clutch. This being the case, try the 3/8 assist. Going through the process again, the 3/8ths assist gives 250 pounds assist at 4000 RPM:

Subtracting 3360 − 250 = 3110 pounds static plate load.

At 3000 RPM, plate force is 3245 pounds with a corresponding pedal force of 54 pounds. Hardly enough difference to bother with—only 2 pounds lower pedal force than if it were 100 percent static. At the higher shifting revs, the plate load would be 850 lbs. assist + 3110 lbs. static plate load = 3960 pounds: 66 pounds of pedal force.

By staying with the minimum required load in static load only, the 7500-RPM pedal force would be five pounds less. It would be best to use 100 percent static pressure and live with the extra two pounds pedal force for street driving.

A final thought, if the car is already set up for the diaphragm, strong consideration should be given it. The reason is, given equal pressure-plate loads for the diaphragm, Borg & Beck and Long,

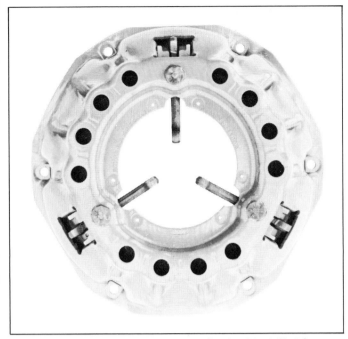

If you are going drag racing and your flywheel is drilled for a diaphragm or Borg & Beck bolt pattern, the combination Long/Borg & Beck is a good choice. Note the reinforced windows and removed CF weights.

You'd be smiling too if you were the only one at the sand drags with a Hemi-powered Jeep. A Clutchflite behind this engine makes a six-roller Borg & Beck or full CF assisted Long a good choice.

pedal-operating forces will be lower for the diaphragm due to the Belleville-spring force/deflection characteristics. Coil-spring clutches cause an increase in pedal force as the pressure plate is disengaged because as a coil spring is compressed, the loads required to compress it increase. As a diaphragm spring is compressed, the load goes down—*if it is adjusted properly*. This point cannot be stressed enough, the diaphragm clutch must be installed and carefully adjusted before it can operate properly. The tolerance for sloppy installation and adjustment for the Long and Borg & Beck pressure plates is higher. Don't let this be your reason for choosing these styles.

Second Example: Given a big-block engine making 550 foot-pounds of torque at 3500 RPM. The engine is in a four-wheel-drive vehicle intended for off-road racing. The engine revs to a maximum of 6000 RPM and very little shifting is required, at least not at high revs. The car is equipped with an 11-inch clutch.

The first requirement is to determine pressure-plate load. From page 71 graph, the minimum plate load required is 2450 lbs. + 20 percent = 2940 pounds plate load. Resultant pedal force with this plate load will be approximately 49 pounds. Not too bad, however, it should be less in case the little lady were to use it to go shopping. This looks like a good candidate for a full centrifugally loaded Long or a six-roller Borg & Beck. Assuming it was originally equipped with a Borg & Beck, try it first. The assist for a six-roller Borg & Beck at 3500 RPM is 600 pounds.

2940 lbs. − 600 lbs. = 2340 lbs. static plate load.

Because this engine is more of a low-RPM torquer, it would probably be shifted at about 2500 RPM on the street. The plate load at this engine speed is 2340 lbs. static load + 300 lbs. centrifugal assist = 2640 pounds and a pedal force of 44 pounds—a reduction of five pounds. This is worthwhile if the higher RPM range is not excessive.

At 6000 RPM, 1700 lbs. centrifugal assist + 2340 pounds static load which equals 4040 pounds and a 67-pound pedal force. This is on the high side. However, if there is not likely to be much shifting at this rev range, it would be a good choice. Sometimes it comes down to personal preference. Maybe you would prefer less centrifugal assist. If the three-roller setup were used, static load would be 2940 lbs. − 300 lbs. assist = 2640 lbs. At 2500 RPM total plate force is 2640 lbs. static + 130 lbs. assist = 2770 lbs. giving a pedal force of 46 lbs. Resultant pedal force is still three pounds less than the 100 percent statically loaded pressure plate and only two more pounds than the six-roller. At 6000 RPM, load is 2640 lbs. + 860 lbs. = 3500 pounds. Almost ten pounds less pedal force at 58 pounds. If the decision is to live with static pressure-plate loads the diaphragm clutch would be a good setup. Just as in the first example, you would still have the pressure-plate load no matter what RPM and with reduced pedal forces.

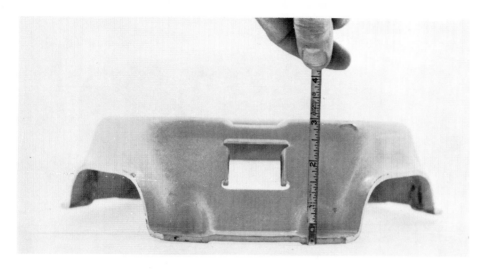

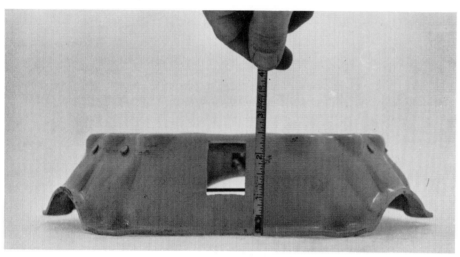

Heights of the three basic pressure-plate covers vary from a high of 3 inches for the Long to a low of about 2 inches for the diaphragm. The Borg & Beck is in the middle at 2-1/2".

Fast lever ratios—One more consideration, pressure plates can be obtained with higher than average numerical lever ratios. The fast lever ratios are about 5:1 and the slower ratios are in the neighborhood of 6:1. The 5:1 ratio is standard for the Long and 6:1 is the Borg & Beck standard. This is one reason why the Long-style pressure plate is known for its quick-release. The Borg & Beck is also available with a 5:1 ratio. The thing to watch for is the faster ratio requires more pedal force, all things being equal. The slower ratio requires less force, but it is also slower to operate, thus the *faster* and *slower* designations.

When it comes to lever ratios, the diaphragm pressure plate is totally different. It has a ratio in the area of 3.5:1—very fast—and the reason for its fast lock-up reputation. Surprisingly, average pedal forces are lower than the slow-ratio Borg & Beck with equal plate loads. This results from the Belleville-spring force/deflection characteristics. So, take a second look at the diaphragm pressure plate because from all indications it is going to be used more and more for its advantages: High plate loads for relatively low operating forces in a compact package.

CLUTCH EFFICIENCY

Slip ratio is the ratio between engine speed and clutch-output speed. It is found by dividing disc speed by pressure-plate, or engine speed. For example, if an engine is turning 4000 RPM and the clutch is being slipped so the clutch-output or disc speed is 2000 RPM, to get the slip ratio, divide 2000 RPM by 4000 RPM. The result is a slip ratio of 0.50. To find *clutch efficiency* at any slip ratio, multiply the ratio by 100 or read it directly off the graph on page 68. In the above case, the clutch efficiency is 50 percent. 0.50 multiplied by 100.

Efficiency is the amount of power on the output side of the clutch versus the power being

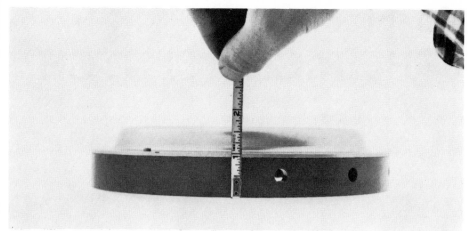

Here's a low-profile clutch assembly. This is Borg and Beck's 7-1/4" three-disc assembly —complete!

produced by the engine. In the example just given, half of the power produced by the engine is lost at the clutch. On the other hand, the amount of torque an engine produces, whether the clutch is slipping or not, is the same torque being transmitted, providing engine RPM is maintained. If the engine in question is producing 500 foot-pounds of torque at full throttle while maintaining the revs at 4000 RPM, the torque being transmitted by the clutch is the same, 500 foot-pounds. Doesn't sound like any power has been lost, does it? If you don't think so, how would you like to put your hand on the clutch? A good example of power transformed into heat energy. Torque is not work, it is force. Power occurs when a *force* applied to an object moves the object a *distance* in a certain amount of *time*. You could push on the corner of your house all day and the only work done would be in the form of burned-up calories and the sweat on your brow. In the case of the clutch, force is torque, the object moved for a given amount of time is the

RPM—revolutions per minute—of the engine crankshaft or the transmission-input shaft.

We are accustomed to expressing engine power in terms of horsepower rather than Joules, watts or foot-pounds per second. To find horsepower when torque and RPM is know, use the formula:

Horsepower

$$= \frac{RPM \times Torque \text{ in foot-pounds}}{5250}.$$

To put this formula to use, plug in the figures from the example: 4000 RPM multiplied by 500 foot-pounds of torque and divided by 5250 yields 380 horsepower. Half of this power is being transmitted to the driveline because of the clutch being slipped at 50 percent efficiency. The other half is being dissipated in the form of heat. To prove this, plug in the figures from the output side of the clutch: 2000 RPM multiplied by 500 foot-pounds divided by 5250 equals 190 horsepower. Half of the power of the engine was being used at this point to generate heat and the other to accelerate the car. We are interested in acceleration.

Chapter Five
CHOOSING THE RIGHT CLUTCH

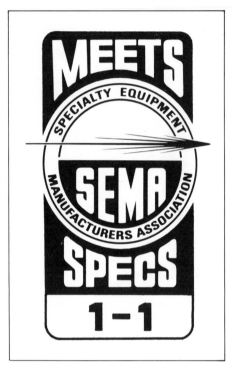

When purchasing a high-performance clutch, look for this label. It assures you that the parts meet minimum performance standards established by SEMA (Specialty Equipment Manufacturer's Association).

Usually the poor old clutch comes as an afterthought when a guy builds up his car. When one is replaced, usually it is because the old one wore out. This is to be expected because what is so dramatic about a clutch when you have things like trick cams, headers, carbs and all that good stuff to think about? Well, the clutch can be very dramatic on one hand and very undramatic on the other.

If you've ever seen the results of an exploded clutch, you'll know how dramatic. A 12-gauge shotgun is kids' stuff by comparison—clutches are more like hand grenades. Take for example any typical small-block engine which redlines at about 5500 RPM stock and receives the full treatment from a roller-tappet cam to double-pumper carburetors. The engine is now capable of nine grand. Somehow the stock clutch finds its way back into the car with disaster just over the hill. Maybe the clutch will last for a little while, but after a few hard starts the disc will have gotten sufficiently hot that the binding has weakened to the point that the next trip to 9000 RPM—BANG!!!

This is minor when it comes to clutch explosions because facing material is relatively light. The bad stuff happens when a pressure plate lets go—you'd think the mob had planted a bomb. What usually goes is the pressure ring. Grey cast iron just can't handle loads for which it wasn't intended. They are not intended for use much over 7000 RPM, but must with-stand periodic trips to 8500 RPM for a safety margin. When one is subjected to the loads imposed by high revs over and over, the pressure ring fatigues and failure results.

Stock clutches can handle much more torque than the stock engines they were designed for can produce. The first reason is due to the safety margin. The other reasons are based on the premise that a clutch must be able to operate under many adverse conditions, some worse than those encountered in high-performance applications. One of the typical tests a clutch must pass before it is given the OK for production is the in-the-car fade test. This is done by pulling the test car up to an immovable wall or barrier, bringing the engine RPM up to maximum rated horse-power and letting the clutch out slowly while maintaining engine speed until it stalls. This must be done a minumum number of times without failing the clutch, say about 20 times. To make things worse, the test is done without letting the clutch cool down. The stock clutch must also with-stand thousands of engagement and disengagement cycles, simulating approximately 50,000 miles of driving. After all of this, a clutch must still operate satisfactorily—no objectionable slipping, grabbing or vibrating.

The type of stock clutch which can cause the most problems when used behind a high-revving high-performance engine uses a centrifugally assisted Borg & Beck or Long pressure plate equipped with

The facing was torn off this disc as a result of being overheated. Assuming this clutch was setup correctly and it has to be slipped for the specific application, a metallic-faced disc would be the answer.

You can't tell this is a stock Long pressure plate. It uses the thinner 0.125" cover material, grey cast-iron pressure-ring and full CF weights. If used behind a high-revving small block, the clutch will not slip because of the CF assisted pressure-plate load, however the pressure plate may explode.

a grey cast-iron pressure ring. The reason for this is, a *centrifugally assisted* pressure plate increases in capacity with RPM due to centrifugal assist. The result is, it *can* transmit the torque of a high-performance engine. Because a stock clutch is not designed to handle high revs and torque for extended use, the result may be an exploding clutch. This can happen because a high-performance engine produces more torque than in its stock configuration—but at higher RPM. At the same time, clutch capacity is increasing at a faster rate with RPM than engine torque. Remember, clutch capacity is directly proportional to pressure-plate load which increases as the square of engine RPM.

An *unassisted* pressure plate does not have an increasing plate load with RPM. Therefore, it will usually end up slipping when additional torque is applied to it. This is due to inadequate plate load. The worse thing that will happen is the disc facings will burn up rather undramatically, possibly ruining the pressure plate in the process. There is a chance that, if the pressure plate does make it through the peak torque range of the engine and get

to high RPM, the pressure ring may come apart.

Most big-block engines begin to lose torque between 3000 and 4000 RPM—say for instance, after reaching a maximum torque of 450 foot-pounds. Take a stock big-block and install a few goodies like a high-lift

cam with solid lifters, a high-rise intake manifold and an accompanying carburetor, headers and the such, and the thing is just starting to wake up at three-grand. Assume it is now capable of 550 foot-pounds of torque at 5000 RPM and redlines at 8000 RPM.

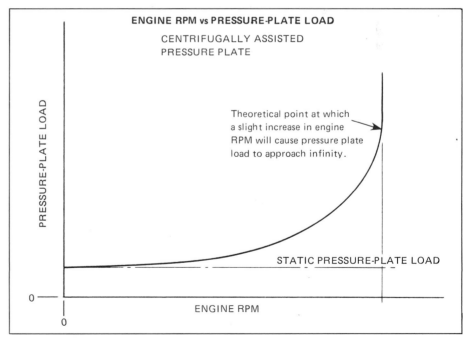

This curve represents centrifugal pressure-plate assist as a function of engine RPM. There is a point where a slight RPM increase will cause centrifugal plate load to approach infinity. The curve is said to go asymptotic (flat) at this point.

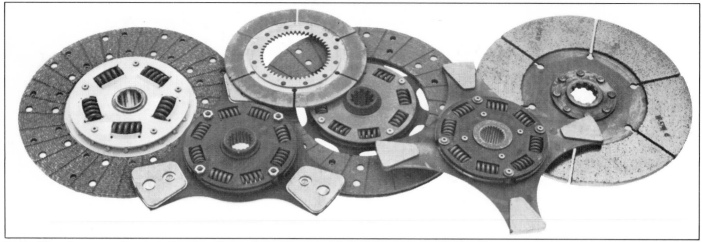

Regardless of your application, there's a disc to fit it. Here are a few of the many available.

Now, if a stock 11-inch, single-disc, Borg & Beck clutch with six rollers having a 2000-pound static plate load was originally used with this engine in its stock form and is retained for use with the modified engine, trouble is sure to result. For example, the 2000-pound plate load works out to about 450 foot-pounds of capacity. At 3000 RPM, plate load increases to 540 foot-pounds, more than enough capacity to handle the stocker, and the modified. At 5000 RPM most stock big-block engines have reached their rev-limit.

Farther up the scale at our self-established limit of 8000 RPM, pressure-plate load climbs outa sight at 5000 pounds. The problem is apparent at this point. Loads are much higher on the disc and pressure-plate components than those for which they were designed. Also, as the clutch is disengaged for shifting, additional load is transmitted to the clutch linkage. Sooner or later one or more of several things can be expected. The clutch disc can shed its facing. The clutch linkage will bend or break. Worse yet, the pressure-plate pressure ring can explode or become separated from the cover or the cover can permanently deform or tear away from the flywheel.

The question is, how to choose a clutch for a particular car? There is no pat answer. If there was there wouldn't be a constant influx of new clutch components. Today's answer may be unacceptable tomorrow. Just pick up a catalog from one of the major high-performance clutch manufacturers—Borg-Warner, Hays, McLeod, RAM, Schiefer, Weber or Zoom. Inside you will see an array of pressure plates and discs. They offer different static loads and centrifugal assists in addition to the various pressure-plate styles. Even more discs—organic or metallic friction material, sprung or unsprung hubs, marcel or no marcel, riveted or bonded, which diameter? Where does a guy start?

Because the large percentage of high-performance clutch applications will be for the street car which will see several trips to the drag strip, I will concentrate in this area. However, I'll also discuss all-out high-performance applications to provide more insight as to why different style clutches are used for different applications. This may also help you understand clutches that much better. I'll also talk about the guy who uses his street car for slaloms or gymkhanas or just everyday fun street driving. No matter which application we look at, the idea is still the same, get the engine power to the rear wheels. One fact remains, no matter what type of motor sport you prefer, drag racing is the toughest application for a clutch. If a clutch holds up under this abuse, it will survive other high-performance applications. Before I trap myself, this is not always true because as I said previously, there isn't *one* pat answer.

Selecting a clutch for your car, whether for the street, for racing or somewhere in between, the pieces must match. The selection process must be orderly. First, you have to consider the car: engine, total weight and transmission. Second, the application must be considered. Is the car going to be used for the street, for drag racing, circle-track racing or what? Finally, you must know what is available. Listing the points of consideration, we have:

THE CAR

1. Engine, the torque it develops and at what RPM?

2. Type of transmission used and the gear ratios, particularly in first gear? Also, is the transmission to be shifted and when must the clutch be disengaged to do so? If it is a planetary-gear type such as a Clutchflite or a Lenco, the clutch does not have to be disengaged to shift.

3. Rear-axle gear ratio?
4. How much does the car weigh?

THE APPLICATION

1. Street.
2. Street and racing.
3. Racing; drag, circle track, road racing, off road or any other type of racing man has dreamed up.

PARTS AVAILABILITY

1. Pressure plate; Long, Borg & Beck, diaphragm or special-application type and the ratio of static plate load to centrifugal assist.
2. The disc; organic facing and how attached: riveted, riveted-and-bonded and bonded. Metallic facing: sintered bronze, sintered iron or copper. Marcel spring or no marcel. Sprung or unsprung hub.
3. Diameter of the clutch and the number of discs.

This gives you quite a lot to consider. By putting everything down in black and white, your selection becomes much easier. One final check can be made to see if you've made the correct selection, particularly if you are heavily into the racing scene. Find out what the fast cars in your class are using. Nothing works as well as success. But don't let this be final. Make sure your findings agree and, if not, find out why. One thing that seems to be consistent when it comes to opinions about clutches, very few agree on any *one* thing. Ask ten people for an opinion and you'll get 11 opinions.

STREET APPLICATIONS

Let's start out on the ground floor, a car with a stock or mildly modified engine intended strictly for the street. This the easiest one to start with because Detroit has already done the work for us. By mildly modified, I mean the engine has been externally modified only—carburetion, headers, spark curve, etc.—excluding turbocharging. The torque output and RPM of this type of engine will not be substantially higher than what it was in its pure-stock form, even though it will be more responsive. When the safety margin

of the stock clutch is taken into account, it will probably have more than enough capacity to handle the engine. Therefore, for a car which falls into this category, the stock clutch will probably do the job. To install a racing clutch would be expensive and wouldn't do a thing for your car in terms of performance. You would only put your money into circulation earlier and make your car uncomfortable to drive. The best thing to do would be to make sure you get a quality factory-replacement clutch, either from your new-car dealer or from a performance shop which carries a reputable brand

Choosing a clutch system for either of these single-purpose cars is relatively simple once you know all the variables. For example, this small-block Chevy-powered street rod should provide years of enjoyable and comfortable street operation. A diaphragm pressure plate with an aluminum-backed organic disc would be an excellent choice. The small-block Ford-powered sand-drag Jeep is strictly meant to go fast. This is a non-shifting application where wheel-spin is desirable. A six-button copper-ceramic disc with a CF assisted Long pressure plate would be just right.

name of performance *street* clutches. Performance-clutch manufacturers offer direct-replacement clutches and they all stand behind their products.

One of the points performance-clutch manufacturers stress over and over, *don't over-clutch your car!* When you install a 3200-pound pressure plate when a 2500-pound one is sufficient or use excessive centrifugal assist or use a disc having a solid hub and no marcel spring, the manufacturer usually hears about it by way of a nasty letter from the customer complaining about a bent clutch linkage, his sore leg or a chattering clutch. All this because he installed the "hot-tip" clutch in his car. He used the same one the big guys at the strip were using or the man behind the counter talked him into buying just to make an extra buck.

What kind of clutch should you expect to see in your car? If you will recall, General Motors products have used the diaphragm-type pressure plate exclusively since the early 60's. Ford products have used the Long-style clutch ever since they gave up spoke wheels.

As for Chrysler and American Motors, they use the Borg & Beck style. Each manufacturer has its own preference when it comes to pressure plates. A trend is shaping up. Ford started changing to the diaphragm beginning with the 302 in the Mustang II. The reason for this is the low pedal force required to operate the diaphragm clutch permits a simplification in clutch-linkage design. Cars using the Borg & Beck or Long-style pressure plates require an assist spring in the clutch linkage which complicates it and makes it more expensive, *expensive* being the key word. Therefore, by using the diaphragm pressure plate, this spring can be eliminated without any increase in pedal forces or loss in clutch capacity.

No matter what make car you have, the basic configuration of the driven member, the disc, will be identical. All have organic facings which are riveted, hubs will be sprung, and all use marcel springs for smooth engagement. In fact, the O.E.M.—original equipment manufacturer—clutch is designed with the objective of smooth operation, after torque capacity and durability. These should be your objectives also.

Even though each car manufacturer may use a different type of clutch, this doesn't mean one will be more streetable or perform better than another. When pressure plates and discs are analyzed separately, they will display different characteristics other than just being a different style. However, when you drive one make car and then another, you'll have a difficult time telling any difference. The reason for this is clutches are designed as a *system* which includes more than the pressure plate and disc. It includes the engine and transmission, their mounts, the driveshaft, the rear axle, rear suspension, and the clutch linkage. Because the manufacturers have the same general objectives such as performance, durability and pedal feel and force, they also have similar test and evaluation procedures. Consequently, differences in clutch operation and performance are not pronounced. The difference really begins to show when a car gets into the hands of the guy who wants to make it

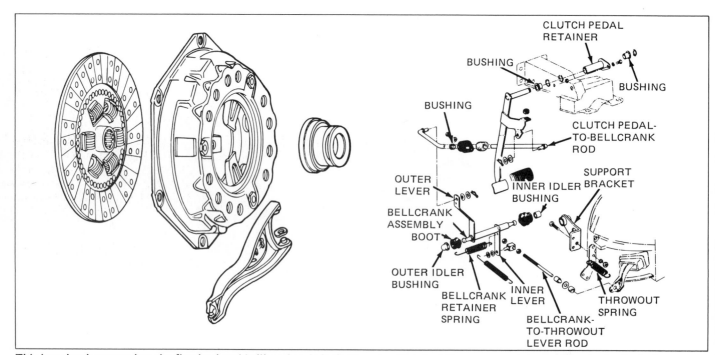

This is a clutch system less the flywheel and bellhousing. It includes more than just the pressure plate and disc. It also includes everything from the clutch pedal pad to the flywheel mounting flange on the crankshaft. *Drawings courtesy AMC*

faster than the next guy. The strong and weak points begin to show up and the proper modifications have to be made.

Let's go over what clutch you should be using in your car point by point. First, the engine is mildly modified, so the amount of torque the clutch must transmit is 20 percent higher at the most without any substantial increase in RPM. The transmission and rear axle have not been changed nor has the weight of the car. As for the application, the car is to be driven on the street, and to be realistic, will have an occasional run at the stop light. Something that should not happen, but we all have our weak moments. With all this in mind and the knowledge the OEM clutches are designed using a large service factor, resorting to anything other than an OEM replacement clutch or equivalent would probably be a waste of money and would unnecessarily increase clutch-pedal efforts and the load on your clutch linkage.

Choosing the right clutch for a double-duty car is a toughy. Chances are if you are going to be the only driver, you'll favor racing when it comes time for compromising. Obviously, this Chevelle wagon is 100-percent in favor of racing.

STREET/COMPETITION APPLICATION

Choose a clutch for dual-purpose street driving and racing is more difficult than choosing one strictly for street or just for racing. The car must be flexible enough to drive on the street and perform well at the track without requiring much more than uncorking the exhaust system and changing tires. Finding a clutch to fit this application is made easier by the performance-clutch manufacturers. They offer a wide variety of pressure plates and discs for various applications. All you have to do is find out what fits your specific application.

Drag, slalom, off-road and gymkhana racing are just about the only types of racing where a guy can run the car he drove up in. Of the three, drag racing is the hardest on a clutch. It's difficult to imagine any tougher clutch application than starting a car by bringing the engine up to 5000-6000 RPM then dumping the clutch. It hurts just to think

about it. As the pressure plate engages the disc, it tries to tear the facing off the disc. Sometimes it is successful. On the other hand, spinning a clutch assembly at 7000-8000 RPM and disengaging and engaging it at speed for shifting is also hard on the clutch as well as other components.

No matter what type of racing you will be doing or the type of car you will be doing it in, make sure you use a good quality clutch—one that will be safe for your application. The best guarantee is to use only those which have been approved by the Specialty Equipment Manufacturers Association (SEMA). If the components you choose are guaranteed explosion-proof under SEMA SPEC. 1-1, you can be reasonably well assured they are safe. This may be required anyway by your sanctioning organization in addition to a safety bellhousing.

CHOOSING A DISC

To make things simpler, let's sort out what must be retained from the street clutch in the street/competition clutch to keep it suitable for

street operation. I can't stress this point enough. The tendency is to over-clutch, to get more than required—in this case, less. First, the clutch must engage and disengage properly, no grabbing or chatter. To avoid this, always use a spring marcel. Pressure-plate load will be modulated during engagement, or will build up gradually, generating

In addition to using a SEMA-approved pressure plate and disc for competition, you may be required to use one of these. Even if there's no requirement, you may want to use one for your own peace of mind.

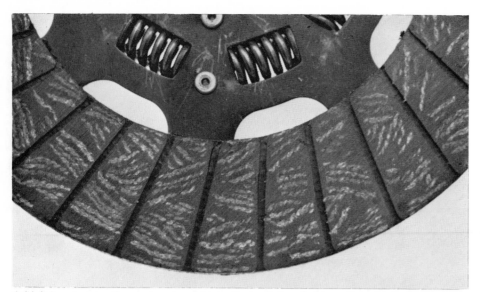

A high-burst-strength spiral-woven facing. Facing is bonded to a disc which does not use a marcel cushion spring. As a result, this is the type of organic facing to use for competition. Grooves in the facing material are molded in rather than cut afterwards, thereby improving burst strength.

CAUTION: When using ceramic button-type disc, allow for expansion of friction material. It expands when hot, thus takes up linkage free play or air gap. If not allowed for, this expansion will prevent clutch from fully disengaging during shifting, causing transmission problems if not discovered.

a gradual increase in driving force on the disc—no on-and-off situation. This will not only prevent harsh engagement, it will also keep driveline loads to a minimum during engagement.

To keep driveline loads at a minimum under all operating conditions, use a sprung hub. Undesirable vibrations will be damped or eliminated completely during the operation of the vehicle without compromising transmission, U-joint and rear-axle life. Street/Competition discs will use heavy-duty hub components—either five or eight alloy springs, stronger hubs, bigger stop pins and thicker plates. So don't worry about a sprung hub not being able to handle the job.

Finally, there is the friction material, the workhorse of the clutch. To be traditional I will discuss organic material first. To start with, high-burst-strength organic lining cannot be the run-of-mill molded and riveted lining. High-burst-strength, high-performance lining is capable of over 10,000 RPM. It is bonded to a thin steel or aluminum

wafer which is riveted to the marcel springs. Aluminum is preferred because of its superior heat-transfer capabilities and lower weight. All of this adds up to higher burst strength because of the reduced weight at the outer periphery of the disc and a subsequent reduction in centrifugal loads at the high revs. In addition, the improved heat transfer of aluminum reduces the possibility of heat reducing the strength of the facing binder.

Lower disc weight is important when it comes to high-RPM shifting. As shifting is done—up or down—transmission synchronizers must accelerate or decelerate the transmission-input shaft to which the disc is attached, to match the speed of the driveline prior to engagement. As the outer periphery of the disc loses weight, so does the rotational inertia of the disc, and less force and time are required to match the two speeds. To complete the assembly of the disc, the facing is riveted to the marcel spring. The disc is now ready to go racing.

Metallic facings are available for street and competition use. One type is available from RAM Automotive and another from McLeod Industries, with other manufacturers surely to follow. Use metallic facings only when organic facings fail to do the job. Metallics are expensive and may tend to chatter or grab. Vehicles which first used the metallic facings successfully other than heavy machinery and trucks are those which experience excessive heat build up in the disc due to slippage. This includes off-road vehicles or those which are used to haul or tow heavy loads such as tow-trucks, campers and motor homes. The street/competition car requiring this type of

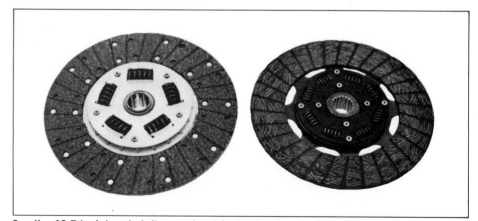

Smaller 10.5-inch bonded disc on the right has less inertia than the 11-inch disc, making shifting faster and easier. If you are going drag racing, this is a very important consideration.

Blocking- and synchronizer-ring assembly from a Ford Top Loader four-speed transmission. It has to do the work of accelerating or decelerating the clutch disc and transmission input shaft during shifts.

When using a metallic-faced disc, it is imperative you use a clean flat pressure plate matched to the disc. The full benefit of metallic facings cannot be realized unless full facing contact is made.

lining would probably weigh 4000 pounds or more.

RAM uses six—three per side—ceramic-copper buttons from S.K. Wellman. They are riveted to a sprung-hub disc in a three-star pattern. Unnecessary portions of the disc are removed between the buttons to keep the inertia of the disc to a minimum. The facings are not cushioned. They do not use marcel springs. This contributes to harsh engagement. The McLeod disc is

full-circle. It uses a backing much in the same manner as an organic disc. Segments of sintered iron are put on the backing during the sintering process. The facing is then riveted to the marcel spring. This disc also uses a sprung hub.

CHOOSING A PRESSURE PLATE

Throw the number of available pressure plates in with the discs and you have the potential for mass confusion. I might add, this is usually the case. Right off the bat, I will establish a few DO'S AND DON'TS'. First the do's because they are more obvious.

DO

• Use a high-performance SEMA-approved pressure plate.
• Use a pressure plate compatible with your disc.
• Use a pressure plate which provides sufficient torque capacity at the RPM where your engine develops its peak torque.

DON'T

• Don't use more pressure-plate load than you need.
• Don't use a centrifugally assisted pressure plate if you intend to disengage it at over 8000 RPM for shifting.

• Don't use a six-roller Borg & Beck pressure plate for shifting applications.

I mentioned the need to use a SEMA-approved pressure plate first because of the need to be safe. As you should be well aware, Uncle Sam and Ralph Nader are always looking for an excuse to take our toys away in the name of the public interest, so play it *safe*. Don't take a chance on getting yourself or someone else hurt needlessly. As for using a pressure plate which is compatible with the disc you are using, it is pretty well explanatory. The pressure plate has to be tailored for a certain thickness disc to obtain the proper plate load and prevent over-stressing the pressure plate, particularly in the case of the diaphragm. Also, the pressure plate and disc should be the same diameter.

One exception, some professional drag racers use 11-inch pressure plates with 10.5-inch-diameter discs. The reason is the smaller diameter disc has less inertia, making shifting easier. What's puzzling is, why not use a 10.5-inch pressure plate? The loads are the same and the disc determines the capacity of the

This unique disc uses sintered-iron facings with marcel springs. It makes a very rugged and streetable disc. This type is available from McLeod. *Photo courtesy S. K. Wellman*

An excellent shifting-application setup. Low-inertia 10.5" disc is mated with an 11" pressure plate. Extra half inch of pressure-ring diameter provides more heat-sink volume to keep the disc cooler.

You may not know a heat sink by name, but chances are you've seen plenty of them. A radiator is one of the most common heat sinks. It absorbs heat from your engine coolant and dissipates it just like a pressure ring and flywheel.

One sure way to get your car launched quicker is to install a higher numerical ratio rear-axle gear set. *Photo courtesy Schiefer*

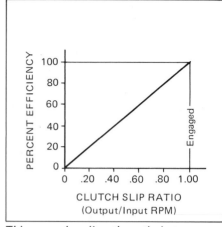

This curve describes the ratio between clutch slip and clutch efficiency. Slip Ratio is the relationship between transmission input-shaft speed and engine speed. The more a clutch slips, the lower the slip ratio and efficiency. The area above the curve represents lost power, or heat generated due to slippage. The area under the curve is power to the driveline.

clutch. The only logical explanation I can come up with is the larger 11-inch pressure plate has a 0.5-inch-larger-diameter pressure ring, naturally. This means 0.25 inches of pressure ring extends beyond the outer periphery of the disc. Now, the only explanation I can give as to why this setup may work better than one with a matching pressure plate is the larger pressure plate provides more *heat-sink* for cooling the clutch.

A *heat-sink* is a device used to absorb heat from or cool another device. The radiator in your car is a good example. As for the clutch, the pressure-plate ring absorbs heat from the disc and transfers it to the air. With the additional pressure-ring area extending beyond the disc, extra pressure-ring-to-air heat transfer takes place. Therefore, the total clutch assembly runs cooler—most important for the life of a clutch.

You are interested in more than just getting from point A to point B, you want to be the fastest from A to B. If any portion of getting from point A to point B involves accelerating from a dead stop, it is impor-

tant to prevent your engine from "bogging" and to make sure the maximum amount of torque is applied to the driveline. Both of these involve keeping engine revs up. For maximum acceleration without spinning the tires, the clutch should be slipped in first gear with engine revs at the low end of the

maximum torque range. Keep in mind that heat buildup will limit slipping time to not much more than one second. If fading results, the clutch may continue to slip as the coefficient of friction drops below 0.20. If this occurs, you will have to engage your clutch sooner.

For quicker times and faster

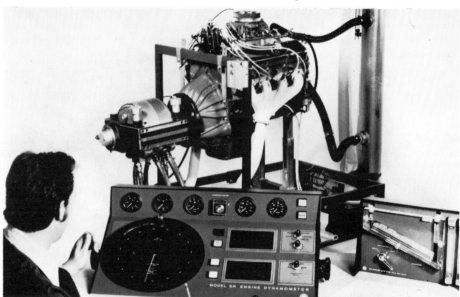

Torque without movement, or RPM in the case of an engine, does not produce power. This dynamometer is monitoring the torque output of this engine at different RPM settings so the specific power-output of the engine can be arrived at. *Photo courtesy Go-Power Systems*

Quick-change rear-axle in Gary Beck's Top-Fuel dragster illustrates the need for proper gearing for a specific situation. Track conditions can change to such a degree that what's right for one run won't be for the next. Rear-axle ratios can be changed very easily with this type of axle. Just remove rear cover plate and slip in another pair of gears.

Hays slider ready to accept its cover. Two interesting points to note are the replaceable wear shims (arrow) on the drive side of the pressure-ring-drive lugs and the lack of insulators under the springs. These springs can operate at temperatures up to 475°F (246°C) because they are manufactured from SAE 9254, a high chromium-silicon spring steel. This is a tremendous advantage because the springs assist in cooling the clutch as heat is transferred directly from the pressure ring to the springs—then to the air.

clutch lockup, use the lowest possible transmission and rear-axle gearing you can find or are permitted to use. For rear-axle gearing, choose the ratio which will permit the engine to rev to the limit on the fastest part of the track providing you don't care what happens

A very important little asbestos ring. It insulates the pressure springs from the heat absorbed by the pressure ring. If your racing involves much clutch slippage, make sure your pressure plate is so equipped or has chrome-silicon springs.

to your fuel economy during street driving. The next best thing is to get your car as light as possible. Fewer pounds means faster acceleration. The car will also corner and brake better. Taking these two steps will get your car away quicker, permitting engine revs to build faster and clutch lockup to occur sooner.

To get on with choosing the proper pressure plate, first a little refresher as to the the features of a high-performance pressure plate. There is more to a high-performance clutch than just pressure-plate load and the resulting stiff clutch pedal. Heat warps pressure rings and takes the temper, or springiness out of springs. Alloys of nickle and silicon can be added to spring steel to increase a spring's ability to handle temperatures. Asbestos insulators can be placed between the springs and pressure rings so the clutch can withstand higher operating temperatures without damaging the springs. No matter how much the springs are insulated, the pressure ring must still absorb and dissipate most of the heat.

If you are certain your clutch

will require a lot of slipping, then you should install a pressure plate which permits maximum cooling of the pressure ring—preferably an aluminum pressure ring. A Long pressure plate has its pressure ring extending outside of the cover to provide maximum exposure to the air for cooling. If you cannot use the Long style due to a different flywheel-bolt pattern or insufficient room in the bellhousing, the next best bet would be the Long/Borg & Beck which has a bolt pattern matching the Borg & Beck or the diaphragm. This is not because the combination Long/Borg & Beck shrouds the pressure ring less than the others, the Long action is easier to control while being slipped. The next choice is the Borg & Beck. Last choice is the diaphragm because it tends to lock up quickly once it begins to engage with the disc due to the over-center action of the Belleville spring.

For street/competition clutches not requiring excessive slipping, your choice of which pressure plate to use remains more flexible. The important point to remember

GEARING YOUR CAR

What is gearing and how do you determine the proper gearing for your car? Gearing provides three functions for your car, it multiplies the torque output of the engine, it lets the driver match engine RPM and torque output of the engine to the speed of the car. It also provides a tool by which the maximum economy can be squeezed from your car. This explanation will be confined to torque multiplication and engine RPM. To find out how gearing affects economy, get H.P.Books' *The Whole Truth About Economy Driving.*

Gears are like a lever. A gear receives torque from a shaft and transmits it to another gear. The first is the input gear and the second, the output gear. First, let's look at the input gear. See the first sketch. Torque T_1 is transmitted to the input gear. The output gear is removed from the sketch so we can look at the force **F** which is applied to the teeth of the gears. Distance r_1 is the pitch radius of the gear. Torque T_1 is equal to force **F** multiplied by pitch radius r_1.

The second sketch shows the output gear with the input gear removed with force **F** shown. Force **F** is applied at the tooth-contact point of the two gears. If pitch radius r_2 is twice that of r_1 then output torque T_2 is twice that of input torque T_1.

To prove this, let the input torque equal 200 foot-pounds. If r_1 equals one foot, force **F** is found by dividing T_1 by r_1. Therefore, **F** equals:

Force F
$$= \frac{200 \text{ foot-pounds}}{1 \text{ foot}}$$
$$= 200 \text{ pounds}$$

To find the output torque, multiply the 200-pound force by pitch radius r_2. Remember, r_2 is twice as large as r_1. Therefore, r_2 is equal to two feet—quite large for transmission or rear-axle gears, but

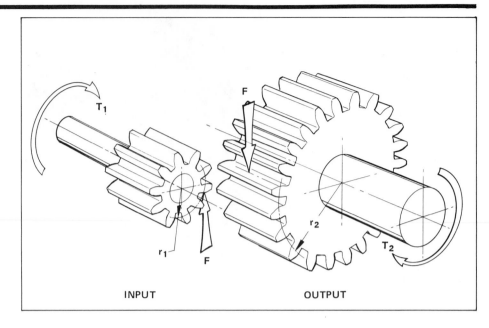

INPUT   OUTPUT

a lot easier to work with as an example. Therefore, torque T_2 is equal to:

$$T_2 = 200 \text{ pounds} \times 2 \text{ feet}$$
$$= 400 \text{ foot-pounds}$$

—twice the torque. After all this mess, you'll be wondering if there isn't an easier way to go about it. Well, there is, and it is much easier.

Finding torque multiplication by measuring the pitch radius of the gears is nearly impossible. So we find it by another method. The number of teeth a gear has is directly proportional to its pitch radius and the amount of torque transmitted is a direct function of the number of teeth of the two gears. For instance, T_2 in the above example is equal to:

$$T_2 = \frac{r_2}{r_1} \times T_1$$
$$= \frac{2 \text{ feet}}{1 \text{ foot}} \times 200 \text{ foot-pounds}$$
$$= 400 \text{ foot-pounds}$$

If N_1 is the number of teeth on the input gear and N_2 is the number of teeth on the output gear,

$$\frac{N_2}{N_1} = \frac{R_2}{R_1}$$

This relationship is called the *gear ratio.* In this example, the gear ratio is two to one, usually shown as 2:1. If the ratio had been 4:1, the torque would have been four times 200 foot-pounds., or 800 foot-pounds on the output side. This is much simpler than trying to measure gear-pitch diameters.

Just as torque is multiplied as it is transfered by two gears, the speed of the output shaft is reduced from the input side by the same ratio. Using the example, if the input shaft is turning 4000 RPM, the output shaft speed is found by dividing the input shaft speed by the gear ratio, or:

$$\textbf{Output RPM}$$
$$= \frac{\textbf{Input RPM}}{\textbf{Gear Ratio}}$$
$$= \frac{4000 \text{ RPM}}{2}$$
$$= 2000 \text{ RPM}$$

If, in the case of an overdrive gearbox, the gear ratio is less than 1:1, torque will be reduced and shaft speed will be *increased.* When finding the overall drive ratio between the engine and the rear axle, the transmission and the axle ratios must be multiplied. In high gear, the transmission ratio will be 1:1, so the final drive ratio, or the rear-axle ratio, will be the overall ratio. If the transmission is in first gear, the overall ratio is:

Overall ratio = Transmission ratio X Axle ratio

If the 1st gear ratio is 2.6:1 and the rear axle ratio is 4.11:1, the overall ratio is

2.6 X 4.11 = 10.686:1

Now that you know what gear ratio is, we must be able to find the proper ones to use. First, the rear-axle ratio is derived from the maximum speed of the car, tire size and the rev-limit of the engine, as recommended by your cam manufacturer, using the formula:

$$R = \frac{n \times r}{168 \times V}$$

Where:

n is engine RPM.
r is loaded radius of the tires in inches.
V is speed of the car in MPH.

To put this formula to work, let's go through a typical problem. Assume we have an engine which redlines at 8000 RPM, the maximum estimated speed of the car is 120 MPH on the fastest part of the track and the loaded radius of the tires is 12 inches. Because the transmission should be in top gear—1:1 ratio, the rear-axle ratio will be solved for:

$$R = \frac{8000 \text{ RPM X 12 inches}}{168 \text{ X 120 MPH}}$$
$$= 4.76:1$$

Choose the next closest ratio available. If you want a higher engine RPM, go to the next higher *numerical* ratio. If not, go the next lowest.

As for transmission gear ratios, if you are going drag racing, use the highest numerical first gear ratio you can find, or are permitted to use by the rules. Obviously, you can overgear your car in theory, but not in practicality because of the limited availability of transmission gears.

is, a pressure plate must be tailored to do a specific job. The most common error is choosing pressure-plate loads, both static and centrifugal, which are on the high side. This is especially true with centrifugal loads. Remember, static load doesn't change with RPM but, centrifugal loads go up as the *square* of the RPM.

Organic facings have fairly constant coefficients of friction and domestic-car-clutch diameters range between 10 and 11.5 inches, so *pressure-plate load has the greatest effect on single-disc-clutch capacity*. With this in mind, the three most important considerations when choosing a pressure plate have the

Light paint on these pressure rings caused by painting after pressure-plate assembly illustrates how much each one is shrouded by its cover. It is obvious the Long pressure ring has the maximum exposure to the air giving it an edge on cooling.

TORQUE CAPACITY vs PRESSURE PLATE LOAD FOR VARIOUS CLUTCH DIAMETERS
SINGLE DISC-ORGANIC FACING

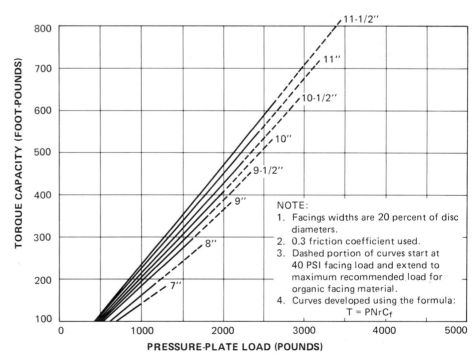

NOTE:
1. Facings widths are 20 percent of disc diameters.
2. 0.3 friction coefficient used.
3. Dashed portion of curves start at 40 PSI facing load and extend to maximum recommended load for organic facing material.
4. Curves developed using the formula: $T = PNrC_f$

Knowing the torque output of your engine and the diameter of your clutch, use this chart to determine minimum required pressure-plate load. Torque capacity shown is for single-disc clutches, so divide the amount of torque you want your clutch to transmit by the number of discs your clutch has before using the graph to determine plate load.

Great fun on the weekends, but if the clutch is too stiff, it won't be fun for the weaker members of the family. A good candidate for a fully assisted Long.

following order of importance:
1. Maximum developed engine torque.
2. RPM at which maximum torque is developed.
3. Maximum usable RPM of the engine.

Once you know the maximum torque of your engine you can find the correct pressure-plate load using the graph on page 71 or by using the formula on page 51. First, determine clutch diameter. If you decide to increase the diameter over that of the original clutch, your required pressure-plate load will be less. Keep in mind that a large disc has more inertia, making fast shifts more difficult. This is a very important consideration if the car is to be used for drag racing. To give the clutch a little margin, add 20 percent to the figure for pressure-plate load. This will make up for lost capacity the clutch may experience from wear and fatigue.

Multi-disc clutches—Normally reserved for the 100-percent competition car, the multi-disc clutch has found its way into the street/competition car class. One popular unit is Borg-Warner's 10-inch dual-disc clutch used behind the 427 and 454 CID big blocks. Its diameter was reduced to 10 inches as the smaller discs reduced the inertia to a point comparable to the 11-inch single-disc unit. It also reduced clutch-operating forces because the plate

load was reduced approximately 700 pounds even though torque capacity was increased. With a pressure-plate load of 1950 pounds, the resultant capacity is 800 foot-pounds. To check this out, look at the graph on page 71. The capacity for a 10-inch single-disc clutch with this plate load is 400 foot-pounds. Doubling this figure for a dual-disc clutch we get 800 foot-pounds. This clutch can handle most race-prepared engines.

COMPETITION CLUTCHES

Choosing a clutch purely for competition is not as compromis-ing as for the dual-purpose street/competition application. You don't have to worry about using your Pro-Stocker or sprint car for grocery shopping. They are intended for one purpose—racing. About the only driving condition approximating street driving would be encountered in the pits or garage area. The best rule to follow here is don't compromise the speed or durability of your racer for this convenience, better to push or tow it.

Of the many types of racing that go on in the world, clutch applications can be classified into two groups. The first is drag racing and the second is closed-course racing. Drag racing includes everything from the stockers to Funny Cars to Tractor pullers. Closed-course includes the likes of sprinters, Indy cars and Can Am cars. This aproach doesn't separate clutch applications as cleanly as you might think but, it does create two major groups:

Shifting and non-shifting applications—The reference to shifting and non-shifting applications has yet to be made. Mainly because there was no need for it. Now there is, because I am talking about pure racing. All

With a dog clutch, you have no choice about being push-started. This sprint car has just fired its engine as is pulling away from its push vehicle.

You'll never see an Indy Car driven in the pits simply to move it. Cars are being rolled to the starting grid prior to start of a 150-mile race at Phoenix.

What could be better than the efficiency of a clutch and the peace of mind of never missing a shift? This is what B&M's Clutchflite does. *Photo courtesy B&M Performance Transmission Products*

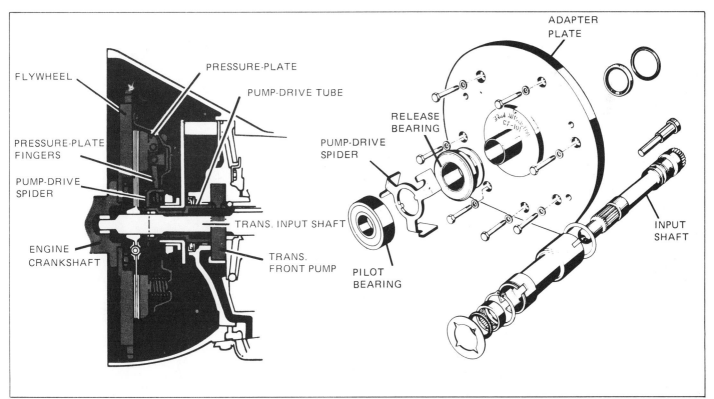

Here's what it takes to convert an automatic transmission from a torque convertor to a clutch drive. First, the convertor housing is removed and replaced with a bellhousing adapter plate with a clutch-release-bearing pilot. A new transmission input shaft is installed which accepts a clutch disc and pilots in the engine crank shaft. Transmission front pump is driven by a spider which engages with the pressure-plate release levers. *Drawings courtesy B&M Performance Transmission Products*

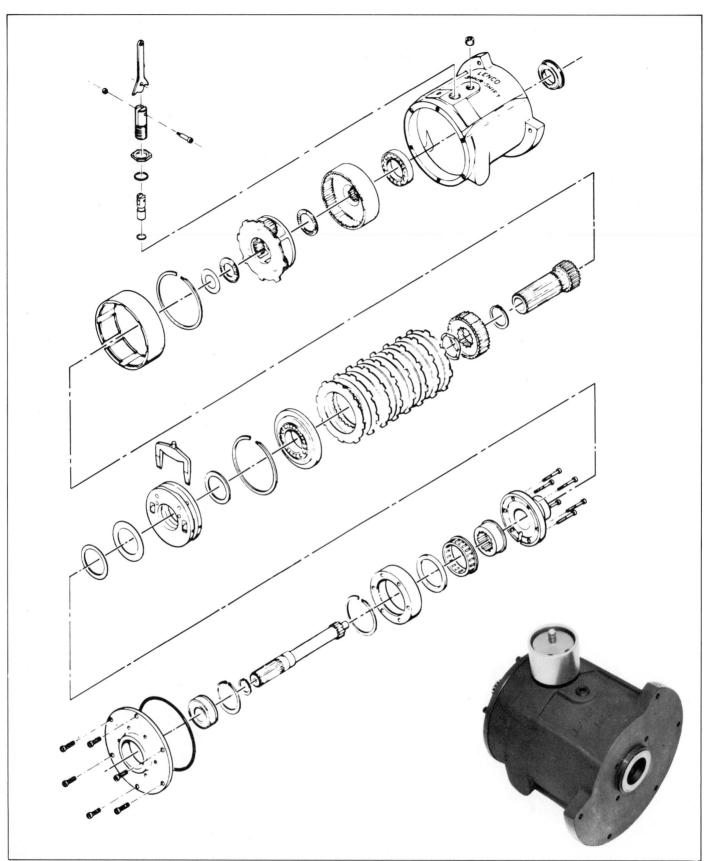

In addition to tire technology and the slider clutch, the Lenco transmission has been one of the biggest improvements in drag racing. Pictured is an air-operated two-speed unit used in Top Fuel and Funny Cars. The exploded view is of an earlier two-speed cable-operated unit. Heart of this transmission is the planetary-gear assembly which permits shifting while the clutch is engaged. *Photo and drawing courtesy Lenco Equipment Company, Inc.*

Pro-Stockers have discovered the advantages of "clutchless" shifting. These shifting levers operate the four-speed Lenco in Kevin Rotty's Townsend's Racing Works Camaro—a non-shifting application.

A shifting application. For this Muncie four-speed transmission to be shifted, the clutch must be disengaged. *Photo courtesy Hurst Performance Inc.*

high-performance manufacturers refer to this in their literature when recommending a specific clutch. Non-shifting is emphasized, which is an inaccurate use of words. The typical catalog will state, "Intended for nonshifting applications only." This infers the car doesn't have a transmission. What they really mean is, the clutch needn't be disengaged to shift the transmission. Such is the case when the clutch replaces the torque converter of an automatic transmission. The Clutchflite, which combines a clutch with a Torque-Flite automatic is one example. The Lenco, used for Top Fuel, Funny or Pro-Stock cars, is a transmission designed strictly for drag racing. These types of transmissions use planetary gears for reduction and do not require clutch disengagement for shifting. The conventional, all-synchromesh, three, four or five-speed transmission with its synchro rings, dogs and slip yokes does. Therefore, a *non-shifting* application is one not requiring clutch disengagement for gear changing. The clutch works for all other uses just as with a conventional transmission: Starting from a standstill, starting the engine while the transmission is in gear, pushing or towing the car while in gear or bringing the car to a stop with the

engine running while in gear. Therefore, when you see a reference to *non-shifting* applications, you can be sure the clutch has a *substantial* amount of centrifugal assist. If a nonshifting-only clutch were to be used in a shifting application, it is likely the clutch pedal could not be operated at peak RPM. Nuff said!

Drag Racing—With a few exceptions, different types of clutches used in drag racing represent virtually all the different types of clutches used in racing. The object is the same for all drag cars—to travel the 1/4 mile faster than any-

one else in the same class. The tremendous difference in car types demands a great difference in the types of clutches to do the job. Factors which determine the specific clutch a car uses are the car weight, engine output, tire design, gearing and type of transmission being used. All these add up to the ability of a car to *launch* or to get away from the line. A car launches better if it is lighter, has more engine output, stickier tires and lower gearing. The load on a clutch is less with a lighter-weight car having low gearing and a planetary transmission.

This Funny Car is just leaving the line. Boy, are they noisy!

Due to the tremendous heat generated by a slider clutch, Hays tried this trick. It's a centrifugal fan inserted behind the pressure ring to circulate air through the clutch. It worked well but the idea was not put into production.

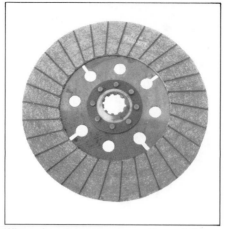
When choosing a disc, regardless of the facing, think twice before using a solid hub. Your driveline will take a beating.

As with any type car, the primary clutch objective is to transmit engine torque to the driveline. For a race car, it must be done as fast and as efficiently as possible. Just because it is a race car doesn't mean the pedal operating forces are to be disregarded. A human being must still operate the car and the lower the operating efforts are, the better the driver can concentrate. Pedal forces are important, particularly with shifting applications. The harder a clutch pedal is to move, the slower and harder shifting will be. Pressure-plate load is the main factor in determining pedal force. It also determines the load on engine thrust bearings. As a release bearing loads the release levers of a clutch, it is also loading the engine thrust bearings the same amount. Loads exceeding much over 3500 pounds will cause excessive bearing wear—another good reason to keep plate loads as low as possible.

SHIFTING APPLICATIONS
Discs—Organic-faced discs remain most popular, even for racing. These discs are available with or without spring marcels and with or without sprung hubs. I highly recommend the use of the sprung hub to reduce driveline shock during high-RPM starts. On the other hand, if you want fast shifts and are prepared to sacrifice transmission and rear-axle gears and axle shafts, don't use a sprung hub. A solid hub reduces disc inertia, resulting in reduced synchronizing time for the transmission.

Chatter, not being a factor in drag racing, permits the elimination of the spring marcel. The use of marcel springs slightly reduces driveline shock, but can also cause problems. At high revs, the marcels tend to open up, or swell as the pressure plate is disengaged. The result is increased clutch-pedal travel and, subsequently slower shifts. No place for the marcel here. Another bonus without marcels is an automatic reduction in disc inertia. Without marcel springs, facing backings and rivets are not required. This gets rid of weight where it does the most good, at the periphery of the disc.

Again, we have a choice of the type of facing material: Organic or metallic. Metallic can't be beaten when it comes to the ability to withstand heat and high revs. Strong consideration should be given metallic linings for stock-bodied cars because heavy cars are very hard on facing material. This is especially true with stockers limited to specific rear-axle and transmission-gear ratios. Two metallic facings suitable for shifting applications are ceramic-copper buttons available from RAM and Schiefer and sintered-iron pucks from McLeod and Hays. Both are

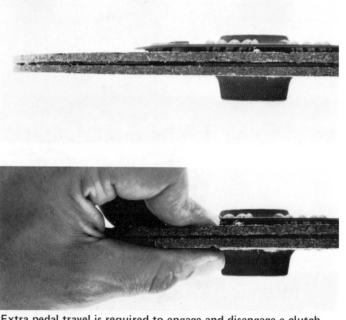
Extra pedal travel is required to engage and disengage a clutch when a marcel-cushioned disc is used. This is due to the "spring-back" of the facings attached to a marcel.

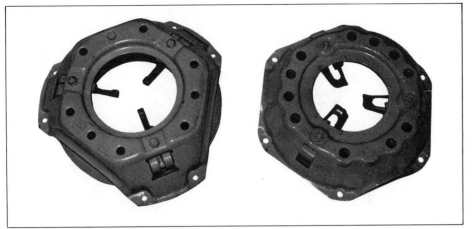

A Long pressure plate has superior cooling because of larger cover openings at the center and around the pressure ring.

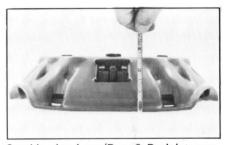

Combination Long/Borg & Beck lets you replace your Borg & Beck or diaphragm unit without changing flywheel-bolt patterns and still get the best features of the Long-style pressure plate. Another plus, the low-profile of this pressure plate, minimizes any cover-to-housing clearance problems.

good candidates for discs experiencing extremely hard usage. These discs are available with or without sprung hubs.

Pressure Plates—Choosing a pressure plate for racing involves the same process as for street/competition applications. The one advantage in choosing a pressure plate for pure racing is, compromises need not be made. The only concern is to get the maximum performance out of every little piece of the car, including the clutch. To do this, it must transmit engine torque efficiently and release and engage quickly.

First, the correct pressure plate must be chosen. The job becomes one of separating opinion from fact. This can be done largely with numbers when choosing pressure-plate load, but the type of style to use is where you run into opinions. Let's do it with facts.

To start off, the best choice for an all-out drag-racing pressure plate is going to be the Long style, or the combination Long/Borg & Beck because of the Long lever design. The Long has the upper hand because its cover doesn't shroud the pressure ring as much. Consequently, it runs cooler.

As for the Borg & Beck and diaphragm pressure plates, they have both been used in drag-race competition, particularly the Borg & Beck. The diaphragm is not often used in drag racing as this book goes to press because of the old high-RPM hangup reputation. Manufacturers seem to have this problem cured and because of the very fast release and engagement features it possesses, its use is bound to increase. It also has the reputation of engaging violently.

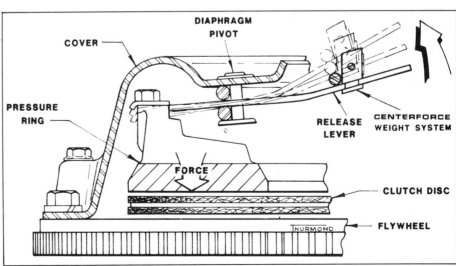

Unique Centerforce diamphragm-type clutch with centrifugal action was developed by Ralph Hays. Weights on diaphragm fingers act similar to weights on levers of Long-type pressure plate. As RPM increases, so does centrifugal assist. Drawing courtesy Midway Industries, Incorporated.

However, proper matching of pressure plate to disc should solve this problem. For instance, a softer-rate disc-damping hub would counteract any harsh engagement. As it stands now, discs are tuned to the Long and Borg & Beck styles. Things will change, what with the simplicity of the diaphragm and its light weight. About the only real obstacle to overcome is cooling. The Long still has the upper hand in this department.

After you've chosen the pressure-plate style you want to use, the next step is to choose the .right plate load. If you are planning on using centrifugal weights, the diaphragm is automatically eliminated. I would recommend eliminating the Borg & Beck because of the problem of disengaging the wedged rollers. Looks like the Long is the one in this case—but stop. Rather than using CF weights for shifting applications, I recommend depending on static spring pressure alone. My reason for this is simple. The purpose of centrifugal assist is to reduce pedal forces at low engine RPM. For the all-out drag-racing car, the only low engine revs encountered are while the car is driven in the pits or being staged. If CF weights are used to obtain the necessary plate load to transmit maximum engine torque, the RPM at which shifting will take place will be at, or near the peak power output of the engine. Because the RPM of the engine at peak power is higher than at peak torque—usually double—pedal forces will be higher due to centrifugal plate load increasing as the square of engine speed. As a result, pedal forces during shifting will be at a maximum which will slow your shifting. On this basis, avoid centrifugally assisted clutches for shifting applications, particularly if you plan to shift in excess of 8000 RPM.

Lever Ratios—Release-lever ratios should be mentioned in more detail because of their effect on pedal forces and travel. The higher numerical lever ratios used with Borg & Beck pressure plates—about

This pressure plate was part of a floater which exited the car at high-RPM. The pressure-ring is bent, gouged and warped, but still in one piece—a credit to the strength of aluminum pressure rings.

6.0:1—reduce pedal forces and increase pedal travel. The lower numerical Long-style lever ratios—about 4.7:1—have higher pedal forces with less pedal travel.

Long and Borg & Beck lever ratios can be changed independently of their springs. For instance, Borg-Warner offers a Borg & Beck style having a 5.0:1 lever ratio and McLeod offers a combination Long/Borg & Beck with a 4.0:1 ratio. The low ratio gives fast plate departure for faster shifting, but with correspondingly higher pedal forces.

Diaphragm pressure plates don't have lever ratios as discussed earlier, ratio is a product of the spring. Diaphragm *travel ratio* works out to about 3.5:1. This is the ratio of the release-bearing travel—after it comes in contact with the fingers—to pressure-ring travel for full clutch release. Pedal forces drop off as the pedal is depressed and

pressure-ring travel increases for a corresponding amount of finger travel. For equivalent plate loads diaphragm-pressure-plate release loads are about 30 percent less than for a coil-spring-type pressure plate.

Pressure Rings—For safety's sake, the first thing to consider is the pressure-ring material. If it is cast iron, it should *not be grey cast iron.* It should be either nodular cast iron or aluminum. For methods of identifying grey cast iron, refer to page 92 in the flywheel chapter. Aluminum pressure rings manufactured from 7075 T-6 or 6061 T-6 forged aluminum alloy and incorporating a heat shield are available. An aluminum pressure ring offers a weight advantage and provides better heat dissipation than cast iron. Whether cast iron or aluminum, the pressure plate assembly should be SEMA-approved, particularly if you are going to use it for racing.

After making sure of the proper cover design, spring retainers and cover-material thickness, calculate the pressure-plate load using the curves on pages 55 and 71. Rather than using the 20-percent service factor as for street/competition applications, use the exact figure you get for plate load. Plate fatigue and disc wear should not be a factor as these components should be replaced long before either gets "too far gone." This is especially true in the case of disc wear. As facing material wears, it provides less *heat sink*. Because cooling is necessary for clutch operation, replace the disc at regular intervals. By following this practice, pedal forces will be less and the clutch will be easier to operate.

NON-SHIFTING APPLICATIONS

Discs—There are two types of non-shifting applications, both used with planetary transmissions. One locks-up soon after launch and the other slips for a good portion of a run. The last one is the slider clutch. Common disc characteristics for these two applications are: Neither uses marcel springs and rotating inertia is not a factor. Slipping action of the slider clutch sufficiently softens (damps) any impact loads so sprung hubs are not needed. For the same reason, marcels are not used. Inertia is not a factor because the clutch does not have to be disengaged for shifting. Therefore, transmission synchronization is not required.

The first type of non-shifting clutch is used in front of Lencos as used in Pro-Stockers or with Clutchflites or Turboclutches. The choice of friction facings is greater here than with any other type of racing application. As for the facing material, organic, ceramic-copper or sintered iron can be used. If slipping of an extended duration is required, organic facing should not be used. This depends on your power-to-weight ratio and your gearing. The higher the power-to-weight ratio and the higher the numerical gear ratio, the less the

Clutch setup to use in Indy Car or formula-type car is obvious when parameters are considered: high-RPM shifting, high engine torque, and low center of gravity. Pressure plate should have no centrifugal assist, but have small diameter and two or more discs. In this case, sintered-iron friction material is used.

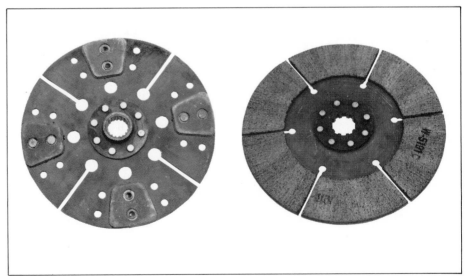

Two different types of non-shifting application discs. The four-button ceramic-copper button disc locks up with very little slippage. Sintered—iron disc is used in slider applications. The button disc can also be used in shifting applications.

As with any slider pressure plate, the Crowerglide uses adjustable CF weights to control slippage. This is the pressure-plate portion of a Crowerglide.

Rather than securing the release-lever yoke against the bottom side of the pressure-plate cover like the conventional Long pressure plate, the yoke is tightened against the adjustable barrel nut on the Long slider. Load is transferred from the yoke through the barrel nut to the cover.

This added-on cover reinforcement (arrow) at the lever yoke serves two important functions—it reinforces the cover and provides additional threads for the barrel nut.

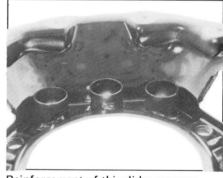

Reinforcement of this slider-pressure-plate cover includes spring cups to contain the springs at high revs, flanged and welded drive-lug windows and reinforced lever-yoke mountings.

need for slipping becomes. It is still best to use metallic-faced discs. Now, if quick lockup is the requirement, use the six-button-per-side ceramic-copper discs or the full-circle sintered-iron facing. The advantage with these materials is their friction coefficients increase with heat, permitting the use of lower pressure-plate loads—always an advantage when possible. Sintered-iron facings are a good choice because the friction coefficient eventually stabilizes with this material whereas it drops off with the ceramic-copper buttons.

Slider clutches are restricted to one type of friction facing—sintered iron. The reason for this is as I just stated, its friction coefficient is stable within broad temperature ranges. This feature is important because of the desirability of letting pressure-plate loads control slip rather than changes in the coefficient of friction. Static plate load and centrifugal assist are much easier to adjust and predict than changes in the coefficient of friction. Your only choice is which brand to use: Crower, Hays, McLeod, Scott, Schiefer or Weber.

Pressure Plates—The feature distinguishing a non-shifting pressure plate from the others is the high amount of centrifugal assist to static plate load. This type of pressure plate derives most of its capacity from centrifugal assist. Apart from the friction facing, slip is controlled by pressure-plate load. The non-slider/non-shifting pressure plates used in front of Clutchflites, Clutchturbos or Lencos are either the fully weighted Long combination, or a six-roller Borg & Beck. Static plate loads are relatively low as compared to its shifting-application cousins—usually around 2500 pounds. This setup permits some slippage coming off the line to keep engine revs up and to damp clutch engagement. Slipping can be controlled by using the adjustable CF weights available with the Long and combination styles. Ideally, the pressure plate should be adjusted so some slipping occurs during shifting. If it doesn't slip, engine RPM will drop to a level below peak-torque output. If the clutch is adjusted for slip, metallic disc facings should be used. Features you should look for in a pressure plate for this application are adjustable springs and reinforced covers at the yoke mountings. This will permit rapid static plate-

load adjustment. And with the very high plate loads, reinforcement at the yokes prevents excessive cover deflection and failure. Finally, to prevent warpage the pressure ring should incorporate a heat shield. Either sintered bronze or iron will do the job.

The use of the two or three-disc slider clutch is presently limited to high-powered drag cars—in excess of 700 HP. Some single-disc sliders are used in lower-powered cars with success. The slider prevents the tires from being shock-loaded on the start. It keeps them from breaking loose and spinning and keeps engine revs above about

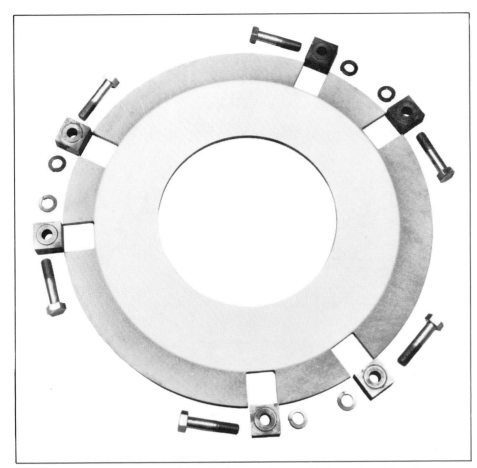

Pressure-plate spacer stands to drive the floater-plate in this dual-disc slider. *Photo courtesy Schiefer*

4500 RPM minimum. The result is a faster car. The two pressure-plate styles available for slider use are characterized by high amounts of centrifugal loading. They include the Crowerglide and highly modified Longs. Both use adjustable weights at the levers for centrifugal-force adjustment.

CLOSED-COURSE RACING

Sprint Cars—Sprint cars don't carry any equipment they don't need for going fast. With the beating they take on the dirt and clay tracks, the fewer parts to break, the better. Most still use the dog clutch which I described earlier. All it does is engage the engine to the driveline—nothing else. This type of clutch is very inconvenient because a car must be push-started and cannot come to a stop with the engine running and start out again on its own. Getting 30 cars push-started for a race is very time-consuming. The problem becomes worse after a race. All the spinouts have to be retrieved due to not being able to restart on their own. On the other hand, the racers are resisting for very good reason. The dog clutch is virtually unbreakable and just about lasts forever. This is due to its simplicity—the only moving part is the sliding coupler. Once engaged there is no relative movement. In addition to being bullet-proof, it offers very little rotating inertia, so a car can accelerate out of the turns faster. Without the conventional

Burnouts are spectacular, but not as fast as runs. The clutch is initially locked-up during the burnout, however the opposite is true during a run.

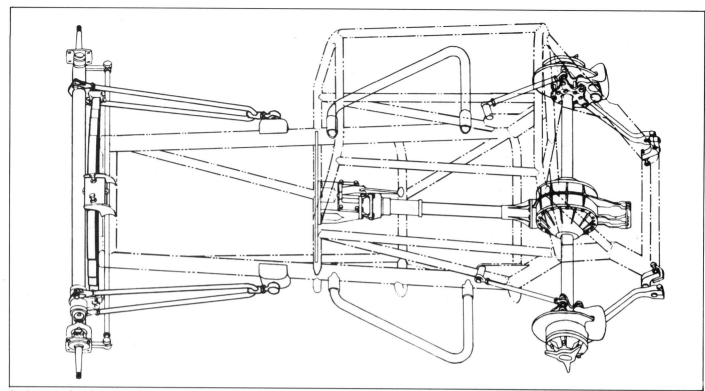

Sprint-car chassis are as strong as they are uncomplicated. The same thing goes for the dog clutch sprinters normally used. *Drawing courtesy CAE*

This sprint car is being rolled out by its crew prior to starting a race. The next push it will get will be from a pickup truck with a big wooden bumper.

clutch, there is no need for a flywheel and because it can't be started from a dead stop, a starter is not required. Another reason for not needing a flywheel or flex plate.

With pressure from race officials, sometimes in the form of bonuses for winning cars having clutches, conventional clutches have begun to appear on the sprint-car circuit. Notable among them are the Crowerglide and the very small diameter—7-1/4-inch—multi-disc unit from Borg & Beck "across the pond." The big advantage with this clutch is the low rotating inertia. It does require an operating mechanism, either foot or hand-operated, whereas the in-out box mechanism is an integral part of the unit with an operating lever and lock-in mounted on top of the box. For sprint-car use, a small diameter flywheel—*button flywheel*—is used as

The two- or three-plate 7-1/4-inch clutch is a good choice for sprint-car applications.

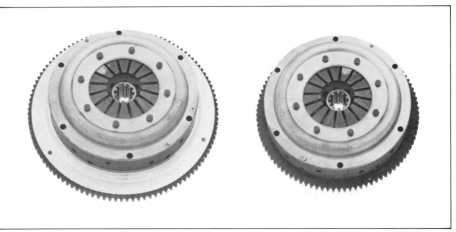

Borg and Beck's 7-1/4" three-plate clutch makes for a very low-inertia setup. Throw one of these small-diameter flywheels in and a Chrysler geared starter and you're in business.

a driving surface for the clutch only. For starting, the standard starter is used with an automatic transmission *flex plate* or a small diameter ring gear and an offset starter. These setups keep the complete assembly as light and low in inertia as possible.

The Crowerglide is used for more than convenience in oval-track racing. Its purpose here is similar to drag racing—To keep engine revs up so the engine won't bog. The only difference, the oval-track car has the problem while exiting turns and the drag car has the problem at launch. As a car is negotiating the turns on an oval track, engine revs are rising and falling. The slider clutch keeps these revs up on the torque curve to give a car maximum acceleration where needed—coming out of the corners. This is particularly true on a track with flat turns and low corner speeds. One notable advantage of this type of clutch for sprint-car use: As a car spins—they do this sort of thing—the clutch automatically disengages. As soon as traffic clears, the car can rejoin the race if everything else is OK. The one problem with this clutch is the maintenance required. For a car which competes two or more times a week, this can become a problem. Frequent adjustments

must be made to the pressure plate to flywheel spacing and stall-speed springs to compensate for disc wear.

Conventional clutches are also used in sprint cars. CAE—Culbert Automotive Engineering—supplies an in-out box which incorporates a conventional clutch for those preferring the convenience and for tracks when sanctioning organizations require it. Some good discs to use for this application are a bonded organic, ceramic-copper or sintered-iron puck facing with a solid hub. This provides for the lightest weight. Chatter or impact loading of the driveline is not a factor. Being this is a *non-shifting* application—in this case, there isn't any actual shifting—a six-roller Borg & Beck or a fully weighted Long pressure plate can be used. Use the plate load to capacity curves to determine the plate-load requirements in conjunction with the appropriate centrifugal-assist curves.

Stocks and Modifieds—I'm going to lump the Grand National Stockers, modifieds, late-model stock cars and all stock-bodied circle-track cars into one group. The same clutch is used for all of these vehicles. Shifting is not required except for getting up to speed after pitting or starting the race. Once the car is up to

A small-diameter flywheel to act as a friction surface mounted on an automatic transmission flex plate such as this eliminates any tricky starter-adapting problems.

Crower's 8-inch slider for oval-track cars is good for keeping the revs up when exiting a turn at low speed.

McLeod's 8-1/2" dual-disc unit is a good low-cost way to go for oval track racing. Whole assembly, including flywheel, weighs in at 27 pounds.

Late-model stock cars exiting turn two at Phoenix International Raceway. Shifting is not a factor here.

speed and in top gear, it stays there. This seems to suggest the use of a centrifugally assisted pressure plate—not so. To avoid unnecessary loads imposed on the clutch assembly, linkage, driver and engine thrust bearings caused by centrifugal assist at high engine revs, only static plate load should be used. Keep in mind CF devices add to pressure-plate weight and inertia. Any of the three basic styles of high-performance pressure plates will do the job. Cooling is not an important consideration, nor is quick release. The clutch is seldom operated and there is little slipping. As a result, there is very little heat build-up. With quick release of minor importance, slower ratio levers can be used. This will reduce the operating loads on the clutch linkage, engine thrust bearings and on the driver. As for the type of disc to use, get a sprung hub. Bonded organic facing has the upper hand but, ceramic-copper pads or sintered-iron pucks will outlast your car. With this type clutch setup, the inertia of the completed assembly is less with improved engine response as the result. You probably won't be able to pick up much difference in lap times on your stop watch, but every little bit counts in racing. The final step

after picking the type of pressure plate and disc is to determine the minimum pressure-plate load from the graph on page 71.

Road Racing—About the only difference between the stock and modifieds and road-racing cars when choosing a clutch is to pay particular attention to the lever ratios. Get the faster-operating levers;

A panic engine change before a stock-car race reveals this diaphragm pressure plate with an aluminum pressure ring. A good reliable setup.

the 4.7:1 Long, 5.0:1 Borg & Beck or the diaphragm. Fast shifts add up to better lap times because of the number of shifts during the course of one lap. For a long-distance race, the number of shifts will be 4,000 or more. As a result, driver fatigue becomes a problem. Shifts are made at high engine revs, so don't use centrifugal assist. Heat is not a factor because clutch slippage amounts to little or none with the shifts being made at speed. Slipping occurs only while in low gear when exiting the pits. Therefore, the Long doesn't have any particular advantage. A small-diameter multi-disc clutch is particularly suited to this application. They have very low plate loads with a correspondingly high torque capacities. The small-diameter discs have low inertia, permitting transmission synchronizing to be quick. On the other hand, the same setup as used for the stocks and modifieds will work well providing the quicker lever ratios are used. The clutch will be a bit more difficult to operate.

For cars using very shallow oil pans, those with *dry sumps* for instance, the engine can be located quite low in the chassis. This will lower the C. G.—center of gravity—resulting in less weight transfer

IROC Camaros are lined up ready to do battle at Daytona. They not only run on the high banks, they must also compete on road courses. A diaphragm pressure plate with an organic-faced, sprung-hub disc works well for both applications.

Tom Monroe averaged 219.418 mph one way in HPBooks Monza to set C/Production record at Bonneville Salt Flats. Clutch selection is very important at Bonneville because of very low rear-axle ratio — 2.25:1 in this case — and peaky engine. Two organic discs were destroyed before success was found with ceramic-faced, three-disc clutch similar to that at top left of facing page.

Engine in this Indy car is a turbocharged Formula I type Cosworth Ford V-8. Extremely low engine position is achieved by the use of a dry-sump oil system and a small-diameter clutch.

The car being constructed here is one I designed for NASCAR Modified racing. Bottom of the clutch housing has been trimmed off to allow setting the engine lower in the chassis. A small-diameter flywheel and clutch were used.

A small-diameter flywheel mounted on a high-output V8 requires a special starter for additional starting torque. A Chrysler geared starter, part number 3755250, accomplishes this in addition to permitting the center of the gear to be moved closer to the centerline of the crankshaft.

from the inside to outside wheels during conering and increased cornering speeds. The only catch is, the clutch housing is the lowest part of the car. To make the clutch housing smaller, the clutch and flywheel have to be reduced in size also. To do this, use a 7-1/4-inch diameter Borg & Beck clutch.

To gain the advantage of the small-diameter clutch, the flywheel diameter must be reduced before the engine can be dropped or the clutch housing changed. Small-diameter flywheels, starters and starter adapters are available from the same sources which supply the clutches.

The final step in this operation is to modify the bellhousing. If you mount your engine amidship, this job will probably already be done for you. Hewland, Z-F and Weismann transaxles have incorporated the small-diameter housing into the transmission case or bellhousing. If you are mounting your engine in the conventional forward position, you'll have to do it yourself. Modify one of the steel explosion-proof housings as described in the bellhousing chapter.

OIL CONTAMINATION

In any type of closed course racing where oil contamination of your clutch could mean the difference between winning or losing, a metallic faced disc is a good insurance policy as opposed to organic. Oil eventually causes an organic faced disc to slip, but oil will burn off of metallic facings harmlessly leaving the performance of the clutch relatively unaffected.

Chapter Six
FLYWHEELS

The flywheel serves three functions necessary to the satisfactory operation of an automobile: It stores energy, provides a second friction surface for the clutch and acts as the driven gear for the starter. Of these three functions, storing energy is the primary one. When it comes to performance cars the order of priorities changes. During the evolution of the automobile, the mere fact that the flywheel was there and was so big prompted automobile engineers to get the most out of it. The need for the flywheel and clutch in the automobile occurred at the same time, so they sort of "grew up together." Not so with the electric starter, it was a Johnny-come-lately. The electric starter didn't appear until 1912 in a Cadillac and was accepted by the public once people were convinced that there was no danger of being electrocuted when using it. The electric starter proved to be more convenient than the hand crank and one didn't run the risk of getting a broken arm when using it.

If you have a car like this, you won't have to read this chapter—unless you're planning to install a clutch, flywheel and starter.

STORES ENERGY

You may ask, "Why worry about storing energy when there is an engine to supply the power?" The reason is because of the nature of the internal-combustion engine. A one-cylinder internal-combustion engine produces power one quarter of the time—180 degrees of crankshaft rotation out of 720 degrees. The engine is on its own after the power stroke to rotate another one-and-a-half times to get back to the next power stroke. The more cylinders an engine has, the better this situation becomes because power strokes of the other cylinders fill in the voids. Remember, the engine is not free-wheeling after the power stroke. It must pump out the exhaust gases, inhale a new fuel charge and compress it prior to ignition. It does all of this against the friction of bearings, piston rings, timing gears, cam, cam followers, oil pump and distributor. Something must keep an engine rotating through the other three cycles. This "something" is called *rotational inertia. Inertia* is the resistance of a weight to any change in motion. If an object is moving at a particular speed or is at rest, a force must be applied to the object to change its speed whether it is going in a straight line or rotating like an engine. The higher the inertia of an object, the higher the force must be. The typical six- or eight-cylinder automobile engine has enough built-in inertia

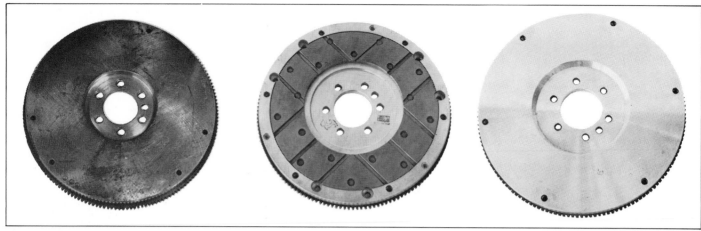

All three flywheels fit the same engine, but they are made from different materials. The first is steel, the second aluminum with a bronze insert and last is an all-aluminum marine flywheel. Because boats don't usually use a clutch, a heat-shield is not required with an aluminum flywheel. The flywheel is really just a convenient way to mount a starter ring gear.

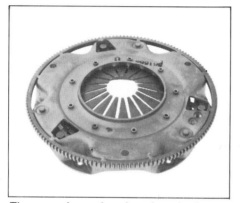

The exception rather than the rule. Corvair starter ring gear is on the pressure plate instead of on the flywheel.

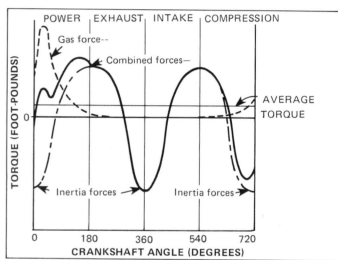

Torque output of a one-cylinder engine. Area bordered by the solid curve and the zero torque line represents this torque with the net sum of this area being average torque. It is represented by the horizontal line. Because torque is produced during the power stroke only, an engine not equipped with a flywheel will have its RPM fluctuate wildly, particularly with fewer cylinders. The flywheel stores energy from the power stroke for smooth engine operation during idling and starting the vehicle in motion.

to keep running at idle. The engine may "lope," or the RPM may fluctuate somewhat but it will keep running. On the other hand, any internal-combustion engine not having sufficient *rotational inertia* will result in a very rough-operating car when it comes to initial clutch engagement. Low-RPM torque of the internal-combustion engine is so low that during normal street operation, additional energy is required

to get a car moving through this transient period without stalling the engine. To keep an engine running which doesn't have enough inertia, the clutch must be engaged at revs higher than normal. The result will be excessive clutch slippage and wear. For the drag racer, it will mean a clutch that will "go south" after a few runs or an engine that "bogs" on the line if the clutch is engaged too soon.

Rotational inertia is found by dividing the weight being rotated by the value of gravity (32.2 feet per second per second) and multiplying it by the square of the distance of the weight from the center of rotation. The equation looks like this:

$$I = \frac{w\,R_o{}^2}{g} \text{ and } R_o = \sqrt{\frac{gI}{w}}$$

1955 Chevy drag car is limited by a three-speed transmission and high rear-axle gearing. It needs a lot of flywheel weight to get launched. The only reason the stock car needs a flywheel is to support the starting gear and provide a friction surface for the clutch.

Where:

I is in slug-feet-squared.

w is in pounds.

R_o is the radius of gyration in feet.

g is the acceleration of gravity in feet per second squared.

The radius of gyration is the distance from the center of rotation all the weight/mass of a rotating object could be placed to get the same inertia as the object itself. Take for instance a 30-pound flywheel. If the 30 pounds could be concentrated at one point and have the same *rotational inertia*—the distance from the axis it is spinning around—or center of rotation— is the *radius of gyration.*

To keep from getting tangled up in more theory, I'll stick to two basic shapes which represent most flywheels, pictured in the sketch. As you can see from the formulas, *rotational inertia* is directly related to weight but, goes up as the square of the radius. What this says is: To increase *inertia* with the least amount of weight/mass, get it farther away from the axis or rotation. On the other hand, if you want to reduce it with the same weight, move the weight closer to the axis of rotation.

What *rotational inertia* gives is the ability to store *energy.* For you engineering types, this is *kinetic energy*—the energy stored as a result of a body in motion. The heavier the body and the faster it is moving, the more *kinetic energy* it has stored up. *Kinetic energy* is expressed in foot-pounds and is found by using the formula:

$$E = .00548IN^2$$

Where:

I is rotational inertia in slug-feet squared.

N is RPM.

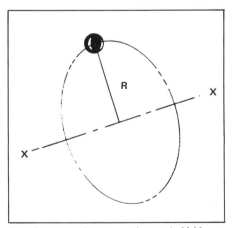

A weight rotating around an axis X-X has a rotational inertia dependent on the weight and the distance R from the center of rotation. As the weight or the radius of gyration is increased, so is the inertia, providing RPM is maintained.

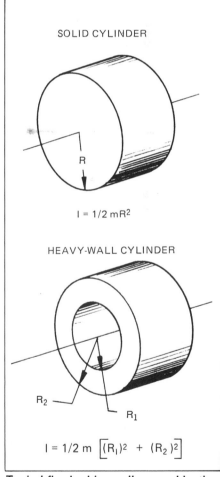

SOLID CYLINDER

$$I = 1/2 \, mR^2$$

HEAVY-WALL CYLINDER

$$I = 1/2 \, m \left[(R_1)^2 + (R_2)^2 \right]$$

Typical flywheel is usually a combination of the two "cylinders" shown here, with holes for mounting the flywheel at the engine crankshaft and the clutch to the flywheel. To find the rotational inertia of a flywheel, calculate each portion separately and then add the results.

MASS

It seems like every time you turn around, someone is trying to make life difficult. Here I go again. Weight must be mathematically converted to *mass* because weight changes with changes in gravity and *mass* does not. Weight is the force exerted by a *mass*. It is independent of gravity. Because physicists deal with the universe, they had to come up with something that is the same on the earth as it is in outer space. The force of gravity changes considerably, depending on the location in the universe and it changes slightly on the earth from one location to another. It is safe to assume you are going to be dealing with your flywheel n the earth, so we'll stick to a nice round figure for the value oτ the acceleration of gravity on earth, 32.2 feet per second squared. To convert pounds of weight to *mass,* divide by the value of gravity and you will get *mass* in terms of *slugs.* Remember, a *slug* of *mass* is the same no matter where in the world or universe it is. Not so with a pound of force exerted by a given mass. An astronaut weighing 180 pounds on earth may weigh nothing in outer space, but he will have a *mass* of 180 pounds divided by

32.2 feet per second squared, or 5.59 slugs *anywhere* in the universe. The force he exerts on a floor, or whatever, while standing still is totally dependent on the force of gravity at that particular location. However, if he runs into a brick wall at five MPH, with the gravity being half what it is on the earth (meaning his weight will be 90 pounds), the force of the collision will be the same as if he did it on the earth because his *mass* is the same. The same goes for a flywheel which varies in weight with changes in gravity. However, the force due to its inertia will be the same, just as with the astronaut, no matter if it is rotating or moving in a straight line. Therefore, it will require the same amount of force to speed it up or slow it down a given amount anywhere in the universe because mass remains constant. The formula for converting pounds of weight, or force, to slugs of mass is:

$$m = \frac{w}{g}$$

Where:

m is mass in slugs.
w is weight in pounds.
g is acceleration of gravity in feet per second squared.

To relate all these numbers and formulas to real life, let's look at a typical flywheel weighing 30 lbs., 11.75-inches in diameter and shaped like a solid disc. Actually, flywheels are a combination of the two shapes. Using the formula for a solid disc:

$$I = \frac{30}{32.2} \left(\frac{5.87}{12}\right)^2$$
$$= 0.1116 \text{ slug-feet squared}$$

where 30 pounds is divided by 32.2 to change pounds to slugs and the 5.87-inch radius is divided by 12 to convert to feet. Energy of the flywheel at 1000 RPM is found using the *kinetic energy* formula, or:

$$E = .00548(0.1116)(1000)^2$$
$$= 612 \text{ foot-pounds}$$

For the same flywheel rotating at 5000 RPM, the stored energy is:

$$E = .00548(0.1116)(5000)^2$$
$$= 15,289 \text{ foot-pounds}$$

Depending on how fast you want to make a standing start you can see from the example: A flywheel turned at higher revs builds up a considerable amount of energy. If your application happens to be drag racing, this is a very important consideration. The quicker you can launch your car, the better your chances are of winning races. This is even more critical if your car is relatively heavy and has a small-displacement engine. A stock 327 CID Nova or a 302 CID Mustang would qualify in this catagory. The object is to get your car launched so the engine revs can be utilized.

Once a car is on its way, the flywheel becomes a detriment. Power is now required to spin up the flywheel. If you can invent one which freewheels soon after clutch engagement in first gear, and is economically feasible, you'll be an instant millionaire. As for light drag cars having large high-output engines such as Funny Cars, they need no flywheel. They all use slider clutches which keep engine revs up and the clutch assembly supplies much more inertia than the typical flywheel.

I'll discuss lightening flywheels after we look at how flywheels are constructed.

Little ray of light under steel rule indicates a slight offset between the clutch friction surface and the pressure-plate mounting surface. A straight cut across the face of this flywheel will eliminate the offset and increase pressure-plate load slightly.

FLYWHEEL CONSTRUCTION

The flywheel has other functions to perform other than storing energy. It has to support the clutch and the starter ring gear. Taking the clutch first, the pressure plate must be mounted to the flywheel to clamp the disc between the flywheel and the pressure ring to transfer engine torque to the driveline. In addition, the flywheel must act as a heat sink for the clutch. Both of these requirements establish a minimum thickness and diameter right off the bat. A 1/8-inch-thick steel plate wouldn't be rigid enough to support the clutch nor provide enough volume to absorb the heat generated in some applications. Just how thick a flywheel should be is a question which has an infinite number of answers—and all of them right.

Generally, if a steel flywheel is used to replace the stock unit, the cross section is dictated by the starter, clutch linkage, the clutch, crankshaft and ring-gear mounting locations. They must all remain relative to each other, otherwise some or all may have to be modified. For example, if the clutch-mounting surface changes position, the clutch linkage will not operate properly, or maybe not at all. Also, the recess at the center of the flywheel must be maintained at a minimum so the flywheel-mounting bolts will clear the clutch disc. As for the ring gear, it must not change position or diameter, otherwise the starter will not engage.

Let's take a look at the different types of flywheels. Three basic materials are used, cast iron, steel, and aluminum. Detroit uses cast iron exclusively. In fact, some engineers refer to cast iron as *Detroit's wonder metal.* Just as with pressure-plate pressure rings, two types of cast iron are used. The first is *grey cast iron.* The name comes from, guess what—its color! It is used for the majority of stock flywheels but, is not strong enough to be used behind a Detroit high-performance engine, let alone one

These cast-iron flywheels illustrate the two types of balancing—zero balance and Detroit balance. Cast-in balance weight on the backside of the Detroit balanced flywheel doesn't include the finger.

which has been modified. As a result, *nodular cast iron* is put into service. Other names for this material are *ductile cast iron* and *ferritic cast iron.* Therefore, if you have a high-performance engine from Detroit, chances are it is equipped with a *nodular cast-iron* flywheel. The other two materials are used by the high-performance industry for the simple fact that they are less expensive to work with on a low-volume basis and

much stronger on top of it. One type of steel is used—*mild cold-rolled.* It is the most popular material because of simple economics. Aluminum flywheels are approximately 30 percent more expensive than steel. When you are considering an outlay of $100 or more, another $30 is hard to part with unless absolutely necessary. Aluminum is more expensive to start with because the raw material costs more and a heat shield must be added.

The parent metal of steel flywheels act as the clutch friction surface. A heat shield, as indicated by the dark area, must be added to an aluminum flywheel. Steel-plasma-sprayed heat shield which is approximately 0.015-inch thick adds very little to the weight of the flywheel. Steel flywheels, like the one on the right, don't need heat shields. *Photos courtesy Schiefer*

GREY CAST IRON OR NODULAR CAST IRON?

An easy way of determining the type of cast iron your flywheel is made from is by the noise it makes when hit with a hammer. Support your flywheel by hanging it with a rope or a piece of wire and tap it lightly with a hammer. A nodular flywheel, or any other high-burst-strength type, will ring like a bell whereas a grey cast iron one won't—it will be more like a thud.

A more sophisticated method of distinguishing grey cast iron from nodular cast iron is to look at your flywheel with a microscope. To do this, you'll need to polish a small area of your flywheel—approximately one-square-inch will do—with 600-grit sandpaper. Graphite is distributed throughout grey cast iron in the form of flakes. You'll need at least a 30X microscope to see them. As for nodular cast iron, the graphite is in the form of nodules, or spheres. These appear as circles about the size of pin points and can be seen under much less magnification—3X should be enough.

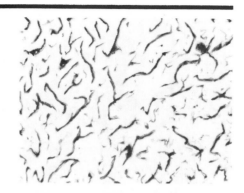

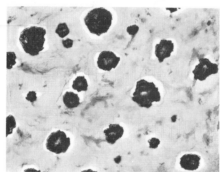

Graphite is in the form of flakes in grey cast iron. It takes a sphere or nodule form in the stronger nodular cast iron. The magnification of these representative samples is 100 times.

The *heat shield* is sintered iron or bronze or a steel disc with the same diameter as the clutch it is to be used with. Some are larger to accept a range of clutch sizes. Sintered shields are sintered onto a thin-steel base disc (0.060-inch). The shield is then riveted to the flywheel and Blanchard ground as a part of the flywheel assembly.

Another process, called *plasma spraying*, involves spraying steel or bronze directly on the aluminum to a thickness of 0.080 inch. The whole assembly is then Blanchard ground. Its advantage over the riveting process is that it is lighter and has better heat-dissipation qualities. This same process is also used with aluminum pressure rings. Steel or bronze must be applied to the aluminum, otherwise the aluminum would gall from the slipping action of the disc.

Aluminum flywheels are either forged or machined from billet stock, using one of two alloys, 6061 T-6 or 7075 T-6. 7075 T-6 has almost twice the strength of 6061 T-6, however, 6061 does the job quite adequately and is much less expensive. To be more specific, the *yield strength*—the point at which a material will permanently deform when loaded—of forged 6061 T-6 aluminum is virtually the same as mild steel and is 42-percent lighter for an equivalent volume.

This aluminum flywheel uses a sintered-bronze heat shield. It is riveted to the flywheel and then Blanchard ground. *Photo courtesy RAM Automotive*

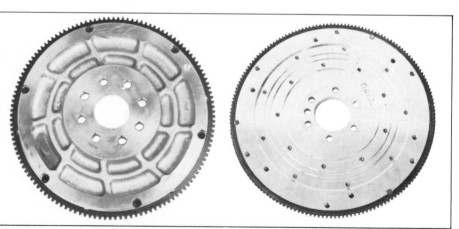

Aluminum flywheels are machined from forgings or from blanks which are sawed from billets. Forgings may be ribbed on their backsides to lighten them while retaining their strength. Theoretically, the forged type is the best, however billet flywheels also work well. Rivets on the back of the machined flywheel attach the heat shield.

This makes for a flywheel which is stronger than steel because the centrifugal loads are less at the same RPM.

FLYWHEEL LIGHTENING

Just to see what a flywheel means in terms of performance, let's take a look at the effect of lightening one. To do this, I am going to use a trick formula which tells how much weight would have to be removed from a car to get the same effect as removing one pound from the flywheel. For example, if the answer came out to be 10, for every pound taken off the flywheel, 10 pounds would have to be removed from the car to get the same result. Now, everybody knows a lighter car means a faster car, so let's take a look at this magic formula:

$$W = \frac{0.5 \times n^2 \times R_o^2 + R^2}{R^2}$$

Where:

W is the weight in pounds that must be removed from a car to achieve the same effect of one pound from the flywheel.
n is total gear ratio found by multiplying the transmission-gear ratio by the rear-axle ratio.

By concentrating all the mass of this flywheel on the radius of gyration R_o the same rotational inertia will result. By locating less mass farther from the center of rotation, the same inertia can be achieved or exceeded.

R_o is the radius of gyration of the flywheel.
R is the radius of the driving tires.

Refering back to the example using 30-lb., 11.75-inch flywheel, if a straight cut is taken across the flywheel to reduce its weight, let's see what effect this has. First, the *radius of gyration* must be found. Because the flywheel is just thinned, the *radius of gyration* will not change. Using the formula for a concentrated weight/mass rotating around a radius, the *radius of gyration* is:

$$R = \sqrt{\frac{I \times 32.2}{w}} = \sqrt{\frac{0.1116 \times 32.2}{30}}$$
$$= 0.346 \text{ feet} \equiv 4.15 \text{ inches}$$

If all the weight of this flywheel could be concentrated at one point 4.15 inches from the center of the crankshaft, it would have the same inertia as the flywheel. It would be tough to mount a clutch or a ring gear on it, though. With 12-inch standing radius tires (measured from the center of the wheel to the ground, not half the tire diameter), a 2.64:1 first gear ratio and a final drive ratio of 4.57:1 giving an overall ratio of 12.06:1, the weight removed from a car for each pound off the flywheel is equal to:

$$\frac{0.5 \times (12.06)^2 \times (4.15)^2 + (12)^2}{(12)^2}$$
$$= 9.70 \text{ pounds per pound}$$

Therefore, each pound taken off of this flywheel has the same effect as removing 9.70 pounds of weight from the car. If 10 pounds were removed the effect would be a 97 pound lighter car. Note: This is in first gear only. As you go through the gears, the effect becomes progressively less, or proportional to the overall gear ratio. For example, the result of being in top gear is:

$$\frac{0.5 \times (4.57)^2 \times (4.15)^2 + (12)^2}{(12)^2}$$
$$= 2.25 \text{ pounds per pound}$$

For a 10-pound lighter flywheel in top gear, the effect is a 22.5-pound lighter car.

This little exercise shows one thing. Cars which use their bottom gears a lot benefit most from light flywheels. Drag cars are definitely in this catagory as are road-race cars. The interesting thing is, road racers get a double advantage. In the first place, they don't need the additional inertia for starting a race. The lighter flywheel is a definite advantage when accelerating out of a tight corner in first or second gear. It is just as important when down-shifting upon entering a turn. The reason is, just as an engine must accelerate a car out of a turn, the brakes must decelerate it going into one. The less inertia a car has, the more effective the brakes will be. A car which can go deeper into a turn before braking has a distinct advantage. An extreme example of this was a four-wheel-drive Can-Am car I was familiar with. The car had so much additional inertia from the front-drive transfer gears and the extra drive shaft, half-shafts and ring and pinion gears that getting the car stopped without over-heating the brakes was the car's biggest problem. Every trick in the book was used to get the car to stop—such as bigger brakes, cooling ducts and a panel which flipped up to act as an air brake just prior to entering a turn—but nothing really worked. The car was a failure as a result.

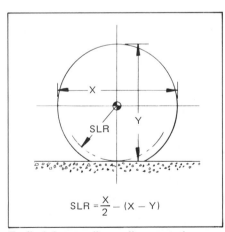

To find the standing radius or static-loaded radius (SLR) of a tire, divide the outside diameter of the tire by two and subtract this number from the vertical height of the tire measured from the ground. Use a square to make accurate measurements.

Low-inertia flywheels are beneficial for brake performance too, particularly in road racing. Compare this photograph with the one on page 53 to get a comparison between braking and accelerating forces. *Photo by Larry Griffin*

You may deduct from everything said up to this point that the lighter the flywheel the better, or none at all. This is true in some cases but not possible in most.

Flywheel lightening is not only an important consideration from a performance standpoint but, is very important from the safety aspect.

If done wrong, disaster may result. Centrifugal loads on a clutch are high but not as high as on the flywheel to which it is attached. This is because the outside diameter of the flywheel has a larger diameter than the clutch. For example, the centrifugal load on the periphery of a 14.5-inch-

diameter flywheel is approximately 30 percent higher than on the periphery of the pressure ring of an 11-inch clutch mounted to the flywheel. Referring back to the clutch chapter, the formula for centrifugal force is:

$$F = 0.0000284 \times W \times r \times n^2$$

Where:

F is the centrifugal force in pounds.
W is the weight of the object in pounds.
r is the distance of the object from the center of rotation in inches.
n is the speed in RPM.

For a one-pound chunk at the outer periphery of the flywheel, the force on it at 8000 RPM is:

$$F = 0.0000284 \text{ (1 pound)}$$
$$(7.25 \text{ inches) (8000 RPM})^2$$
$$= 13,180 \text{ pounds!}$$

With these kinds of forces, I recommend not modifying a flywheel in the first place, no matter what material it is made from. If you plan on lightening one anyway, don't do it to a stock cast-iron one. In fact, a grey cast-iron flywheel should not be used for *any* performance application. The only machining which can be done to a cast-iron flywheel without great risk of weakening it is a light cut for cleaning up the friction surface.

As for steel flywheels, they shouldn't be thinned to less than 3/8 inch. Check very carefully that this thickness is maintained at the center where the clutch side is counterbored to recess the flywheel-mounting bolts. If this area is thinned too much, the result may be a sheared-off flywheel.

Actually, the minimum thickness of a steel flywheel should be maintained at 1/2 inch. Any thinner and warpage and hot spots will be the result. When this happens, the flywheel is instant junk because there isn't enough remaining material which can be removed to straighten it out. A heat shield can be used to

Trans-Am Capris use small-diameter, low-inertia clutch and flywheel assemblies such as pictured at top of page 83.

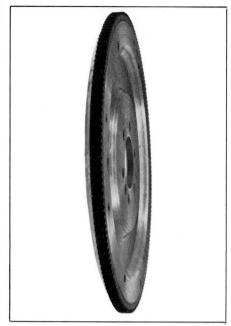

Steel flywheel lightened to the minimum by machining out the crankshaft side. Chances of it warping from clutch heat are high.

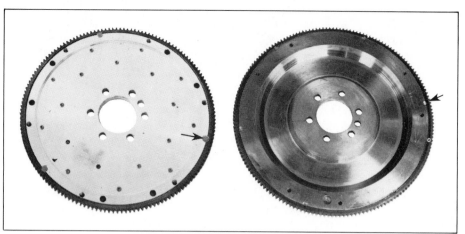

Because ring-gears have been known to work their way off, some flywheel manufacturers attach ring gears positively rather than depending on a shrink-fit. This is particularly true in the case of aluminum flywheels because of the different thermal-expansion rates of the two materials. The two methods shown are riveting on the aluminum and staking on the steel.

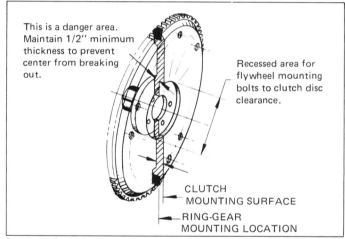

This is a danger area. Maintain 1/2" minimum thickness to prevent center from breaking out.

Recessed area for flywheel mounting bolts to clutch disc clearance.

CLUTCH MOUNTING SURFACE

RING-GEAR MOUNTING LOCATION

Section of a lightened steel flywheel. For a flywheel to replace the stock unit, the crankshaft, ring gear and clutch-mounting surfaces must remain in their same relative positions, and the flywheel must retain adequate strength to ensure against exploding. This limits the extent to which a flywheel can be lightened.

ZERO BALANCE AND DETROIT BALANCE

The engine a flywheel is used with determines how it is balanced. For instance, engines are either balanced *internally* or *externally*. Flywheels used with *internally* balanced engines are *zero balanced*. This means a flywheel and engine are in balance whether they are together or not. It also means the *zero-balanced* flywheel can be indexed on the crankshaft in any position without affecting the balance of the whole assembly.

The *Detroit-balanced* flywheel is a different ball game altogether. It mates up with the *externally balanced* engine to provide a balanced engine assembly. When the two are apart they are both out of balance, but together, they are in balance, providing the flywheel is indexed correctly on the crankshaft. Externally balanced engines use dowel pins with a companion hole in the flywheel to ensure proper indexing.

A word of caution at this point. To make certain an externally balanced engine is balanced when switching flywheels, the engine

prevent warpage or hot spots, however it will bring the weight of the flywheel right back up.

If it is absolutely necessary to use the lightest-possible flywheel, use aluminum. By taking this approach, there'll be no question as to safety and you'll have the maximum amount of heat sink available

with the minimum weight. For example, the lightest steel flywheel weighs about 20 pounds. It is marginal because it provides such a small heat sink and warpage becomes a problem. However, there are plenty of 11-pound aluminum flywheels available, with the majority of them in the 15-pound class.

This was a grey-cast-iron flywheel used to test a safety clutch housing for SEMA certification. Flywheel was partially cut so it would fail between 7000 and 8000 RPM. Heat checks accomplish the same thing. *Photo courtesy Lakewood*

Two methods are used to ensure a counter-balanced flywheel is indexed properly on the crankshaft. One uses a dowel pin in the crank and the other uses staggered mounting holes. Another method isn't as positive as illustrated by the crank on the right. Just make sure any extra hole in the flywheel has an extra hole behind it in the crank.

must be rebalanced with the flywheel. This is in spite of what some manufacturers say. The very nature of an externally balanced engine says metal must be removed from the flywheel to make up for the specific imbalance of that particular engine. Even though two engines are supposed to be the same as they come down the assembly line, it's a coincidence if they are. Therefore, if you install a new flywheel on your engine without balancing it with the engine, chances are the engine will be out of balance.

Some notable engines which are externally balanced are the 400 and 454 CID Chevrolets, all small-block Fords and the 428 CID Ford. In addition, the Chrysler 440-6Bbl. engine in 1970 and '71 was externally balanced as are all the new 360 CID engines from 1971 on plus, all AMC V-8's, Oldsmobiles up through 1967 and all Buick V-8's & V-6's.

DON'T REDRILL

While we're into the "do's and don'ts" of flywheels, one of the don'ts is redrilling a flywheel for a different pressure-plate bolt pattern. The reason for this is a locating error of 0.003 or 0.004 inch will throw everything out of balance. When this happens the pressure plate will orbit around the center of rotation rather than being on center.

If you must use a pressure plate requiring a different pattern then install a flywheel which is drilled for it. All of the high-performance-clutch manufacturers offer flywheels which are drilled for just about any clutch you may want to use. Many are drilled for more than one pattern. This includes changing clutch diameters or styles of pressure plates.

Crankshaft damper pulleys are also used to balance an externally balanced engine.

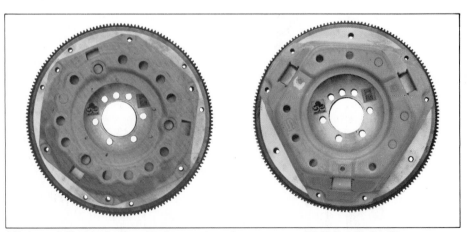

All those drilled and tapped holes are there for a purpose. This flywheel will accept a Long, Borg & Beck or a diaphragm pressure plate.

INCREASING DIAMETER

Final considerations you'll have to think about if you plan to increase your flywheel diameter are the clutch/bell-housing clearances and starter-motor fit. This is one modification you should try to avoid if possible. Increasing the size of a flywheel will not accomplish much in itself. The major reason for doing it is to increase clutch size or to change pressure-plate styles. Because the Long pressure plate has a higher profile than either the Borg & Beck or the diaphragm, changing to the Long may require spacing the housing or replacing it. Let me give you a "for instance." One popular conversion with Chevrolet engines is going from the 153-tooth ring-gear flywheel to the larger-diameter 168-tooth one. To do this will require changing to a larger housing. About the only snag you'll run into is with the starter. For your purpose, all General Motors starters are the same. To make your starter work with the new flywheel, just get a new starter nose—the aluminum piece on the geared end of the starter. The one you'll need is P/N 1968122. This will save the unnecessary expense of a new starter and spaces the centerline of the starter out the required distance.

DECREASING DIAMETER

Refer to the bellhousing chapter for information on what to do when you decrease flywheel diameter.

All GM starter motors are basically the same for the 153- and 168-tooth flywheels. The difference is in the nose—the cast portion which mounts the starter to the engine-block. Chevrolet PN/1968122 will fit your starter to a 168-tooth flywheel.

FLYWHEEL IDENTIFICATION CHART

Make	Year	Engine	# Teeth	Gear O.D.	Tooth Spacing (inches)	Balance (type)	# Bolts
General Motors							
Chevrolet	55-63	All 6's ex. Corvair	168	14.096	0.263	Zero	6
	64-76	All 6's ex. Corvair	153	12.835	0.263	Zero	6
	55-76	All V-8's Lg. hsngs. ex. 400 & 454	168	14.096	0.263	Zero	6
	70-76	400 & 454 Lg. hsngs.	168	14.096	0.263	Detroit	6
	63-76	400 & 454 Sml. hsngs.	153	12.835	0.263	Detroit	6
Oldsmobile	64-67	All V-8's	166	13.879	0.263	Detroit	6
	68-70	All V-8's	166	13.879	0.263	Zero	6
Pontiac	64-71	All V-8's	166	13.879	0.263	Zero	6
Buick	64-71	All V-8's	166	13.879	0.263	Detroit	6
Chrysler	64-68	S/S Hemi ram manifold	130	13.210	0.319	Zero	8
	66-69	426 Street hemi	*172	14.640	0.267	Zero	8
	70-71	426 Street hemi	130	13.210	0.319	Zero	8
	62-76	340, 361, 383, 413 & 426 wedge	130	13.210	0.319	Zero	6
	71-76	360	130	13.210	0.319	Detroit	6
	67-69	440	143	14.590	0.320	Zero	6
	70-71	440	130	13.210	0.319	Detroit	6
Ford Motor Co.	65-71	240 & 300 6 cyl.	164	14.215	0.272	Zero	6
	62-71	260 & 289	157	13.265	0.265	Detroit	6
	64-76	289 H.P., 302, 351, 400	164	14.215	0.272	Detroit	6
	54-63	292 & 312	146	14.774	0.317	Zero	6
	58-64	332, 352, 390, 406 & 427	153	15.457	0.317	Zero	6
	65-71	352, 390, 427 & 429	184	15.532	0.265	Zero	6
	66-71	428	184	15.532	0.265	Detroit	6
	69-72	429	176	15.532	0.277	Zero	6
American Motors	66-75	343, 360, 390	164	13.82	0.264	Detroit	6

*Uses a 12-tooth direct-drive starter motor. All others use 10-tooth geared starters.
Some engines use the smaller 13.265" diameter ring gears. Measure to verify.

Use this table to determine the specifications of your flywheel.

CHOOSING THE RIGHT FLY-WHEEL

Factors which you must consider when choosing a flywheel start out with what the car is going to be used for in the first place. What is its application? Next, you must consider the weight of your car, its engine output, gear ratios and tires. These are particularly critical if your car is going to be used for drag racing. The first objective should be to set your car up so it will launch without bogging the engine. The trick here is to use a flywheel which is heavy enough to get your car launched, but not excessively heavy. Once your car is under way with the clutch fully

engaged and engine revs in the usable torque range, the flywheel becomes a detriment. It turns into a balancing act.

Strictly Street—If you will be using your car only for street driving, my first inclination is to recommend staying with the stock flywheel. However, if you've tweaked your engine to the point it has usable revs over ten percent greater than

the stock revs, then something should be done. Face it, the loads on an engine and flywheel are going to be the same when you're using your newly found ponies to accelerate through the gears just as if you were making a run down the strip.

With this in mind, the first thing you should do is make sure your engine is equipped with one of

When purchasing a high-performance flywheel, do the same thing you should do when purchasing a clutch—make sure it is SEMA-approved.

Light flywheels and the street don't go together unless your car is extremely light such as this 340 CID Dodge powered T-Bucket. Otherwise, don't fiddle with the flywheel unless you want to be leaving stop signs and lights at 3000 RPM.

OEM HIGH-BURST-STRENGTH FLYWHEELS				
Manufacturer	**Part Number**	**Engine**	**Material**	**Notes or Specifications**
Chevrolet	3991406	All V-8's ex. 454	Nodular CI	For 10-1/2" HD clutch
	3963537	454	Nodular CI	Detroit balance
	3992094	454	Nodular CI	For 10" dual-disc clutch, Detroit balance
	3955151	396/427	Nodular CI	For 10" dual-disc clutch
Chrysler	3410258	1970-426 Hemi	CI Alloy	Eight-bolt pattern
	2863069	'67—'69 426 Hemi	CI Alloy	Eight-bolt pattern
	2780619	1966 426 Hemi	CI Alloy	Eight-bolt pattern
	2465123	1965 426 Hemi	CI Alloy	Eight-bolt pattern
Ford	C9AZ-6375-C	Boss 429	Nodular CI	Can be used on 429 CJ
	C9ZZ-6375-B	Boss 302	Nodular CI	Can be used on 289, 302, 302W, 351C and 351W CID Engines, but should be balanced.
	D1ZZ-6375-B	Boss 351	Nodular CI	Can be used on 289, 302, 302W, 351C and 351W CID Engines, but should be balanced.
Listed are high-performance flywheels and the engines they were available with installed from the factory. There were no OEM high-burst-strength flywheels available on engines not shown.				

the high-performance ductile cast-iron units. If it's not, and any are available for your engine, get one. If not, install a high-performance steel-billet flywheel. This will greatly reduce the chances of having the flywheel explode when you are "on it." As far as which weight you should be using, I recommend staying with the stock weight. It is just about impossible to come up with a better setup. The only exception would be if you are using a big-block engine in a tube-framed, glass-bodied street rod. You could get away with a lighter flywheel—say ten pounds less. I still recommend staying with the stock weight for the street—certainly not less than 30 lbs. total.

Street and Competition—First, if your engine is equipped with a grey cast-iron flywheel, *get rid of it* in favor of nodular cast iron or steel. Don't even attempt to use a stock flywheel unless you are 100% sure it is nodular iron. See page 92.

If you are going to use your car for the dual purpose of racing while maintaining it for street use, you are going to have to make compromises. Whether you compromise in favor of racing or street operation is up to you. If it is drag racing you'll be doing, chances are a little heavier flywheel will help. As for why you should choose a heavier flywheel, the very fact that your car is a street machine says it is heavy relative to the power output of the engine. It also means you're not running rear-axle gears in the 5.13:1 range unless you own your own oil well. These factors determine how your car will launch. If it "hooks up" too well—gets too much traction at the starting line—the engine will "bog." Assuming you've done all the tricks in the book to your engine and chassis, including adequate accelerator-pump shot and "shooter" size, look at the flywheel. First, run your car several times to get it sorted out. The next thing to do is check your times against the competition. If you're winning with lower elapsed times (ET's), you can forget about changing anything. Assuming you aren't the quickest in your class, look at your times. If your speeds are higher as well as your ET's and your engine is bogging as you come off the line, go to a heavier flywheel—no more than 50 pounds. By doing this, the loss due to the extra flywheel inertia will be more than offset by a quicker launch and your ET's will drop. On the other hand, your top-end speed may also drop, but who cares? It's ET that counts. The heavier flywheel won't hurt the streetability of your car. In fact, it will help a little bit. Not often do you get two for the price of one!

If you are doing some other type of racing where stand-still starts aren't critical to win the race, consider a stock or *lighter* weight flywheel. Whatever you do, don't reduce the weight of the flywheel more than ten pounds. The car would then become unmanageable on the street.

Drag Racing—Choosing a flywheel for a drag car has to be more complex than for any other application. As I discussed earlier, what's good for launching a car is bad the rest of the time. But, if your car can't launch, you might as well put it back on the trailer and go home. The problem with choosing a flywheel for this application is, it involves the whole car—just about everything but the paint job. For example, following is a list of the key factors you must consider when choosing the weight, or more accurately, the inertia of the flywheel:

1. Weight of the car.
2. Weight distribution.
3. Power output of the engine.
4. Rear-axle and transmission first-gear ratio.
5. Traction of the tires.
6. Chassis setup.
7. Type of clutch being used.

These two cars have four wheels, are station wagons and their engines are supercharged—end of similarities. The old Ford 312 can use a little help from its flywheel at launch time. The Hemi doesn't need much help at all.

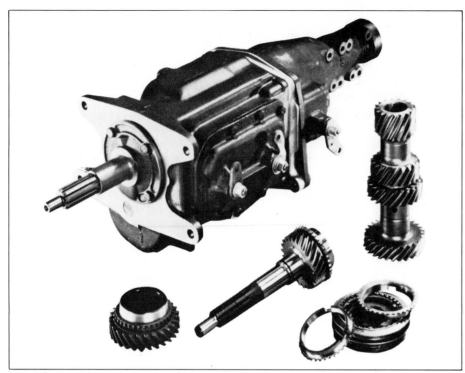

The right combination of transmission and rear-axle gears and you won't need much help from the flywheel during launch. *Photo courtesy Borg-Warner Corporation*

The power output of an engine and the weight of a car must be considered as a team. Divide the estimated horsepower of your engine by the total weight of your car and you get what is known as the *power-to-weight ratio.* As this number increases for a given car, so does the ability of the car to accelerate from a standstill. For example, the power-to-weight ratios for the typical Super Stocker,

40-pound steel flywheel is a typical high-inertia flywheel. It is thick enough so it can easily be lightened by 10 pounds if necessary.

Pro Stocker and Funny Car are 0.15, 0.30 and 1.5 horsepower per pound, respectively. The rate of acceleration each of these cars has in the first 100 feet reflects the power-to-weight ratio. In like respect, the inertia required from the flywheel becomes proportionately less as the power-to-weight ratio increases.

The object of using a flywheel for drag racing is to get your car launched and get it moving so the engine RPM reaches its usable torque range as quickly as possible. Once this is accomplished, it's all up to engine power to accelerate the car through the quarter mile. If you're having engine-bogging problems, the situation can be improved with lower gear (higher numerical) ratios in both rear axle and transmission. Rear-axle gears are available as low as 5.57:1 for most rear axles and 6.50:1 for many, rules permitting. Schiefer offers a real "stump-puller"—a 7.17:1 gear set for the Dana 60 only! This ratio is for the high-revving small block installed in a relatively heavy car. Pick the gear which lets your engine RPM peak as you're going through the lights. After making this change, if your car hooks up without the engine bogging, you've found the right combination. If not, you'll have to make transmission-ratio changes. If, after using the lowest gearing permitted or available, your engine continues to bog, you'll have to use a heavier/higher-inertia flywheel to get the car launched. If you are really serious about getting the most out of your car, go to the heaviest flywheel available—50 or 60 pounds—and compare your before and after times. If you are launching without any bogging, but are getting engine revs up too quick, lighten the flywheel five pounds and recheck your times. McLeod has a nice one for this purpose called the *Centrifugal Flywheel.* Unfortunately it is only available for Chevrolets at present.

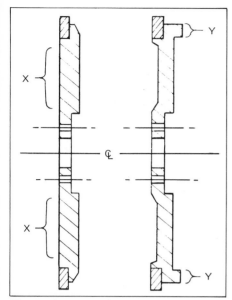

Flywheel on the left is a section of a typical 50-pounder whereas the other is a 36-pound flywheel with the same inertia, or energy-storing capability. This is accomplished by concentrating more mass at the rim indicated by Y and removing it from the area indicated by X.

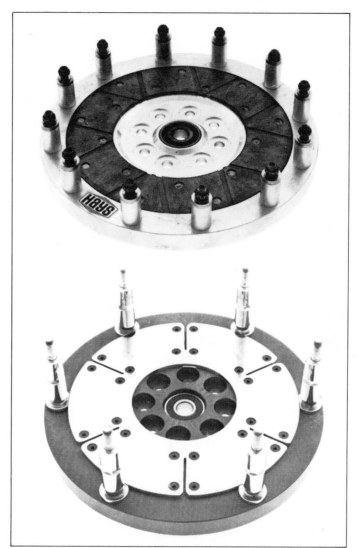

Aluminum flywheels with three-disc slider clutches. Six-stand unit is for a Crowerglide while the other is for a conventional Hays slider. Both use ball-type pilot bearings inserted into the flywheel rather than in the engine crank. Crowerglide uses threaded adjustable drive stands and a steel heat shield attached with countersunk screws. Hays uses shims to space the pressure plate and has a riveted sintered-bronze heat shield.

The reason for its name is it weighs 40 pounds, but has the inertia of a 50-pound conventional flywheel. This is done by concentrating more weight toward the outside periphery. The result is a more effective flywheel. A car will end up weighing less toward the front where you should try to get your car lighter and the flywheel will have the same launching power as a 50-pounder. If you find out you can reduce the flywheel inertia, only the outer edge needs lightening rather than having to hollow out the engine side as with a conventional flywheel. This makes the modification simpler and less expensive if you have to farm out the work.

The need for high-inertia flywheels came about as a result of improved traction brought on by advancements in chassis and tire designs. The days are long gone when a set of Traction Masters and some recaps or Atlas Bucrons on the rear would do the job. The present cars and tires hook up right now! This depends on your class, but if you're running wrinkle-wall drag tires, the only significant wheel spin you should be getting is during the burnout. The answer to engine bog may seem to be, use tires which spin during launch so engine revs won't get pulled down excessively. One thing for sure, this will cure the bogging problem. Another thing for sure, it will also eliminate any chances of winning. You have to have traction first. After getting it, you then must utilize the power of your engine to the maximum through proper gearing, flywheel design and the right clutch.

The last major factor you'll have to deal with is the type of clutch you're using. As for the majority of cars using conventional clutches, they are limited by how much heat the lining can withstand before it self-destructs. In this situation, maximum use will have to be made of gearing and flywheel inertia for launching.

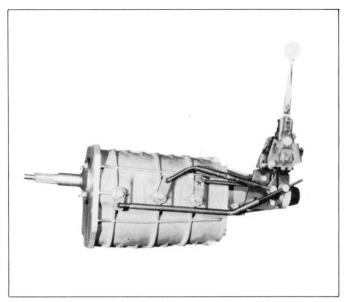

Great use has been made of five-speed transmissions to get the most out of an engine. This is Doug Nash's super-strong unit which is used with great success in drag racing and is finding its way into oval-track and road racing. *Photo courtesy Doug Nash*

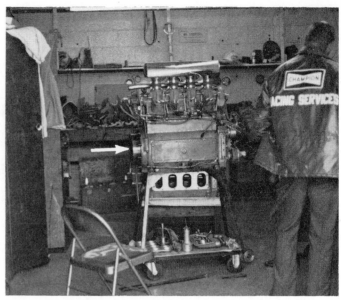

Here's some exotic hardware in Gasoline Alley at Indy. This Offy engine has just been pulled out of its car exposing the floater-plate drive ring (arrow).

If you're using a slider, you don't have to concern yourself with a flywheel because the clutch should be set up to to prevent engine RPM from falling below a predetermined figure. Engine bog will occur if the clutch locks up prematurely. This usually happens when an engine is down on power and the clutch isn't readjusted to compensate. The right way to correct this problem is with a healthy engine.

A metallic-faced disc used with a centrifugally adjustable Long pressure plate can be set up to act like a short-duration slider. A setup like this used with a non-shifting application and low gearing can use a minimum-weight flywheel. If you are using a steel flywheel, you'll still need a heat shield to prevent flywheel warpage and heat checking from the excessive heat generated by clutch slippage. If you can use a light flywheel, I recommend using aluminum because of the additional volume. It will absorb and dissipate heat more efficiently than a steel flywheel of equal weight.

Closed-Course Racing—Just as I did in the clutch chapters, I'll throw the sprint cars, stocks, modifieds and road-race cars all under the closed-course heading. These cars are as different as night and day, but the flywheel applications turn out to be the same except in special instances. The factors in choosing a flywheel for a drag car are largely based on getting a car moving or launched from a standstill. In

Because of low RPM engine torque and two-speed transmissions, Indy cars need a little hand getting out of the pits.

closed-course racing, about the only launching done is while exiting the pits. In many cases, pitting doesn't even enter the picture. If it does, the fraction of a second saved getting out of the pits isn't worth the loss in acceleration you would experience coming out of the turns with a heavier flywheel. Therefore, the recommendation as to which type of flywheel to use is the lightest and lowest-inertia one you can find. Why? Because you don't need to store any energy. That is strictly for the asphalt burners! Still, your engine needs a flywheel for other purposes. You have to start the engine, mount the clutch and provide a friction surface for the clutch. Therefore, the factors requiring consideration change. They are as follows:

1. Starter requirement.
2. Type of clutch.
3. Vertical location of the engine.

Rather than breaking down the different types of closed-course racing to consider each factor and getting a lot of overlap, I am going to take each one separately and point out any exceptions related to a particular situation. Just

remember, a lighter flywheel is worth horsepower at the rear wheels once a car is under way and the clutch is fully engaged. This is more pronounced when lower gears are used while exiting relatively slow speed turns—30 to 50 MPH.

There are only two types of closed-course race cars I know of which do not use on-board starters. They include some sprint cars and all championship cars. Without a starter, the flywheel doesn't need a ring gear. This is nice because the ring gear is weight removed from the outside diameter of the flywheel, right where it has the biggest effect on reducing rotational inertia. For starting, sprint cars are pushed, nothing tricky. As for championship cars, they are started with a hand-held portable electric starter. It engages the transaxle/transmission input shaft at the back of the car and when starting, the transmission is placed in neutral with the clutch engaged. The starter is then free to turn the engine over without the car rolling. As soon as oil pressure is up, the ignition is switched on and the engine fires. For all other types

of racing, a starter is required. If you aren't running a sprinter or championship car, plan on using a flywheel to mount the starter ring gear.

After the starter comes the clutch. Having taken up the sprint car first, I'll do it again because it is a special case. The sprint car which normally doesn't have a starter won't have a friction clutch, either. It uses a *dog clutch* without any flywheel. This is a "perfect" situation because engine power used to accelerate the flywheel can go to the rear wheels instead. Championship cars require a clutch for getting in and out of the pits, so a flywheel has to be used for mounting the clutch. If you don't have a sprint or championship car, you'll have to provide for both a starter and a clutch no matter if it is a Formula 5000 road racer, a NASCAR Grand National stock car or an IMSA GT. Just make certain the flywheel and clutch bolt patterns match. Also, if you are using a conventional 10 to 11-inch diameter clutch, use an aluminum flywheel for the lowest possible inertia. However, if you use the small-diameter 7-1/4-inch Borg & Beck

Here's a sprint car in a classic pose. A flywheel isn't needed because storing energy is not required, a clutch isn't used and the starter, a pickup truck in this case, pulls behind the fence once the car is under way. *Photo at left by John Mahoney*

Starter plugged into the transaxle of A. J. Foyt's Indy car. Because these cars don't carry on-board starters, flywheel ring gears are not required.

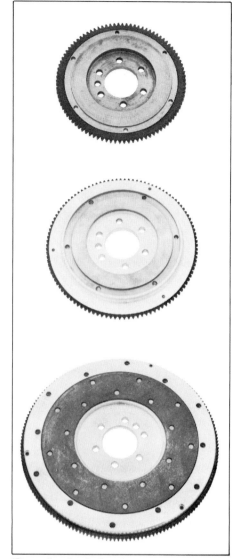
Three flywheels for the same engine—all with provisions for a starter and a clutch. Two smaller flywheels are designed to be used with the 7-1/4″ multi-disc Borg and Beck clutch while the larger one is for a conventional 10-1/2″ or 11″ Borg & Beck or diaphragm clutch.

unit, use the small 94-tooth 9-5/8-inch ring gear steel flywheel. The inertia from the small-diameter flywheel doesn't justify the complexity of an aluminum, heat-shielded flywheel. The ring gear alone accounts for the greatest portion of the inertia, and you need the starter ring gear. However, if you are determined to get your rotating inertia down to a minimum, ARC Industries can supply you with an aluminum flywheel. Its loose heat shield is retained to the flywheel by the pressure-plate-attaching bolts.

Another consideration is the vertical position of the engine in your chassis. If you don't plan to lower the engine to get your car's C.G. down, use a standard-diameter flywheel and avoid the complication of a special starter. If the class you're running in permits the use of a dry-sump lubrication system, by all means take advantage of it and use the smallest flywheel you can lay your hands on. If you're running a sprint car, you have it made in this department providing your car is one of the many not using a starter or clutch. But wouldn't you know it—the setup which is the least complicated to lower isn't going to be an advantage. In fact it's going to hurt. A relatively high C.G. is desirable

for cornering when running on dirt because of "sidebite." However, if most of your races are on pavement, you might strongly consider the idea of dropping your engine.

One final consideration before I leave the subject of which flywheel you should be using. As I've said over and over again, it is to your advantage in circle-track or road racing to reduce the rotational inertia of your driveline as much as possible. The flywheel is a large part of this inertia. Just as the diameter and the weight have a substantial bearing on this inertia, so does the weight and diameter of the clutch. Therefore, the combination of a small-diameter flywheel and clutch not only makes it possible to lower the engine in a chassis, it also reduces overall driveline inertia.

ARC's neat little flywheel for the 7-1/4-inch Borg and Beck clutch. Heat shield is retained to the aluminum flywheel by the clutch-attaching bolts.

Chapter Seven
CLUTCH LINKAGES

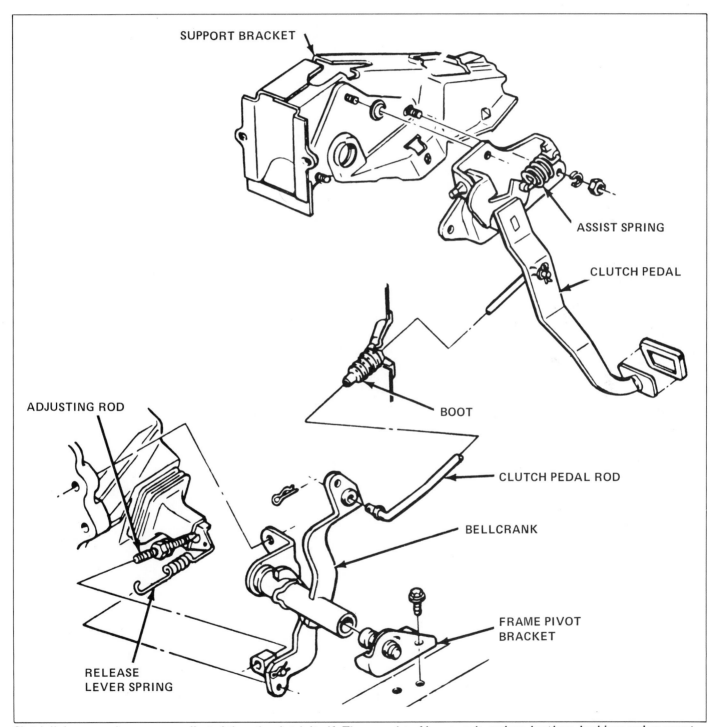

SUPPORT BRACKET

ASSIST SPRING

CLUTCH PEDAL

ADJUSTING ROD

BOOT

CLUTCH PEDAL ROD

BELLCRANK

FRAME PIVOT BRACKET

RELEASE LEVER SPRING

Clutch linkages can be more complicated than the clutch itself. They consist of levers, rods, springs, bearings, bushings and an assortment of various retainers and fasteners. *Drawing courtesy Ford Motor Company*

The clutch linkage transmits force and motion from the driver to the clutch to engage and disengage it. Linkage includes everything from the pad on the pedal, or the grip on the handle, to the release bearing.

There are two types of clutch linkages, *mechanical* and *hydraulic.* Mechanical is most common. Your car probably has a mechanical linkage. If your car is not a subcompact, its linkage will be made up of pushrods and levers. If yours is a race car, only *you* know what type it is.

Hydraulic linkages are mainly reserved for application where space is so tight in the foot and transmission areas that it would be very difficult or impractical to use a mechanical system. Foreign-made cars and trucks often use hydraulic clutch linkages regardless of engine location.

A common use for hydraulic linkages is when the engine is located so far from the driver that a mechanical linkage would be too clumsy. Mid- and rear-engine cars are in this catagory.

One common factor to consider in relation to every automotive clutch is the human one. No matter what type of clutch a car is equipped with, it must be operated by the driver, a human. With this in mind, there are practical limits on how much force and travel can be applied at the pedal to operate a clutch. Maximum force required to operate the average passenger-car clutch is about 35 pounds through a travel of about six inches. Travel includes one inch of free play and one inch of pedal reserve. Actual travel for operating the pressure plate is four inches: Six inches minus one inch of free play and one inch of pedal reserve. For a high-performance car or a truck, this load can easily be doubled, although this would be excessive. One major car manufacturer used the following design parameters in the days of high-performance production cars—6.50 inches maximum pedal travel

Space is precious in Formula 1 cars, as can be seen at rear of this car with bodywork removed. This is why hydraulic clutch linkages are used exclusively.

A clutch linkage can be mechanically perfect and still not be right if the pedal is not positioned properly in relation to the driver and the other controls. Kevin Rotty's Pro-Stock Camaro works well because it was carefully thought out.

and 40 pounds maximum pedal force. These are nice numbers to talk about, but sometimes very difficult to meet. For a road-race car, I try to limit pedal forces to 60 pounds because of the number of times the clutch must be operated during the course of one race. For a drag car, this can be higher because fatigue doesn't become a problem. Increasing pedal force is more tolerable than increasing pedal travel. The human leg can operate effectively through just so much travel, 6.50 inches is just about maximum. Pedal load and travel are tied together. If you want to reduce pedal travel, then pedal load will increase in the same proportion. On the other hand, if you want to reduce pedal load, travel has to increase. This is taking advantage of *lever ratios* or *mechanical advantage.*

Lever Ratio—Now is a good time to bone up on a little theory. *Lever ratio* is used to advantage in just about every mechanical system. A term which is interchangeable with *lever ratio* is *mechanical advantage.* It is taking advantage of mechanics to do something. That something is to translate motion and force. The first thing needed is a lever. The clutch-pedal assembly is a lever. Next is an axis or a *fulcrum point* for the lever to pivot about. The *fulcrum* supports the lever and provides a point for the lever to pivot as in the case of the clutch pedal. Above sketch illustrates the clutch pedal as a lever showing the relationship between the force applied at the pedal and the reaction at the pushrod relative to their distances from the *fulcrum* or pivot points. If the distance from the pedal pivot to the center of the clutch-pedal pad is 15 inches, and from the pivot to the pushrod is three inches, the *lever ratio* is equal to:

$$\text{Lever ratio} = \frac{A}{B} = \frac{15 \text{ inches}}{3 \text{ inches}}$$
$$= 5.0{:}1$$

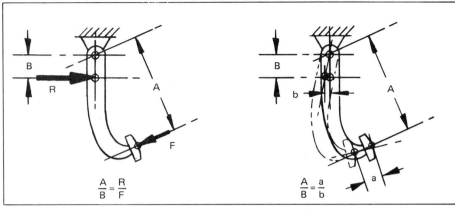

Illustration at left shows relationship between a force applied at the clutch pedal and the reaction force at the pushrod to distances from the clutch-pedal pivot point. One on the right shows the relationship of the clutch travel at these points and the same distances. Forces are inversely proportional and travels are directly proportional to A and B. In other words, where big dimension A is, the small force is, but with greater travel. The term for this is *mechanical advantage.* Mechanical advantage is determined by the lever ratio A/B.

Where:

A is the distance from the center of the pad to the pedal pivot in inches.
B is the perpendicular distance from the pushrod to the pedal pivot in inches.

What this means in terms of pedal force and the resulting force at the pushrod is, the pushrod force is five times the amount of the applied pedal force. Therefore, if you have a clutch with this lever ratio and you apply 40 pounds to the pedal, the force on the pushrod will be 200 pounds—a real mechanical advantage. The force out is five times what you put in. Now, the law that says you can't get sumthin' for nuthin' applies. Load at the pushrod was five times that put in, but the pushrod travels only one-fifth the amount of pedal travel. Therefore, the forces and the travels are inversely proportional to each other. Going back to the *lever ratio,* the forces are *inversely proportional* to the lever ratio and

the travels are *directly proportional.* In equation form this looks like:

$$R = F \times \frac{A}{B}$$

Where:

R is the reaction force at the pushrod in pounds.
F is the applied force at the pedal in pounds.
$\frac{A}{B}$ is the lever ratio.

So as distance B from the pushrod point to the pedal pivot is reduced with the pedal-pad-to-pivot distance A remaining the same, the reaction force is increased for a given applied force. On the other hand, the pushrod travel is reduced for a given pedal travel. What this means in the real world, if you want to reduce your clutch-pedal operating force, the pushrod pivot can be relocated closer to the pivot, but the pedal has to be moved farther to operate the clutch. The reverse happens if you

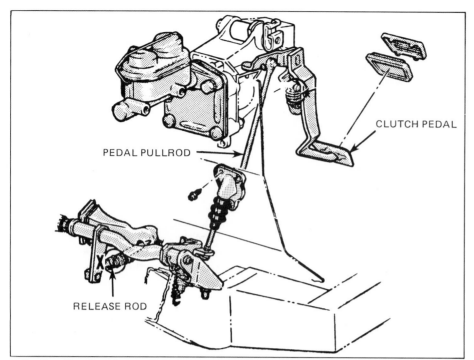

A "pullrod" rather than a pushrod is used from the clutch pedal to the bellcrank in this 1970 Ford clutch linkage. This is accomplished by locating the rod-attaching point on the opposite side of the pedal pivot. *Drawing courtesy Ford Motor Company*

want to reduce pedal travel. Move the pushrod farther from the pivot and the required travel is reduced, but the pedal-operating force increases in the same proportion. A good move if you want quicker operation of the clutch and the operating force doesn't end up too high.

Application of the *lever-ratio* principle is pretty simple, but if you're not careful you can get into trouble. For example, the lever, or clutch-pedal assembly I've shown in the previous example has the pedal-pivot point above the other two points to make it nice and simple. This doesn't have to be, and in many cases it's not. These points can be located any distance from or around the fulcrum and the A/B principle still applies. Just observe which direction the points move. For instance, the clutch-pedal illustration shows the applied force and reaction force moving in the same direction. If the pushrod was located above rather than below the pivot, motion

would be reversed.

Something else to watch out for is making the common mistake of measuring dimensions A and B incorrectly. Rather than a point-to-point measurement, they are a line-of-action measurement. Instead of

measuring from the center of the pedal-pivot point to the center of the pushrod pivot, the measurement should be taken from the center of the pedal pivot to the *line of action* of the pushrod, link or leg. If the pushrod happens to be straight, measure perpendicular to the center of it. If the measurements are taken incorrectly, a substantial error may result in calculating the lever ratio.

One final point to consider is the lever-ratio change as the clutch pedal, or any lever for that matter, goes through its travel. If you are designing your own clutch linkage, this is a very important consideration. You can try to minimize this effect, but you should always try to use this lever-ratio change to your advantage. How it is used depends on the type pressure plate you are using. If your car is equipped with a coil-spring pressure plate, it is desirable to have the pedal-lever ratio rise as the pressure plate is disengaged because of the increase in release lever load due to the compression of the coil springs. Just the opposite is wanted with the diaphragm pressure plate. As it is released, the spring load drops. It would be helpful to have the lever ratio also drop to speed up

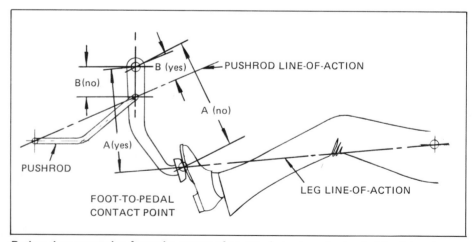

Rather than measuring from the center of an attachment or pivot point to determine a lever ratio, measure from the center of the fulcrum point to the *line-of-action* of the pushrod or link. For a clutch-pedal assembly, determine A and B as shown.

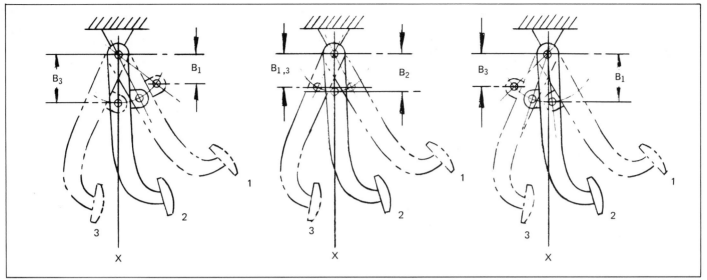

Three sketches illustrate what can happen to *lever ratios* at different pedal positions. Position 1 is full clutch engagement. Position 2 is midpoint of the pedal travel and position 3 is full disengagement. The configuration on the left results in an A/B ratio which falls as the clutch is disengaged. I prefer the one in the middle because A/B remains relatively constant and it is uncomplicated. Setup on the right has an increasing A/B ratio. One on the extreme left would be suitable for a diaphragm pressure plate whereas the one on the right would be for a coil-spring pressure plate, assuming the rate of ratio change remains unchanged between the clutch pedal and pressure plate.

clutch release. I prefer to end up with the same ratio at the engagement and disengagement extremes of pressure-plate travel. This doesn't involve any tricks where they're not needed and may avoid trouble which may result otherwise. Automobile engineers use this method unless there is an unusual design situation.

The theory of levers as applied to clutch pedals is the same no matter what type of system is used or how it is mounted. It could be a rod-and-lever, cable, or hydraulic system. The pedal can be suspended from the steering column to firewall bracket in the conventional manner or floor-mounted. Sketch at right shows the different systems and how they can be mounted. There are many variations from what I've shown, but definite rules must be followed, depending on the system. The first rule is to minimize lever-ratio changes no matter which system you are using.

Rod and Lever Linkage—Most flexible, durable and least troublesome to work with is the rod and lever, as evidenced by its broad use by the U.S. auto industry. The rod can be mounted in any position relative to

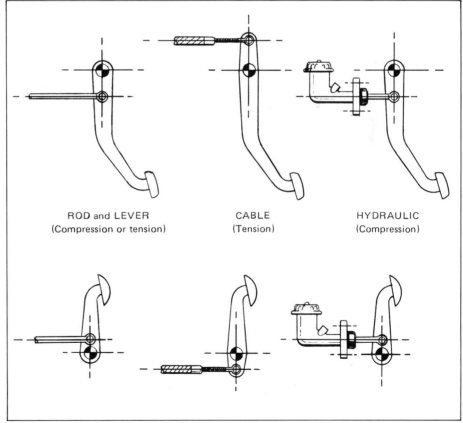

ROD and LEVER
(Compression or tension)

CABLE
(Tension)

HYDRAULIC
(Compression)

Basic clutch-pedal configurations: Three are floor-mounted and three are suspended or hanging. Many different setups can be derived from the more conventional or common ones shown. The method each one can be operated is shown. Compression means to push, tension means to pull.

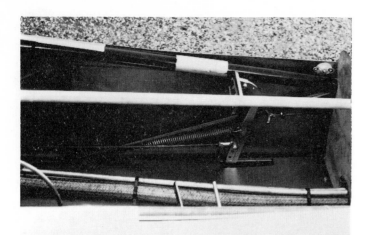

Clutch linkage in this Top-Fuel dragster is a basic rod-and-lever linkage. A long rod extends from the pedal to a bellcrank at the rear of the car. This rod is hidden by the bottom frame tube at the rear of the car. Another rod connects the bellcrank to a release lever which extends out of the bellhousing. Note the adjustable pedal stop and the "cheater holes" in the pedal, bellcrank and the release lever. Extra holes let the car owner set his car up to suit him and lets the builder get by with some guesswork.

the pedal pivot, putting it in tension (pulled) or compressed (pushed) when the clutch is operated. I will cover the most common designs which let *you* apply the principles to different arrangements.

The first thing is to take a look at the job. A typical 2000–3000-pound pressure plate must be moved 0.030–0.085 inch to disengage the clutch, depending on whether the disc has marcels or not. If the combined ratios of all the links and levers from the pressure plate to the clutch pedal were one, the force and travel required to operate the pressure plate would be the same, assuming the system was rigid and friction-free. A 0.030–0.085–inch pedal travel sure would make for fast shifts, but only King Kong could operate it.

Returning to reality, let's look at a typical situation. A 3000-pound pressure plate used with a disc having a marcel spring with 0.045" spring-back and a 0.035" air-gap at full release requires a total plate travel of 0.080 inch. If the pressure plate is a Long style with a release-lever ratio of 4.7:1, the load at the release-lever is equal to 3000 pounds divided by 4.7, or 638 pounds and the travel is equal to 0.080" multiplied by 4.7, or 0.376". Picking a pedal travel

of 4.0 inches, the overall ratio of the clutch linkage is equal to 4.0 inches divided by 0.376", or 10.64:1. Force at the pedal is then equal to 60 pounds, all of which assumes the system is 100-percent efficient and rigid.

Rather than achieving the total lever ratio from the clutch-pedal assembly, it is spread out over the remainder of the levers which make up the rod-and-lever system. The reason for this is the pedal-pivot-to-pushrod-pivot dimension would be so small that there wouldn't be enough room for bushings, bearings and attachments. Also, the loads transmitted by the pedal would be so high that the size and strength of the components required to transmit them would result in unnecessary expense and weight. There are other reasons, but I think you get the idea.

Rod-and-lever clutch linkages are made up of six major components, starting with the clutch pedal. Taking them in order from the pedal to the pressure plate, there is the pushrod, the *bellcrank*, another pushrod, the release lever and release bearing. The first pushrod attaches to the clutch pedal and goes through the firewall to the *bellcrank*. The pushrod transmits force and motion from the pedal to the *bellcrank*

without changing either. What comes from the clutch-pedal rod goes directly to the *bellcrank* unchanged.

Other names for the *bellcrank* are *equalizer bar, torque shaft* and *cross shaft*. Independent of the name, it still does the same job. A bellcrank is used to transmit motion—usually in a direction different from that applied by the clutch pedal.

Finally, the bellcrank transfers force to the clutch-release lever so the force is canceled out on the engine and transmission. What this means is, the engine isn't forced to move on its rubber mounts during clutch operation. I'll talk about this important point in the section on race-preparing your clutch linkage.

A *bellcrank* is two arms or levers welded to a steel shaft, called a *cross shaft*. One end of the cross shaft is mounted to the frame or body of the car and the other end is mounted to the engine. Both ends are in bearings or bushings so it can rotate freely. Arm lengths and the pushrod-mounting points determine the lever ratio of the bellcrank and the overall ratio of the clutch linkage. For example, if the primary arm from the center of the shaft to the center of the pedal-to-bellcrank

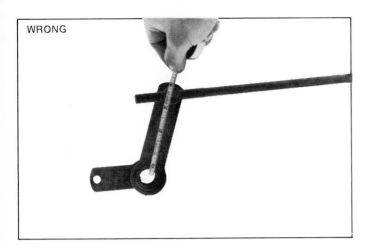

WRONG

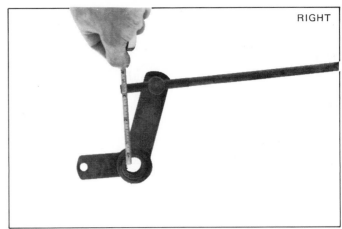

RIGHT

The difference between measuring a lever arm distance the right way and the wrong way can introduce a considerable error. In this case the error is 1/4". Always measure from the pivot center perpendicular to the line-of-action.

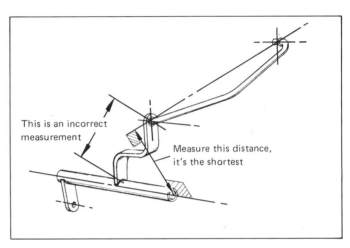

This is an incorrect measurement

Measure this distance, it's the shortest

Bends in bell-cranks tend to make them weaker or heavier. They are necessary to get around exhaust pipes, frames, steering columns and so forth.

Looking into an engine compartment at the bellcrank as it disappears into the rat's nest of parts. You can see the reason for their odd shapes.

pushrod pivot is nine inches and the secondary-arm length is six inches from the center of the shaft to the bellcrank-to-release-fork pushrod pivot, the A/B ratio equals nine inches divided by six inches, or 1.5:1. If the pedal ratio is 3:1, the bellcrank *multiplies* this ratio, increasing the lever ratio up to this point. That is, the lever ratio *out* of the bellcrank is 3.0 *multiplied* by 1.5, giving a 4.5:1 ratio at the secondary arm.

A very important point to remember when measuring dimensions A and B: Use the same method as for measuring the clutch-pedal pivots. Make each measurement perpendicular to the center of the shaft. This is the shortest distance between the two lines. Chances are, the rod-pivot points will be relatively close, but check to be sure. Also, don't let all the bends and kinks in the lever arms bother you. They have no effect on the lever ratio—they are there to get around components such as an exhaust pipe or steering column.

The next link is the bellcrank-to-release-lever pushrod. Just as with the pedal-to-bellcrank pushrod, it doesn't change the motion or force it is transmitting. It does have another function in addition to transmitting force and motion. It is designed to allow adjusting the clutch linkage. This is accomplished by two methods. First, and most common uses a threaded pushrod and swivel/trunion at the bellcrank. The only one I could find which is different is the 1963 to 1977 Corvette. The linkage adjustments on these are made at the bellcrank end of the pedal-to-bellcrank pushrod. The rod threads into the swivel—a block with a threaded hole in it. A pin from the block is retained in the bellcrank by a cotter pin, clip or spring, leaving the swivel free to swivel. Makes sense doesn't it? To adjust clutch free play, air gap or whatever, the distance between the bellcrank and release lever is changed by threading the pushrod in or out of the swivel. When the desired

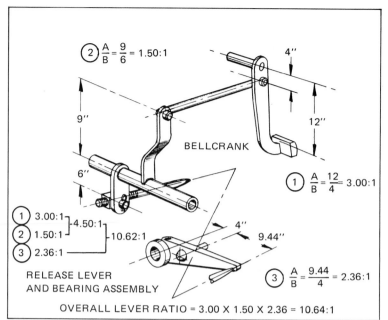

Overall lever ratio of a clutch linkage is a multiple of each of the ratios of the levers which make up the system. Rather than having one component supply the required pedal-to-pressure-plate ratio, it is spread out over the total clutch system.

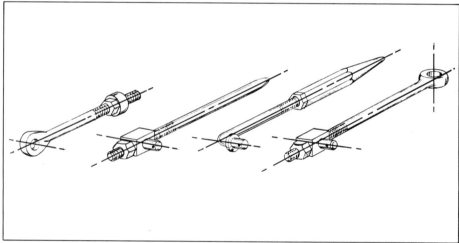

These pushrods represent most of those presently being used. They are characterized by their adjustability.

adjustment is reached, the rod is locked in position with a jam nut. The release-lever end of the pushrod is usually bullet-shaped. This end fits into a mating depression in the release lever and is free to rotate. A tension spring keeps the rod from falling down and away from the lever. This is possible because the pushrod is strictly a compression member. Another setup also uses a threaded rod, threaded into a long bullet-shaped nut locked by a jam nut and adjusted in the same manner. There are variations on the two types I've explained, but there isn't enough difference to waste any more words.

Strange-looking piece of rubber seals the release-lever opening in a bellhousing. It helps keep water, oil, dirt and the like from contaminating a clutch.

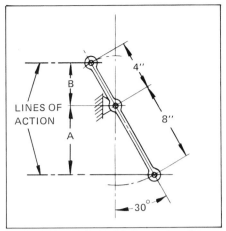

Because this bellcrank's lines-of-action are parallel and all three points are on a common line, dimensions A and B can be measured directly. For example, if the lever is pivoted 30° as shown, A and B will equal 6.92″ and 3.46″, respectively. Therefore lever ratio A/B is equal to 2.00:1. In this particular case you don't have to go through all the gymnastics because 8.0″ divided by 4.0″ also results in a 2.00:1 ratio.

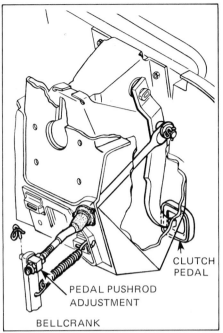

Corvette clutch-linkage adjustment is done at the lower end of the pedal-to-bell crank pushrod rather than at the release-lever pushrod. *Drawing courtesy Chevrolet*

The release lever is the final reduction in motion or increase in load between your foot and the pressure plate. You can think of it either way. This lever is usually a stamping shaped like a two-pronged fork—that's why it is sometimes referred to as a *clutch fork*. The lever extends through a hole in the bellhousing and is sealed with a rubber boot to prevent any contaminants from entering the housing—oil, dirt or water—and flexible enough not to interfere with the operation of the lever. The inner end of the lever is a fork which straddles the release bearing. The lever pivots on a ball stud or bracket as it moves the release bearing back and forth. Release-lever lever ratio is determined in the same manner as was done with the pedal and bellcrank. The A dimension is measured from the line of action of the bellcrank-to-lever pushrod to the center of the lever pivot. The B dimension is taken from the lever

pivot to the lever-and-bearing contact point which should be in the center of the bearing or very close to it.

One helpful point to take advantage of, when dealing with a straight lever having lines of parallel action: Lever attitude (angle) will have no effect on the lever ratio because the foreshortening of the A and B dimensions will be proportionately the same. As a result, there is no ratio change, regardless of lever attitude. Because most release levers meet these conditions, you won't have to go to the trouble of trying to get into the clutch housing to do your measuring *if* your lever is straight and the pushrod is parallel to the transmission-input shaft.

Cable Linkage—As for the cable system, it must be mounted so it is in tension during clutch operation—cables do not like to be pushed on. They are also subject to high wear and frictional losses as they are used. Some must even be adjusted

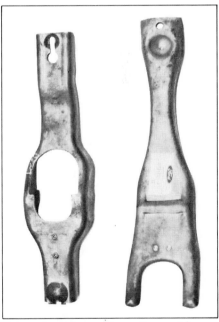

Release lever transmits motion and force from outside the bellhousing to the release bearing. Lever at the left is for use with a cable and the one at the right is used with a rod-and-lever system.

113

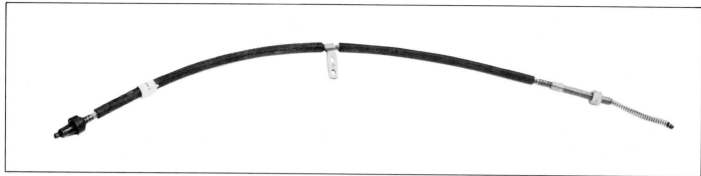

The clutch cable is used rather than the bellcrank and accompanying pushrods of the rod-and-lever type clutch linkage. Cables have limited use in high-performance applications because they stretch and develop high frictional losses as they wear.

periodically to compensate for stretch.

I won't take up much space discussing cable linkages because they are used mainly in sub-compact cars and I wouldn't recommend the use of a cable in a high-performance car. However, they do exist and are starting to show up in the U.S. due to their low cost. If you get the idea I'm prejudiced, you're right. If you've been stranded as often as I have by a broken cable, you would be too. Seriously, a cable is a very good way to transmit force and motion in tight places if the cable doesn't have to bend tight radii, the loads it must transmit aren't high, the travel isn't much or the area the cable must pass through isn't hot—such as near an exhaust pipe. With all of these conditions met, the efficiency of a cable will drop from about 90 percent when new to less than 70 percent when worn as a result of increasing friction between the cable and conduit or housing. What this means in terms of pedal force is if a theoretically 100-percent-efficient cable required 45 pounds to operate the clutch, then 50 pounds will be required to operate it when it is new at 90-percent efficiency and 64 pounds at 70-percent efficiency when worn.

Cables are almost always used when the engine is mounted in the middle or rear of a car as on Porsches, VW's and Corvairs, for example. The cable replaces the bell-

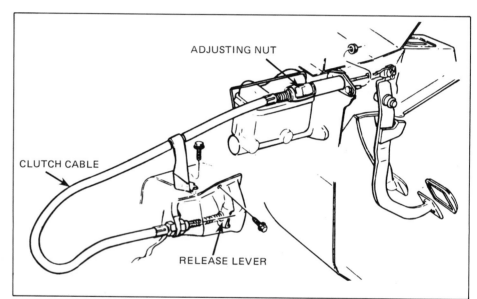

Typical cable clutch linkage. It is low cost and good for fitting in tight places, but has excessive internal friction for high-performance use. *Drawing courtesy Ford Motor Company*

crank and pushrods of the conventional clutch linkage. The differences are it can only be operated in tension and the cable has a 1:1 ratio only. This means the total required clutch-linkage ratio must come from the pedal-assembly and release-lever ratios.

Because the cable is strictly a tension member, it must be compensated for in the mechanics of the pedal and release-lever design. For example, as the pedal is depressed, the cable must be pulled. This can

be accomplished in one of two ways on a front-engine car. Attach the cable on the opposite of the pedal pivot to the pedal pad. The cable can then go through the firewall to the release lever.

The next method requires more parts such as a pulley to reverse cable direction. Using this method permits locating the cable attachment on the same side of the pivot as the pedal pad. The advantage is to shorten the clutch-pedal assembly and the disadvantage is more

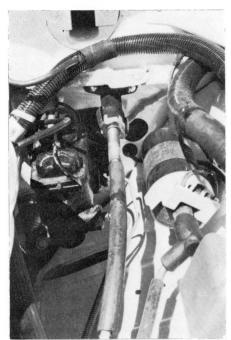

Clutch-cable conduit starts at the firewall. The end of this one is threaded so the clutch linkage can be adjusted.

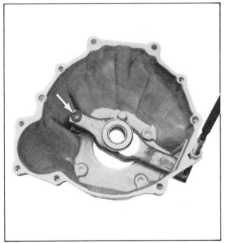

Lever-pivot for a cable linkage (arrow) is on the opposite side of the bearing from the cable attachment so the release bearing moves forward when the cable pulls the outer end of the lever.

parts and another source of friction in the linkage. After leaving the pulley, the cable can then go through the firewall to the release lever. At the release lever, the cable will be pulling the same distance as at the pedal, thus the 1:1 ratio.

Because it is pulling rather than pushing, the release-lever-pivot location must be changed from that used in the lever-and-pushrod system for a front-engine car. If it weren't, the release bearing would move away from the pressure-plate levers as the pedal was depressed. The release-lever pivot must be located on the opposite side of the bearing from the cable-attaching point. Now, as the cable pulls the lever, the bearing moves in the same direction as the cable. The method for determining the lever and the pedal A/B ratios is the same, just keep in mind you must measure from the *line-of-action* of the cable to the pivot points.

With a rear-engined car using floor-mounted pedals, the cable can be mounted on the same side of the pivot as the pedal pad. For rear-engined cars, the release lever can operate on a pivot between the cable and the release bearing.

Finally, the outside, or conduit of a cable must be attached near the pedal and the release lever. The usual place near the lever is the firewall. At the lever it is at the rear face of the engine block and bellhousing. This end is usually threaded for linkage adjustment. If not, the end of the cable has a threaded rod for adjustment at the release lever.

Hydraulic Linkage—Hydraulic pressure is just another way of transmitting force and motion from the clutch pedal to the clutch-release lever. Unlike the cable system, it is capable of *multiplying* force and travel. Just the opposite of cables, the hydraulic master cylinder must operate in compression. It's not that one couldn't be designed to work the other way, it would just be more complex and expensive. Consequently, the only types available operate in compression with a pushrod.

Three basic components make up the hydraulic portion of a hydraulic linkage. They are the master cylinder, the connecting line and the slave cylinder. As the master-cylinder piston is pushed by the clutch pedal, hydraulic fluid is transferred from the master cylinder to the slave cylinder, displacing its piston by an amount determined by the fluid displaced by the master cylinder. This determines the load-and-travel ratio of the hydraulic portion of the linkage. Remember, the pedal-lever-ratio is applied to the hydraulic-cylinder pushrod, reducing the required pedal force.

It is common practice to mount the slave cylinder so it operates the release lever like the pushrod of a lever-link type system. If a cable system is being converted over to hydraulics, a slave cylinder which works in tension is available from Neal Products in San Diego, Calif. It was developed for VW-powered dune buggies.

When mounting a hydraulic master cylinder, there are two important rules to follow:

1. Mount the master cylinder so it is in compression when being operated.

If you are mounting a hydraulic master cylinder with integral reservoir, mount it level so it can be filled with fluid. This is the clutch master cylinder in a 280-Z Datsun.

2. If the cylinder has an integral reservoir, it should be mounted level, otherwise it can't be properly filled with fluid. If it has a remote reservoir, the cylinder can be mounted in any position so long as it is operated in compression. The reservoir must be mounted level and higher than the cylinder so the fluid will feed the cylinder.

The theory of hydraulics, as applied to the hydraulic clutch linkage, is based on the piston areas of the master and slave cylinders. For example, piston travel is inversely proportional to the areas of the pistons. Because the area of a piston is equal to *pi* (π), or 3.14, multiplied by the piston diameter squared and divided by four, pi and four drop out, leaving the diameters squared. Therefore, piston travel is *inversely proportional* to the diameters squared.

$$T_s = T_m \times \frac{D_m^2}{D_s^2}$$

Where:

T_s is slave-cylinder piston stroke in inches.
D_m is master-cylinder bore diameter in inches.
D_s is slave-cylinder bore diameter in inches.

What this says is, if the master-cylinder and slave-cylinder bores are the same, the travels will also be the same. On the other hand, if the master-cylinder bore is smaller than the slave-cylinder bore, slave-piston travel will be less than the master-cylinder piston travel, based on the formula. The reason is simple enough. The larger a piston is, the less distance it must travel to displace a given amount of fluid. The opposite is true if it is smaller.

As an example; a master cylinder with 0.50-inch bore and a slave cylinder with 0.75-inch bore. Slave-cylinder-piston travel for one inch of master-cylinder-piston travel is:

$$T_s = (1.00) \times \frac{(0.50 \text{ inch})^2}{(0.75 \text{ inch})^2}$$
$$= 0.444 \text{ inch}$$

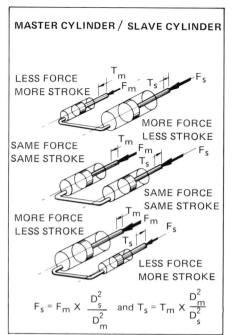

MASTER CYLINDER / SLAVE CYLINDER

LESS FORCE MORE STROKE

MORE FORCE LESS STROKE

SAME FORCE SAME STROKE

SAME FORCE SAME STROKE

MORE FORCE LESS STROKE

LESS FORCE MORE STROKE

$$F_s = F_m \times \frac{D_s^2}{D_m^2} \quad \text{and} \quad T_s = T_m \times \frac{D_m^2}{D_s^2}$$

Effect of master-cylinder and slave-cylinder bore sizes on input to output travel and force. F_m and F_s are the forces of the master and slave cylinders, respectively. T_m and T_s are the strokes of the master and slave cylinders. D_m is the bore of the master cylinder and D_s is the slave cylinder bore.

Therefore, the travel ratio is 1 inch divided by 0.444 inches, or 2.25:1—equivalent to the A/B ratio of the mechanical system.

Now for the part which is just a little more difficult to understand because it involves pressures—travel is something you can see, but pressure you can't. Force exerted by a slave-cylinder piston is a function of the square of the master- and slave-piston diameters. Taking a look at pressure, if 100 pounds force is exerted on an area of 1.00 square inch, the pressure is equal to 100 pounds divided by one square inch, or 100 pounds per square inch (psi). If the same force is exerted on half the area, 0.50 square inch, the pressure doubles to 200 psi. If a force is exerted on a column of fluid, the resulting pressure is the same on all surfaces containing the fluid: Lines, cylinder walls and pistons. Using the previous example of the 0.50-inch-bore master cylinder and the 0.75-inch-bore slave cylinder, the areas

Girling has done something helpful by indicating cylinder-bore size on the sides of their reservoirs. Bore sizes of these two cylinders are 5/8" and 3/4", respectively.

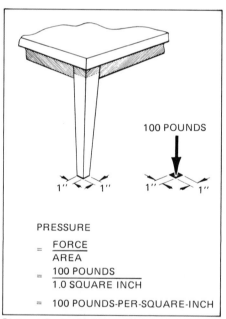

100 POUNDS

$$\text{PRESSURE}$$
$$= \frac{\text{FORCE}}{\text{AREA}}$$
$$= \frac{100 \text{ POUNDS}}{1.0 \text{ SQUARE INCH}}$$
$$= 100 \text{ POUNDS-PER-SQUARE-INCH}$$

Piston of a hydraulic cylinder exerts pressure on fluid like this table leg exerts pressure on a floor with the major difference being the fluid must be contained in a cylinder. If 100 pounds is supported by the table leg and the contact area of the leg with the floor is one square inch, the pressure exerted on the floor is 100 pounds-per-square-inch. For twice the area, two square inches, the pressure will be half as much at 50 pounds-per-square-inch.

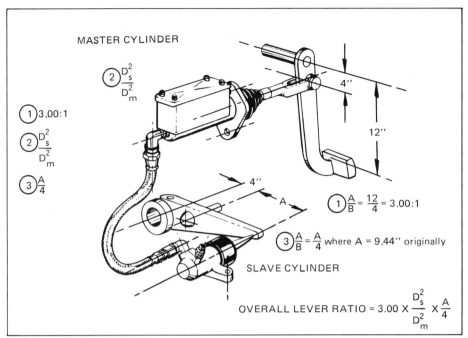

MASTER CYLINDER

① 3.00:1

② $\dfrac{D_s^2}{D_m^2}$

③ $\dfrac{A}{4}$

4″

12″

4″

A

SLAVE CYLINDER

① $\dfrac{A}{B} = \dfrac{12}{4} = 3.00:1$

③ $\dfrac{A}{B} = \dfrac{A}{4}$ where A = 9.44″ originally

OVERALL LEVER RATIO = $3.00 \times \dfrac{D_s^2}{D_m^2} \times \dfrac{A}{4}$

This linkage is the same as the rod-and-lever linkage on page **112** with the bellcrank having been replaced by the master and slave cylinders. If the ratio of the bellcrank cannot be matched using hydraulics, either the pedal or release-lever ratio will have to be changed.

of the two pistons are:

Master-cylinder area

$= 3.14 \times \dfrac{(0.50\ \text{inch})^2}{4}$

$= 0.196$ square inch

Slave-cylinder area

$= 3.14 \times \dfrac{(0.75\ \text{inch})^2}{4}$

$= 0.442$ square inch

With a 200-pound force exerted on the master-cylinder pushrod, pressure in the system is 200 pounds divided by the 0.196 square-inch area of the master-cylinder piston, or 1020 psi. Now comes the interesting part. Pressure pushing in every direction in the fluid is also pushing the slave-cylinder piston at a pressure of 1020 psi. Force exerted on the release lever by the slave cylinder is equal to this pressure multiplied by the piston area, or 450 pounds. The load ratio is then equal to 450 pounds divided by 200, or 2.25:1—the same as the travel ratio. Therefore, force out of a hydraulic clutch linkage at the slave cylinder is this ratio multiplied by the force

exerted on the master-cylinder piston and the travel is the inverse. Divide the master-cylinder travel by the same ratio to get slave-cylinder travel.

Now that I've gone through the theory of hydraulics as applied to clutch linkages, I will say the best practice is to use the same size master and slave cylinders. In this case, the effective A/B ratio is 1:1, resulting in the same load and travel at both cylinders. The hydraulic portion of the clutch linkage is then used strictly to transmit the force and motion of the clutch pedal to the release lever as with the cable. If this is not the case, you'll know how to deal with it.

Let's look at an example where you are replacing a bellcrank with a hydraulic setup because of an engine transplant taking up too much room. Starting out with the premise that you are going to maintain the clutch-pedal and release-lever lever ratios, you must determine the master- and slave-cylinder-bore sizes. Using the ratios shown on the sketch

on page 112, the A/B ratio for the bellcrank is 1.5:1. This must also be the ratio of the hydraulic cylinder bore sizes squared. Therefore, D_s^2/D_m^2 must equal 1.5:1. This is where some trouble can be encountered because of the limited number of bore sizes available. If you can't hit it right on, you'll have to use what is available and make the necessary adjustments in the pedal or release-lever ratios. Getting on with the problem, if you choose a master-cylinder bore size of 5/8″ (0.625″), the slave-cylinder size will have to be:

$$D_s = \sqrt{A/B \times D_m^2} = \sqrt{1.5 \times (5/8)^2}$$
$$= 0.765\ \text{inch}$$

This is not a common bore size for a slave cylinder. The closest available size has a bore diameter of 3/4″. Therefore, the new D_s^2/D_m^2 ratio is equal to

$(0.75)^2 / (0.625)^2$, or 1.44

versus 1.50:1. To the the job right—the only way to do a job—the pedal- or release-lever ratio will have to be changed to maintain the overall ratio of 10.64:1. Assuming the release-lever ratio is the easier of the two to change, its new A/B ratio must be determined. To do this, the overall ratio of the system, 10.64, is divided by the combined ratios of the clutch pedal and the hydraulic system, or 3.0 multiplied by 1.44. The new release-lever ratio is equal to 2.46:1. Now, the only thing left is the length of the lever from the slave cylinder to the pivot, dimension A. You find this by multiplying the desired ratio, 2.46 by 4.0″, which equals 9.85 inches. The length will then have increased by 9.85 inches minus 9.44 inches, or 0.41 inches.

This example illustrates the amount of jockeying it will probably take when you convert from a lever-and-linkage system. When changing a cable system to hydraulics, the problem is simplified because the cable has a 1:1 ratio to start with. You can mount the cylinder pushrods at the same points on the clutch pedal and release lever. Make certain when doing this that the two cylinders have the same bore diameters or the clutch-linkage ratio will change.

One final thing to look out for when working with hydraulic cylinders: If the pressure side of the cylinder is on the pushrod side of the piston, the amount of area displaced by the pushrod must be compensated for when calculating ratios. This is no trouble to do, it just may be trouble if you don't.

Let's just take for example a slave cylinder which pulls rather than pushes when pressurized. It has a 3/4" bore and a 1/4" pushrod and is used with a 0.50" master cylinder, the ratio will not be

$$(0.75)^2 \ / \ (0.50)^2, \text{ or } 2.25{:}1.$$

It will be

$$[(0.75)^2 - (0.25)^2] \ / \ (0.50)^2$$

which equals 2.00:1. Therefore, the area displaced by the pushrod reduces the ratio by 12.5 percent, meaning the force exerted by the slave cylinder will be 12.5-percent *less*. Travel at the slave cylinder will be affected by the same amount, but in the opposite direction. It will increase by 12.5 percent for given amounts of pedal travel.

Release Bearing—The last major part of the clutch-linkage system is the *release bearing*—or *throw-out bearing* as most folks call it. I personally prefer *release bearing* because it describes what the bearing does. Just the same, throw-out bearing is an excellent name for one very good reason: When a clutch is being replaced, the old throw-out bearing *should be thrown out.* Considering the cost and effort to replace it when everything is already disassembled—it is not worth the risk to put up with the hassle of going through almost the same job just to replace it later on.

The release bearing deserves a closer look because one is required regardless of the type of clutch linkage or clutch used. The bearing is moved fore and aft on the front bearing retainer of the transmission by the clutch linkage. As it moves

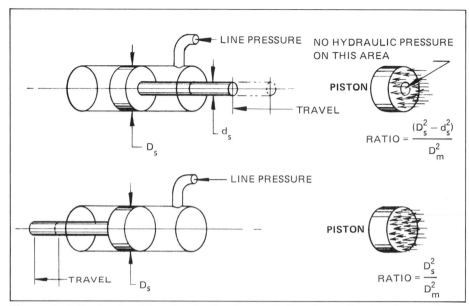

When calculating load and travel ratios for slave cylinders that pull rather than push, the area on the head of the piston displaced by the "pullrod" must be considered. If you don't, you'll end up with more travel and less load than you planned for at the slave cylinder. More importantly, you'll end up with higher pedal forces.

Indy Car bellhousing, transaxle and rear-suspension assembly: Hydraulic-type release bearing eliminates pedal-to-release bearing clutch linkage. Hydraulic lines are routed directly from clutch master cylinder to release bearing-and-hydraulic cylinder assembly in bellhousing (arrow).

forward it must also be able to rotate at engine speed the instant it contacts the pressure-plate release levers. To do this, a release bearing with a carrier or hub slip-fits on an extension of the input-shaft bearing retainer. The hub is designed with clips or a groove to hold the bearing-and-hub assembly onto the release lever without binding as the bearing is moved back and forth. When the clutch is fully engaged, the release bearing is retracted from the pressure-plate fingers approximately 0.1 inch so the bearing does not have to continue rotating at

Here's a bearing and pressure plate you're not likely to see unless you've been around some imported cars. This unit is for a VW. Release bearing is a circular block of carbon retained in a steel housing. For clutch release, the bearing is forced against the steel ring attached to the pressure plate release levers. Eventually the carbon block wears down and has to be replaced.

This is the type of bearing you'll see most often. It is a rear-axle bearing designed to support radial loads whereas a clutch release-bearing is for thrust loads, thus the name thrust bearing.

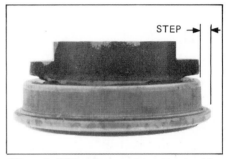

"Step-shell" bearing can be recognized by the offset or step in the shell (arrows).

engine speed. This prevents premature bearing failure and excessive release-lever wear.

Two types of release bearings are used. One is a carbon-block bearing—a flat circular-shaped piece of carbon mounted in a carrier. It operates the pressure plate by pushing against a flat circular ring mounted to the pressure-plate levers. This type bearing is not used on U.S.-made vehicles. It is used by some British and European manufacturers.

U.S. car owners are accustomed to seeing a ball-bearing type designed for taking thrust loads (pushed on) rather than radial loads like rear-axle bearings.

There are three significant design variations in the ball-bearing-type release-bearings. First is the conventional *thrust bearing* followed by a variation of this design called a *step-shell* bearing. Finally, the latest and most significant design is called

an *angular-contact* bearing. The reason for the departure from the conventional thrust-bearing design was improved durability, even though all three types are still used. To understand why the difference in durability between the three designs and how they operate, let's look at each design.

The conventional thrust bearing differs from the usual bearing in that it doesn't have inner and outer *races* as such. A race provides the track or groove for the ball bearings to roll in and transfers the load through the balls. The thrust bearing has a front and rear race, the front race contacting the release levers and rotating. The rear race is fixed to the hub which holds it stationary. The rotating race has a shell crimped to it and overlapping the fixed race to hold the bearing together and to contain lubricant, making it a sealed bearing. There is sufficient

clearance between the shell and fixed race so the bearing is free to rotate. The final part making up the bearing is the ball separator which spaces the balls and assists in lubricating them. So, we have five parts, the two races, the shell, ball separator and the ball bearings —a nice even dozen. Of course, grease is required for lubrication. Molybdenum-disulphide is usually used.

The *step-shell* bearing is a second-generation design. It came about in an attempt to keep the grease in contact with the balls.

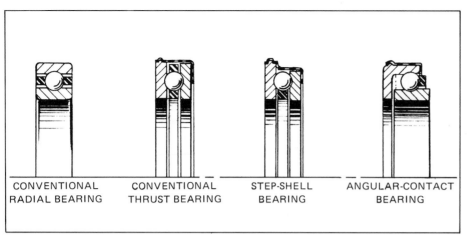

CONVENTIONAL RADIAL BEARING   CONVENTIONAL THRUST BEARING   STEP-SHELL BEARING   ANGULAR-CONTACT BEARING

Bearing on the left is a conventional radial bearing. The other three represent the types used as clutch-release bearings. On the right is a high-performance bearing which is a necessary part of a high-performance clutch system.

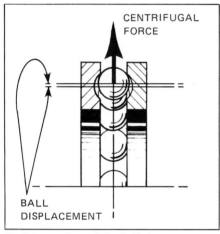

CENTRIFUGAL FORCE

BALL DISPLACEMENT

Wedging action of the balls in a conventional thrust bearing is one reason for their relatively short life. Most damage occurs just as the bearing is unloaded at high-RPM, letting the races open up.

As the conventional thrust bearing rotates during clutch operation, grease is thrown outward against the shell because of centrifugal action. The shell held the grease, but the bearings were not lubricated, resulting in early bearing failure. The name *step-shell* was derived from *stepping* the shell closer to the balls in an attempt to keep the grease closer to the balls. This change, in addition to bearing separators made out of moly-disulfide-impregnated nylon, resulted in a fractionally more durable bearing. This bearing can be recognized by the significant step in the shell behind the area where it is crimped to the front race.

A significant advancement in release-bearing design came with the introduction of the *angular-contact* bearing. Rather than two flat races sandwiching the ball bearings between them, the front race wraps around the outside of the balls and the back race fits inside them similar to a radial bearing. As a result, the load is transmitted at an angle rather than directly parallel to the loads on the bearing, thus the name *angular-contact*. This reduces the absolute load capacity of the bearing, but that's not the problem. Other than loss of lubricant, an additional problem is encountered with the conventional thrust bearing, step-shell or not. As the bearing is spun at high RPM, the balls are forced outward from the center of the bearing and they try to wedge the races apart like the rollers on a Borg & Beck pressure plate. When this happens, the bearings are not riding in their races. They are on the sharp outer edge of the races. Contact pressure on the balls becomes excessive and galling and pitting results. The angular-contact design eliminates this problem and the one of lubrication. Consequently, the durability of the angular-contact bearing exceeds that of the step-shell by at least five times. I've reduced this claim from what it actually is because of the risk of sounding like I'm exaggerating. To compare the durability of the angular-contact bearing versus the step-shell, refer to the graph on the right. This graph was constructed using actual test data.

Let me tell a bit about the superiority of the angular-contact bearing. In the "good old days" of manufacturers' involvement in racing, I was with the Ford racing group when Henry had his sights on Le Mans. Of the many problems encountered with running a 24-hour race, the big one is durability and the release bearing was a durability problem. It wouldn't last 24 hours without failing. This was in 1966 when the angular-contact bearing was just being tested for installation as original equipment in production cars. Everyone knew they were better, but no one knew just how much. Because time was short, a few bearings were scraped together and installed on the Mark IV's. They all finished the race without a failure—release-bearing failure, that is. The Fords finished one, two and went

You can recognize a conventional thrust bearing by holding the hub and trying to force the front face sideways. If it moves like this, it's conventional and if it doesn't, it is an angular-contact bearing.

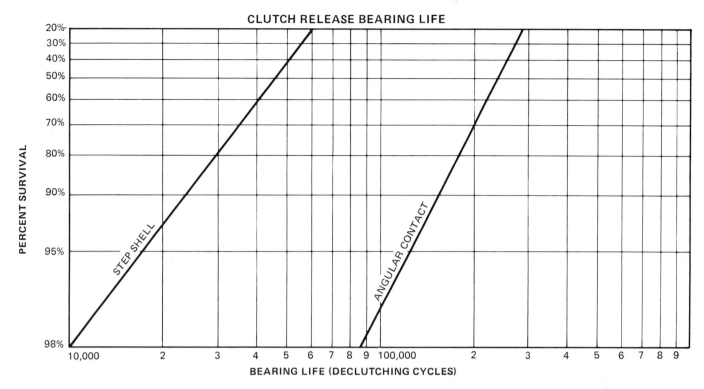

CLUTCH RELEASE BEARING LIFE

PERCENT SURVIVAL

20%
30%
40%
50%
60%
70%
80%

90%

95%

98%

STEP SHELL

ANGULAR CONTACT

BEARING LIFE (DECLUTCHING CYCLES)

10,000   2   3   4   5   6   7   8   9   100,000   2   3   4   5   6   7   8   9

Durability of the angular-contact release-bearing design. 80-percent of the step-shell bearings have failed before 2-percent of the angular-contact type fail.

on to finish out the season with the same bearings. To the best of my knowledge, the same ones are still in the cars wherever they are.

Depending on the particular bearing, it is sometimes difficult to distinguish one bearing from another. The easiest way is to hold the bearing hub in one hand and with the other, try to move front race sideways. If it moves a noticeable amount, it is a conventional or step-shell bearing. If it feels solid when you try to move it, it is an angular-contact. This is the one you want, particularly if you are going to install it in a car where the release-bearing durability may mean winning or losing a race.

RACE-PREPARING YOUR CLUTCH LINKAGE

If you've set up your car to race and have installed a high-performance clutch, your next step is to make sure you have a high-performance linkage to go with

it. If you don't, your troubles may just be beginning. What you have to do depends on the clutch you've installed, the type of racing you'll be doing and the environment for the linkage. One thing for sure, it is nearly impossible to beat the durability of a factory clutch linkage when it is used with the original clutch. When you change to a high-performance clutch there may be a problem in the strength department. One thing the factory can't be expected to do and that is to design cars and their components for what folks like you and I are going to do with them. It's up to us to do this.

Reducing deflection and friction in a clutch linkage and reinforcing it so it will not be overstressed and break in operation are the top priorities when your are race-preparing your linkage. For example, when a pressure plate with a distinctly higher load is installed in a car, the linkage and surrounding structure must be capable of supporting more load.

This is a good example of a bad bellcrank design. The attachment of the lever-arm to the cross-shaft will fail under any appreciable load.

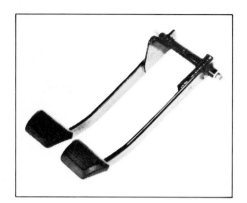

If weight reduction is your number-one objective, here's a clutch and brake pedal assembly fabricated from titanium. *Photo courtesy Trick Titanium, Inc.*

If pressure-plate load is substantially higher or a Long or Borg & Beck style pressure plate is used in place of a stock diaphragm-type clutch, the deflection due to the substantially higher load at the release bearing may cause the clutch linkage to deflect so much that the pedal won't have enough travel to engage or disengage the clutch fully. Even worse—parts may permanently bend or break from being overstressed. To avoid this, let's look at the problem areas and see how to remedy them.

I'll deal mainly with the rod-and-lever systems because there is not much you can do with a cable setup except keep your eye on the cable and replace it when friction becomes excessive from wear or it stretches beyond its adjustment range. As for the hydraulic systems, none are installed as original equipment on U.S.-built cars, so I'll reserve this one for when I talk about the "ground-up" race car.

Rod-and-Lever Linkage Modifications—Number-one culprit when it comes to bending and breaking is the bellcrank. In many instances, they are weak. The problem is usually in how the lever arms are attached to the cross shaft, or tube. The arm should be fitted to the backside of the tube—the tension side—so at least 180° of weld is

HYSTERESIS

Hysteresis is a term used to describe the work lost in a system when energy is changed from one state to another, then returned to the original state. The system may be electrical or mechanical, but the principle is the same. The cause of hysteresis in a mechanical system is friction. An example of this is pushing a car up a hill and then letting it roll back down while holding it back. If the brakes drag, the force required to push it up the hill will be *more* and the force to hold it back while coming down will be *less* than if the brakes weren't dragging.

A graph of this travel and force is called a *hysteresis loop.* The area inside the loop represents energy or work lost due to friction. The loop shows a high force required to push the car up the hill and a lower force to hold it back while returning to the original starting position. The dashed line is what the curve would look like if the car rolled friction-free. The cross-hatched area is work supplied but lost in friction. A clutch linkage exhibits friction in a similar manner. Because of friction, the force to depress the pedal or disengage a clutch is higher than the engagement force. For high-performance clutches having high pressure-plate loads, it is very important that hysteresis be minimized by reducing friction. The hystersis loop for a clutch shows increasing force for increasing amount of pedal travel due to the compression of the pressure-plate springs as the clutch is

disengaged. If the curve drops below the zero-pedal-force axis, the pedal will stop in that position without returning to its full up, or engaged position.

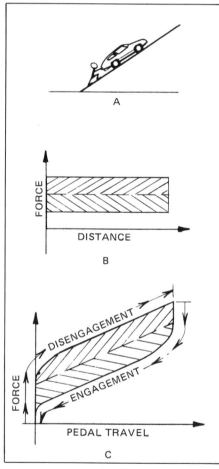

These curves are called hysteresis loops. Figure B represents the work required to push a car up a hill and let it roll back while holding it. Figure C is a curve representing pedal travel versus force required to operate a clutch. Areas inside the curves represent work lost due to friction.

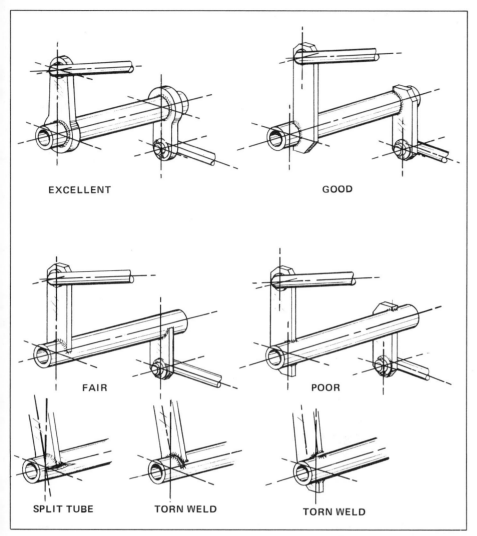

EXCELLENT GOOD

FAIR POOR

SPLIT TUBE TORN WELD TORN WELD

The majority of bellcrank lever-arm to cross-shaft designs rated from excellent to poor. Failures mostly occur when a weld is put in tension as shown.

Here's how a bellcrank lever should look. A full 360° weld attaches the lever to the tube.

1966 Mustang bellcrank was reinforced after failing at the lever-to-shaft joint. Reinforcing shown is crude but effective.

applied to the tube and arm. If the arm has a hole in it for the tube to slip through the arm, it should be welded 360°. Or, the arm-to-tube joint should be gusseted or reinforced in some manner on the backside. Otherwise, the arm will tear away from the tube or the tube will split. Always try to avoid putting a welded joint in tension. They should be in compression or shear if at all possible. If you have a bellcrank that violates this rule, you'll have to do some reinforcing.

The kind of reinforcing you do to a bellcrank depends a lot on how much room there is to work in around the bellcrank area. It's located in a pretty tight area and, more often than not, the reason for a poorly designed clutch linkage is the clutch engineers were not given enough room for the linkage. Things like the frame, bellhousing, engine, exhaust headers, and steering column all have to share the same area. Some notables which should have their bellcranks reinforced for high-

performance use are the early Hi-Performance Mustangs and all GM products, excluding the Corvette. For some examples of reinforcing bellcranks, refer to the sketches on page 124. No matter which method you choose, make sure you check clearances around the bellcrank for interferences during the operation of the clutch.

The next most likely weak link in the clutch-linkage system is the bellcrank-to-release-lever pushrod. Most are 3/8" diameter and this

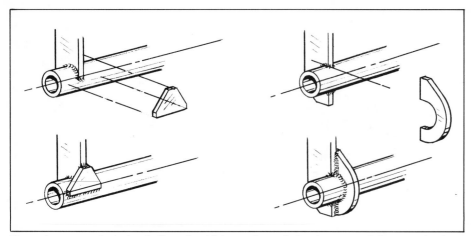

If you have a weak design bellcrank which requires reinforcing, one of these methods should work for you. Be sure to check around the bellcrank area for possible interference.

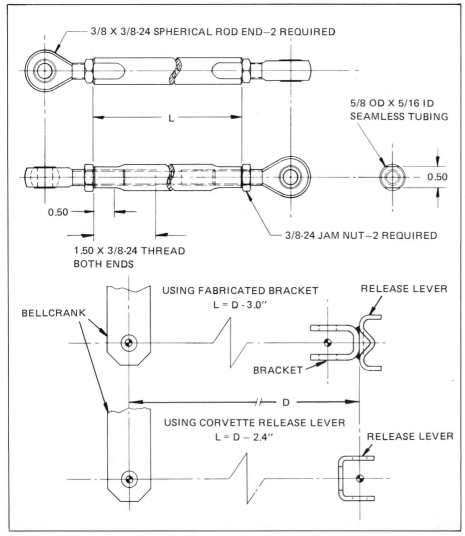

A threaded tube and two spherical rod ends make for a strong pushrod. To determine the correct tube length, determine distance D between the bellcrank and release lever and use one of the formulas.

isn't large enough to handle the extra loads. As a result they will buckle. Direct-replacement larger-diameter pushrods are available from Hays, McLeod and Rocket.

If you really want a professional job, make an adjustable rod using two 3/8" male spherical rod ends which thread into a 5/8" O.D. by 5/16" I.D. tube. With flats milled (ground) on the tube to accept a 1/2" open-end wrench and jam nuts to lock the rod ends in place, you'll have a first-class setup. If you want to go one better, use right- and left-hand-threaded rod ends. Then for adjustment, all you'll have to do is loosen the jam nuts and rotate the tube rather than having to disconnect one end of the linkage. Now, the bellcrank end of the rod will usually bolt right up providing you've drilled the mounting hole out to 3/8". However, it isn't that simple at the release lever. You can take two approaches here if you have a GM product. The first method which applies to GM products only, and the best in my opinion, is to get a Corvette release lever, P/N 3887177—it'll fit your housing. So the lever will accept your new pushrod, you'll have to open the end of the lever up to 9/16". Drill the mounting holes out to 3/8" and make some washer-type spacers to center the rod end in the release lever. This will also prevent the lever from collapsing when the bolts are tightened.

Now, for plan two. This is the one you'll have to use if you have an AMC, Chrysler or Ford product, providing you want to go to the rod-end link. Start with 1/8" steel stock and fabricate a little bracket using the sketch on page 125. Before welding the bracket to the lever, center the mounting holes in the bracket directly over the pushrod pocket in the release lever so the lever ratio will not change. This, of course, assumes you don't want it to. On the other hand, if you do, this is your golden opportunity. Locating the bracket closer to the lever pivot will reduce the

A/B ratio. You can't locate it farther outboard without extending the lever. Turn the bracket so the pushrod-mounting bolt will be vertical as installed in the car. This will prevent the spherical bearing from bottoming out, or running out of angular travel. If there isn't enough travel in the bearing, the bearing or lever will bend or break.

The pushrod-tube length depends on the method you use to mount the pushrod at the lever and the distance your bellcrank is from the release lever. If you are using the Corvette release lever, measure the distance between the original push-rod-mounting points when the clutch is adjusted. This distance minus 2.4" will give you the correct tube length. The formula is:

L = D - 2.4

Where:

L is tube length in inches.
D is distance between the correctly adjusted pivot points in inches.

Therefore, if distance D measures 8.5", then the tube length is equal to 8.5" minus 2.4" or 6.1".

The formula for using the second method with the weld-on bracket is:

L = D - 3.0

Where:

L is tube length in inches.
D is the distance from the center of the bellcrank pivot to the front surface of the release lever at the center of the pushrod.

You'll have to measure from the center of the pushrod-pivot point on the front surface of the release lever at the center of the pushrod pocket. This is the surface the bracket will be welded to. Subtract 3.0" from this number to get the tube length L.

If distance D measures 8.0", then the correct tube length is 5.0".

Because I am talking about rod-ends and threaded-tube linkages, now is a good time to suggest the use of this type of an arrangement to replace your pedal-to-bellcrank pushrod. If yours is bent, it will

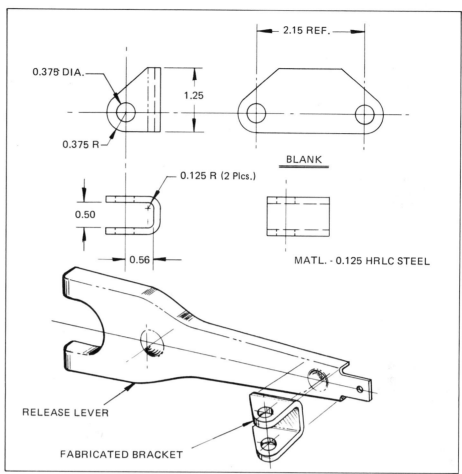

If you are planning on using a spherical rod-end setup and have a release lever similar to the one shown, you'll have to fabricate a bracket and weld it to your release lever.

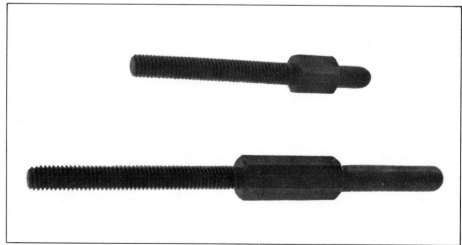

Hays pushrods are manufactured from 4140 chrome-moly steel and fit 1967—1974 Camaros and Firebirds. Replacing your stock pushrods with one of these is an easy way to upgrade your clutch linkage.

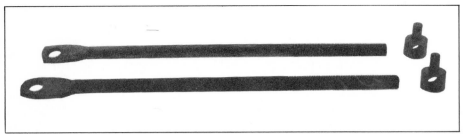

Both bellcrank-to-release-lever pushrods are for 1955—1974 Chevrolets using clevis-pin attachments. They represent two different approaches to the same task by performance-equipment manufacturers. Thread sizes are the same, but threads on one are rolled and the other has machined-in (cut) threads. Cut-thread pushrod has a larger-diameter stronger shaft, however rolled threads are stronger than cut threads. Pay your money and take your choice. It's a toss up.

make the job of fabricating a tube somewhat more difficult because you'll have to match the bend of the original pushrod. Use your old rod as a pattern to bend the new tube while being careful not to wrinkle the inside of the bend/s. If this happens, your new pushrod will be weaker than the original and it will look bad. To prevent this from happening, use the old trick of packing the tube with dry sand and plugging the ends of the tube with wooden plugs. If the sand isn't dry, steam will form and blow the plugs out when the tube is heated. Heat the tube to a dull red

and bend it over a round object such as a pipe to form a neat continuous radius while using the old rod as a pattern. Leave the tube long at the ends to begin with and cut it to length after you have the bends right. The tube should be approximately 1.25" shorter than the original rod at both ends to allow for the rod ends, jam nuts and adjustment. Before doing any more, pull the plugs and pour the sand out. Now you're ready to cut the tube, thread it and put flats on the ends for a 1/2" wrench.

If your pushrod happens to be straight, you are lucky. You won't

have to do any bending. Regardless of whether you have a curved or straight rod, you'll have more adjustment and more importantly, less friction in your clutch linkage. One thing you won't get that you did with the bellcrank-to-release-lever pushrod is much more strength, if any. The stock pushrods from the pedal to bellcrank are generally strong enough to handle any high-performance clutch. If it's strength you're after, don't bother making a new clutch-pedal pushrod. Use the same 3/8" rod ends and 5/8" O.D. by 5/16" I.D. tube, drill the pedal and bellcrank-attachment points to 3/8" and you're ready to install your new rod.

Lever Fulcrums—Now, for the final Achilles' heel of the clutch linkage. If you have a Chrysler or '74 or earlier Ford product, the lever fulcrums, or *release-lever-pivots* as some people prefer to call them, are stamped angular-steel brackets which have a tendency to break at the bend. Ford has switched over to the ball-type fulcrum, starting with the '74 Mustangs, therefore eliminating the problem. However, if you have the angle fulcrums your fulcrum should be gusseted to ensure you won't experience any problems in this area. The Chrysler and '68 and later Ford products have a square hole in the fulcrum to accept a spring retainer off the back of the release lever. This type will

Hays Dzus pedal stop. It's used to limit pedal travel to no more than is necessary to gain full clutch disengagement—a very important consideration in drag racing. The device is fully adjustable and can fit numerous applications.

Most common angle-type lever pivots. They have a tendency to crack and break at the bend when used in high-performance applications.

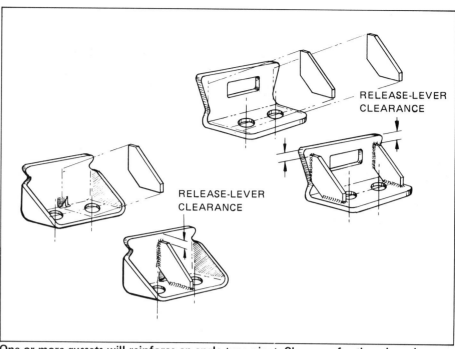

One or more gussets will reinforce an angle-type pivot. Clearance for the release-lever clips and attaching bolts must be maintained.

require two 45° gussets located to straddle the hole without interfering with the spring retainer. The '67 and earlier Fords use a wire clip which attaches to the release lever and hooks over a tang on the backside of the fulcrum. You'll only need one gusset for this fulcrum. Regardless of the type you have, make sure the gusset won't interfere with the operation of the release lever or the attaching rivets or bolts before welding it in place.

If you have a GM product, you won't have any problems with the fulcrum breaking, however one thing you can do if you plan on switching pressure-plate styles is to install an adjustable fulcrum from one of the high-performance manufacturers. By doing this, if you replace your diaphragm pressure plate with a Long style, you can adjust the lever pivot rearward to prevent the release lever from coming out of the bellhousing at an odd angle.

If you are building a "ground-up" racer such as a Pro-Stock drag car, a late-model stock car or a super-modified, your best bet for the clutch linkage is to pick up a bellcrank and clutch pedal which are the strongest combination available for the engine and clutch combination you are using. For example, if you are using a big-block Chevy in any one of the cars I've mentioned above, use the Corvette bellcrank (cross shaft), pedal assembly and release lever. By doing this, you'll retain the correct lever ratios and you can use the stock bearings and bushings to mount a bellcrank and pedal. All that would be left to do is to provide a bracket at the frame for the bellcrank and one at the pedal and to make up the pedal and release-lever pushrods using the method I described earlier. Getting these parts from a scrapyard is a good way to do it providing they are in good condition. You can grab the pedal-mounting bracket while

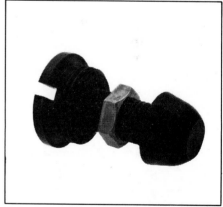

Adjustable release-lever pivot for use in a safety bellhousing. If you have a GM product, you can replace your fixed pivot with this type to get the best release-lever geometry.

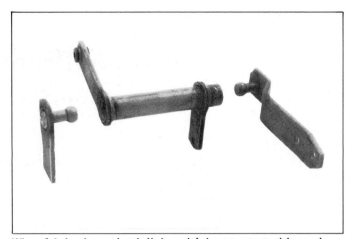

When fabricating a clutch linkage it's best to start with good hardware. McLeod's 1955—1957 Chevrolet bellcrank and pivots can be adapted to just about any rod-and-lever setup.

You can pick up all sorts of ideas from this photograph. For one thing, the driver is located far back of the bellhousing as indicated by the floor-mounted clutch pedal. The bellcrank pulls a rod to operate the release lever. This is perfectly O.K. because the link operates in tension rather than compression as would normally be the case. Engine-mounting bracket is welded to the bellhousing and bolted to the frame.

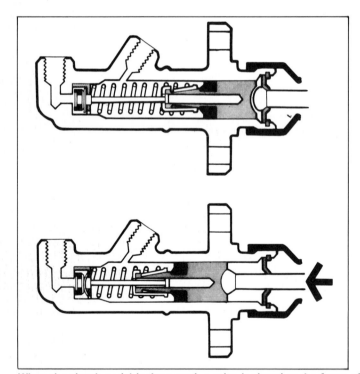

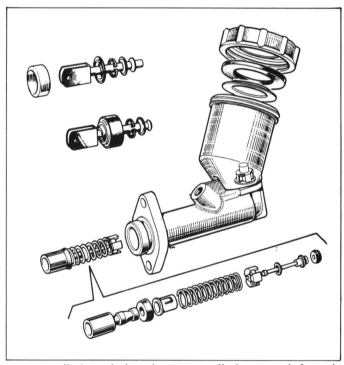

When the clutch pedal is depressed, a valve is closed at the front of the master cylinder to isolate the master cylinder reservoir from the rest of the system. Fluid can then be pressurized and transferred to the slave cylinder to operate the release lever. When the pedal is released, fluid can be drawn into the system from the reservoir if any fluid loss occurs. *Drawings courtesy Lucas Industries*

Master cylinder and slave cylinder are used on right-hand-drive Jeeps because of the complexity involved with routing a mechanical linkage from the relocated clutch-pedal position to the left side of the bellhousing. All a hydraulic linkage needs is a longer hose. Bore sizes are identical at 7/8'', making the hydraulic ratio 1:1. They are available from Lucas, part numbers 68820 and 64068897.

These two master cylinders look quite different, but they are interchangeable. Only the reservoir designs are different. *Photo courtesy Neal Products*

you're at it and use it to hang the pedal by mounting it to the front hoop of the roll cage and firewall. If you decide to modify the clutch linkage to suit the design of your car, you have the basic hardware to work with. An example of this is the clutch linkage shown on page 128. It is for a late model stock car I designed which locates the driver so far rearward that the conventional hanging pedals would have been too difficult to mount. Therefore, they were located on the floor with the bellcrank used strictly to transfer motion inboard from the clutch pedal without changing the direction of motion. The important point is, the linkage was fabricated with stock components to make the job much simpler.

Hydraulic-linkage modifications—If you must use a hydraulic linkage due to the layout of your car or you are replacing your cable linkage, the only mechanical components you'll need are the clutch pedal and the release lever. To save yourself time and grief, use production components and modify them where necessary. At the pedal, fabricate a bracket to mount the master cylinder and use a threaded pushrod which will accept a spherical rod end, but this time, use a female rod end with an externally

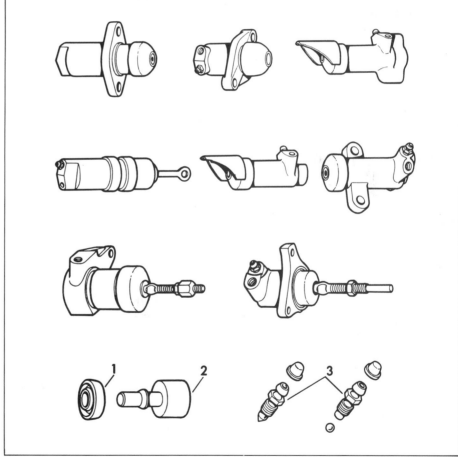

A few slave cylinders available from Girling (Lucas Industries). 1 and 2 are a typical seal and piston from a slave cylinder. 3 shows two styles of bleeder screws. *Drawings courtesy Lucas Industries*

Front bulkhead of an Eagle Indy car on which the clutch and brake master cylinders and their remote reservoirs are mounted. Large reservoir supplies the two brake cylinders and the small one feeds the clutch cylinder. They are mounted above and left of the master cylinders so gravity and cornering forces will assist in feeding them. Due to tight quarters in the foot area, the brake and clutch-pedal positions have been reversed for left-foot braking.

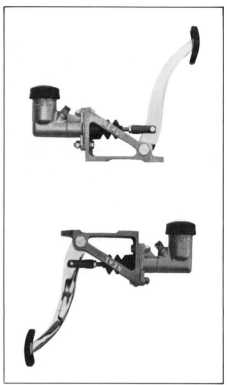

Neal Products offers a nice clutch-pedal, bracket and master-cylinder assembly which can be mounted one or two ways by rotating the master cylinder in the bracket.

threaded rod and a jam nut. Another type of end treatment is to use the clevis type supplied with most hydraulic master cylinders. This will save you the time and expense of fabricating your own. A word of caution here, the clutch pedal and master cylinder should be mounted on the same structure so if there is any deflection, the two will not move relative to each other.

At the slave cylinder, mount it so you will get the desired ratio. If you are using the push-type cylinder, chances you will have to fabricate your own pushrod. A bolt will do the job. Just cut the hex-head off and round it into a bullet shape so it will seat properly into the slave-cylinder piston. a 5/16" female rod end and bolt will do the job if you limit the length of the rod to no more than 3-1/2". Other-

wise, you should go up to 3/8". At the release lever, use the same method I described for that used when modifying the lever for a rod-end-type release lever. Just make sure to mount the master and slave cylinders rigidly. Any deflection will reflect as extra travel at the pedal.

When computing ratios, allow 0.10" travel at the master cylinder for *take-up*. This travel is required before the master cylinder can develop any pressure to transmit force or motion to the slave cylinder. Therefore, if the A/B ratio for your clutch pedal is 4:1, the take-up at the pedal will be 0.40" before *any* movement at the release bearing will take place. This figure adds to the pedal *free play* meaning if the *free play* required to move the release bearing into contact with the

pressure plate levers at the pedal is 0.50", then the total *free play* will be 0.90". Therefore, if you have a shifting-application drag car, I suggest that you not use a hydraulic linkage. The extra pedal travel required to operate the clutch will have an adverse effect on super-fast shifting. Otherwise, it is a very good substitute for the rod-and-lever linkage and definitely superior to the cable.

Where can you get all these "trick" hydraulic parts? Try starting at your local Ford or Chevy dealer. Hydraulic clutches have been used extensively in domestic trucks and are currently used in the small Ford Courier and Chevy Luv. Ford Courier master and slave cylinder are D27Z-7A542-B and D27Z-7A542-A, respectively. And for the Luv, they are 94024512 or

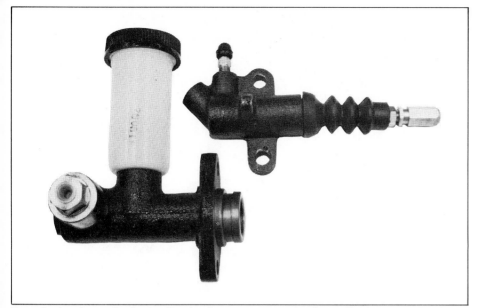

If you're in a hurry for hydraulic-clutch components, they're available at your local Ford or Chevy dealer. These are from the Ford Courier. Part numbers for the master and slave cylinders are D27Z-7A542-B and D27Z-7A542-A, respectively.

Aeroquip or Weatherhead steel-braided hydraulic hose can be used if you keep the total length under 24 inches. This is because a flex line swells slightly under pressure. Consequently, you could end up with a spongy pedal if too much hose is used. Therefore, use as much steel line as possible.

Some applications require flexible line. For instance, rubber engine mounts mean a slave cylinder is going to move around more than can be compensated for with a service loop in a steel line. Therefore, a flex line from a frame member or the body to the slave cylinder should be used.

If you are using one of the automobile manufacturer's hydraulic cylinders, an easy way to minimize your plumbing problem is to purchase the accompanying flex line and hardware. You'll still have to make your own steel line to fit your car, but most of your plumbing problems will be solved.

94025085 for the master cylinder and 94021443 for the slave cylinder. Part numbers for the past model Ford master cylinders are B8TZ-7A543-A and C1TT-7A543-G. Both are used with slave cylinder C3TZ-7A508-D. Chevy part numbers for master and slave cylinders are 2621033 and 5465146, respectively. The problem with this Chevy master cylinder is it is integral with the brake master cylinder. As a result, you would be buying more than you needed, but you can eliminate it by cutting it off. The best choice in hydraulic clutch parts from the dealers are the Courier and Luv units because they are in current production and will probably be in stock. If they aren't, you can get them in a few days.

Girling and Hurst-Airheart also manufacture hydraulic clutch components. They can be purchased from Citation Engineering, Neal Products or Karl Haas Automobile Imports, Inc. Neal Products specializes in clutch and brake systems.

Neal offers complete hydraulic clutch-linkage assemblies including the master cylinder, pedal and mounting bracket which can be mounted on the floor or in a hanging position by swapping the pedal and master cylinder around on the bracket.

A final note about hydraulic-clutch linkages. One thing you will be confronted with is plumbing— a method of containing and transferring hydraulic fluid under pressure between the master and slave cylinders.

The best type of line to use is steel brake line—*not copper line*. Steel line is low cost as well as being the most reliable—provided it is used properly. The ends should be double flared and *service loops* used from the chassis to both cylinders. Service loops consist of bending the line in a loop or spiral so any flexing will be distributed over a greater length of line. This will prevent overstressing and potential line failure.

The more expensive flexible

Radius-face release bearing must be used with a flat-fingered diaphragm pressure plate. A flat-face bearing is used with a Long, Borg & Beck or bent-finger diaphragm pressure plate as shown.

Make – Year	Description	Borg-Warner	Hays	McLeod	RAM	Schiefer	Weber	Zoom
GM 55-76	Flat diaphragm Bent finger diaphragm or B & B Long Special	N1086 HP N1488 HP	70-102 70-101 70-111 70-103☆	1601 1600 1602*	488	628-0001 628-0002	381010 381011	050001 050008 050016
FoMoCo 69-73 58-68 66-74 57-68	Ex. 427, 428 & 429 1"—23 spl. or 1-1/16"—10 spl. 427, 428 & 429 1-3/8" 10 spl. Ex. 427, 428 & 429	N1439 HP N1493 HP	70-115 70-120	1603 1604	485 486 487	628-0006 628-0007	382015 382016	050015 050010
Chrysler 70-75 68-69 62-76 62-76	426 Hemi 426 with 11" clutch 273, 318, 330, 340, 360 & 383 with 10" or 10.4" clutch and 1"—23 spline.	N1498 HP N1490 HP N1463 HP	70-113 70-112 70-110	1606 1605	482 484 483	628-0003 628-0005 628-0004	383014 383013 383012	050012 050011 050007
AMC 67-73 67-73	3 spd. trans. 4 spd. trans.	N1701 HP N1701 HP	70-125 70-125	1607 1607	480 481	628-0008 628-0008	384016 384016	050013 050014
Special	Dragsters 1-3/8" spline (direct drive) Clutchflite & Turboclutch					628-0009	388017 387018	

*Intermediate bearing length. Use when 1600 and 1601 are too short.

☆ Use when converting from diaphragm to Borg & Beck or Long pressure plate.

Use this table to select the correct release bearing for your application.

Regardless of the type line/s you're using, route them away from exhaust manifolds and pipes. If you can't do this, at least shield them from the exhaust heat. Otherwise you're risking boiling the hydraulic fluid. As the fluid heats up and expands, the clutch gradually disengages without your foot on the pedal. A fried clutch is the next occurence in the sequence of events if you don't get wise to what's going on and stop your car.

Release Bearing—The last clutch-linkage component is the release bearing. As I mentioned before, the best type to use is the *angular-contact* because of its durability. However, the important thing to watch out for is to match the release bearing to the style of pressure plate you are using. Make sure the pressure-plate release-lever fingers fit correctly with the release bearing. For instance if you are using a flat-fingered diaphragm pressure plate, even though it's as far from being high-performance as a 7.0:1 engine compression ratio, you must use a radiused-face release bearing. Hope-fully you won't be using the flat-fingered diaphragm pressure plate unless you *like* your clutch to disengage automatically at high revs. On the other hand, this type of bearing cannot be used with any other kind of pressure plate—bent-fingered diaphragm, Long or Borg & Beck, If you change to one of these types, you'll have to change to a shorter flat-faced bearing.

For the release bearing you should be using, refer to above table. This chart will generally tell you which bearing you should be using, however, there are other factors which can cause problems. For example, if you have a light steel flywheel, it will be thinner as a result and will move the pressure plate forward and away from the release bearing's normal position. In addition, if you are using an explosion-proof bellhousing/scattershield with an engine shield, the bellhousing and transmission will be spaced rearward, moving the release bearing and lever even farther away

An example of the different release bearings available for GM products. Medium-length bearing is for use with the Long or Borg & Beck pressure plates. Short one is for bent-finger diaphragm pressure plates. For situations where neither the medium nor the short ones will do the job, McLeod offers the longer bearing shown at right.

One way to keep your engine from moving is to install solid engine mounts. These are for Corvettes and are direct replacements for the production rubber mounts.

If you have a ground-up race car like the Townsend Pro-Stock Camaro, an engine-plate (arrows) eliminates any clutch-linkage problems caused by engine movement.

Other Considerations—You can have the strongest most rigid clutch linkage going, but if it isn't mounted rigidly, then you haven't gained a thing. For example, when you depress your clutch pedal, things move other than the pedal and linkage. Things these are mounted to also move to some degree. Your job is to minimize this movement or deflection. If you don't, you'll end up with excessive pedal travel and a clutch that may not stay adjusted.

Two areas need attention, the firewall and the engine. If your car has a roll cage, you shouldn't have any trouble with the firewall if you've tied the clutch and brake pedal bracketry into it. If you get noticeable deflection, then you need more bracing. If you have a stock-bodied car with a high-performance clutch, you may have to provide additional structure at the firewall. The best way to do this is to run a brace from the firewall inside the engine compartment on the opposite side of the clutch and brake-pedal-support bracket down to the frame. If you have a '67–'69 Camaro or '63–'67 Corvette, both without power brakes, Mr. Gasket already has one made up for you. For other cars, they are simple enough to make. A firewall

from the pressure plate. What will happen when you adjust your clutch linkage is the angle on the release lever may be excessive and you may run out of adjusting thread on the release-lever pushrod. If the pushrod can adjust all the way out, it will be weaker and may bend as a result. If you are using an engine-mounting plate between the bellhousing and engine, the problem will even be more acute. Therefore, a longer release-bearing assembly should be used to restore the release lever to its original position. This, in addition to the adjustable ball pivot which accompanies most safety bellhousings, will solve the problem.

Finally, when checking and adjusting your clutch linkage, make sure there is enough room between the release levers on the pressure plate and the front surface of the transmission-bearing retainer for the release bearing to clear the pressure-plate levers when the clutch is fully engaged. If the release bearing doesn't pull back from the pressure

plate, the clutch may not fully engage, causing it to slip and burn up. Or, the release bearing may prematurely fail as may the pressure plate due to worn release levers or an overheated pressure ring.

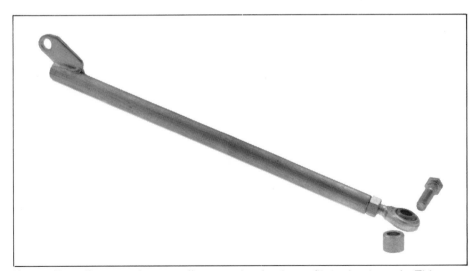
If your firewall moves when you disengage the clutch, you'll need to brace it. This Corvette brace attaches to the bottom of the brake master cylinder and the top of the steering-box. Mr. Gasket has this one, plus one for the Camaro. If none are available for your car they are easy to make.

To cancel loads imposed on an engine by the clutch linkage, the pushrod-to-bell-crank mounting points must be located in the plane-of-rotation of the cross-shaft pivots, or a proportionate distance from them. Note that the long arm of this bell-crank is located farther from the left of the end of the tube than the short arm is from the right end.

brace is merely a tube with a plate with a hole in it welded to one end of the tube and a rod end threaded into the other end. This makes the rod adjustable for mounting. If you decide to build your own brace, measure the exact length you'll need and do away with the rod end. Just add another drilled plate, but tack-weld it in place on the car. You'll then know the brace will fit after you finish welding it. With the firewall brace in place, you've eliminated the flexible-firewall problem.

The problem with rubber engine mounts is they let the engine move. Street cars are supposed to do this to isolate the passenger compartment from engine noises and vibrations. Unfortunately, this does not work too well with a race car, particularly one with a clutch. Cars with cable or hydraulic linkages don't have this problem, only ones with the rod-and-lever type linkage. The reason is one end of the bellcrank is mounted on the engine and when it moves, so does a large portion of the clutch linkage. When this happens, you may experience excessive pedal travel

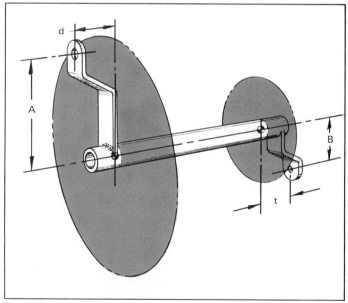

To prevent a rubber-mounted engine from moving back and forth during clutch operation, offsets d and t must be located in proportion to the A/B ratio of the bellcrank. This will cancel the loads applied to the engine by the clutch linkage.

when disengaging the clutch, *if it will disengage,* or the linkage may even bind up. Now, when I say one end of the bellcrank is mounted to the engine, I'm referring to the typical factory setup. If it weren't, the problem would be worse. Before talking about how to fix it, let's take a look at what causes the problem.

An engine with rubber mounts can move two ways which are detrimental to the operation of the clutch. It rolls or rotates from engine torque and it can move fore and aft due to loads imposed by the clutch linkage. The first is by design but the second is by error. If the bellcrank is not designed correctly, there can be an unequal load condition at the engine causing it to move as the clutch is disengaged. Using the conventional bellcrank setup as an example, if the load on the release lever is higher than the load on the bellcrank-pivot at the engine, the engine will move back during clutch operation and it will move forward if the opposite is true. If you'll remember, one of the names I mentioned which is used in place of bellcrank is *equalizer bar.* This is because one of its functions is to cancel the load on the release lever at the frame pivot, *equalizing* the two forces. Assuming the bellcrank wasn't mounted on the engine, then the full force of the release-lever-pushrod would try to push the engine rearward. By pivoting the bellcrank on the engine, an opposite force pushing forward on the engine prevents the engine from moving. For this to happen, the two forces must be equal.

If you have a street rod or street car and want to retain the rubber engine mounts while also using a bellcrank, let's look at what conditions must be to make it right. The simplest setup is to keep the pedal attachment at the bellcrank in the *plane of rotation* of the frame pivot. The *plane of rotation* is an imaginary disc which, if located at the center of the bellcrank frame pivot, would not wobble when the bellcrank is rotated.

The same thing goes for the release-lever pushrod. It must also be located in the *plate of rotation* of the engine pivot. With these two conditions met, the loads on the engine and transmission will cancel, keeping the engine from moving as the clutch pedal is depressed.

Now the question becomes, what do you do in the case of not being able to locate the pushrod attachments in their respective *planes of rotation?* This may occur if you are correcting your bellcrank or building one from scratch and you don't have the room. First, you must know how to measure this distance, or offset. It's the lateral distance from the plane of rotation of the pivot you are measuring to the center of the parts which are pivoting. For a rod going into a bushing, measure from the center of the bushing. If you are using a spherical rod end, it is to the bearing center. The rule is, if the release-lever-pushrod pivot is inboard the plane of rotation of the engine pivot (toward the engine), the pedal pushrod must be outboard the frame pivot (away from the engine) by the A/B ratio of the bellcrank. The opposite goes when the release-lever-pushrod pivot is outboard of the engine pivot. The pedal pushrod must be inboard the frame pivot by the same ratio. Use the following formula to calculate the correct offsets:

$$d = t \times \frac{A}{B} \text{ or}$$
$$t = d \div \frac{A}{B}$$

Where:

d is pedal-pushrod pivot offset in inches.

t is release-lever pushrod pivot offset in inches.

$\frac{A}{B}$ is lever ratio of the bellcrank.

Therefore, if the A/B ratio of a bell-crank is 2:1 and the offset t for the release-lever pushrod is 1.0" inboard the *plane-of-rotation* of the engine pivot, the pedal pushrod will have to be offset outboard the

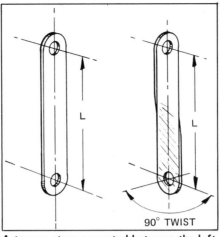

A torque strap mounted between the left side of a rubber-mounted engine and the frame will restrict engine roll. Fabricate a strap from 1/4" X 1" hot-rolled steel after determining the length of the strap and the mounting-hole sizes. Strap can be twisted in a vise for mounting to holes which are not parallel to each other.

frame pivot by the amount 2.0 multiplied by 1.0", or 2.0".

As for engine torque moving the engine, there is one way to fix the problem *only if you're going racing.* Your car will end up unfit to drive on the street. Mount the engine solidly in the chassis by using solid engine mounts which replace the rubber ones or use front and/or rear torque plates to mount the engine. Either of these methods will take care of any problems which may come from the engine moving.

Now, for the car which must race and also provide you with reasonably comfortable transportation. Two things can be done which will let you retain rubber engine mounts. First, to restrict engine roll, a simple *torque strap* fabricated from 1/8" X 1.0" flat steel stock with holes drilled in both ends should be installed between a relatively strong bolt on the left side of the engine—such as an exhaust-manifold bolt—down to the frame so the strap is in

tension when the car is under power. To attach the strap to the frame, you can drill a hole in the frame if you can get into the frame for holding a nut with a wrench. If not, you may be able to find an existing bolt such as a steering-box-mounting bolt. Or, finally, you may have to weld a bracket to the frame and bolt the *torque strap* to it. Any of these methods will do the job.

The next thing you should do if you can't get your bellcrank sorted out for one reason or another is to use another strap to keep the engine from moving back and forth when the clutch pedal is depressed. To do this, you must first find out which direction your engine is moving. Have someone push on the clutch while you watch the engine. If your clutch is centrifugally assisted, run the engine up to the RPM you'll be shifting at and then check movement. If the engine moves forward, the strap should run from the engine back to the frame cross-member or side rail so the strap will be in tension when loaded. On the other hand, if the engine moves back, the strap will have to run forward. For installing the strap, make sure you use sufficiently strong bolts, at least 3/8" grade 5. Also, use the same 1/8" x 1.0" steel stock as was used for the torque strap. Of equal importance is how you mount the straps. Make sure you get them as close to parallel to the release-lever-pushrod as possible. You may have to deviate somewhat to be able to get from the engine to the frame, but try to minimize it as much as possible.

One possible fix is to use 1974 or later engine mounts. They are designed so the steel in the mount is interlocked, restricting engine movement in all directions. These mounts won't stop engine movement completely, but may be enough to cure clutch-linkage problems. If they don't do the job, you'll have to install one or two straps.

Chapter Eight
BELLHOUSINGS

The driver of this car highly recommends the use of an explosion-proof bellhousing. Pictures like this one are hard to come by now because rules and regulations imposed by the various sanctioning organizations have dramatically reduced this problem through use of the correct parts. *Photo courtesy NHRA*

The *clutch housing, clutch-and flywheel housing, bellhousing, can, scatter shield* or whatever you prefer to call it is one of those parts of a car which is usually taken for granted. Take it for granted and you may have serious trouble. It doesn't have any moving parts nor can it make a car go faster. It can make a car slower and unreliable if set up incorrectly. On some occasions, it is essential to protect your life and limbs.

Bellhousings are made from cast aluminum, hydroformed steel or spun titanium. The first is used for production and some race cars and the other two exclusively for performance cars. These are commonly referred to as *safety* bellhousings because they are explosion-proof. Cast iron housings were once used on production cars. It is very heavy and has been replaced by aluminum. Cast aluminum was tried as an option in the manufacture of safety bellhousings, but the material does not have sufficient ductility to absorb the impact of an exploding flywheel. When enough material thickness was used so the housings would contain an exploding clutch or flywheel, they became heavier, bulkier and much more expensive than hydroformed steel. The result is they aren't available anymore.

OEM aluminum bellhousings are pretty but they can't contain an exploding clutch or flywheel. This is a big-block Chevy ready for installation in a Corvette. Note the husky release lever. Don't forget the release bearing!

After the aluminum has cooled sufficiently, the part is removed from the mold and finish machined. It is drilled for mounting, faced so the front and rear sufaces will be parallel, and bored in a fixture to ensure accurate alignment of the transmission with the engine.

As for *hydroforming,* it is an amazing process which gives the explosion-proof bellhousing its "performance image" right from the time it is manufactured. The majority of formed-metal parts, called *stampings,* are made by stretching or drawing a sheet of metal with a *male die* or *punch* into a *female die* with a mechanical or hydraulic press. To do this, a sheet of metal is cut into a *blank* which resembles the outer periphery of the finished part plus some additional material to hold onto to prevent the blank from being indiscriminantly forced into the female die by the punch. In the hydroforming process, the punch is replaced by a rubber diaphragm which seals the blank

HOW ARE THEY MADE?

To begin building your appreciation for the bellhousing, I'll briefly describe how the three types of housings are manufactured. First, the cast aluminum. Two methods are used—*high-pressure* and *low-pressure casting. High-pressure* is used in mass production and is accomplished by injecting molten aluminum under pressure into a *permanent mold* or *die* which has the shape of the finished part, plus an allowance for shrinkage after the part has cooled. The part is removed or *stripped* from the die after it has cooled. The *low-pressure* method is used in relatively low-volume production. Molten aluminum is poured at atmospheric pressure into sand molds which are destroyed after each part is cast and removed from the mold. You can recognize parts manufactured using each method by the texture of the part, a *high-pressure* casting has a smooth finish and a *low-pressure sand casting* is rough.

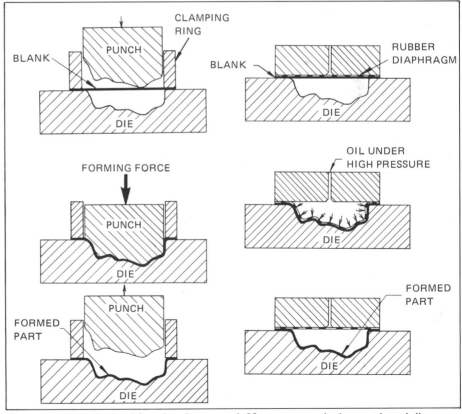

Here are two methods of forming sheet metal. Most common is the punch-and-die method shown at left. Steel bellhousings are made by hydroforming (right). The flat-steel blank is forced into a die with high-pressure oil behind a rubber diaphragm.

down against the female die which will give the part its shape. After this, hydraulic fluid is pressurized against the back of the diaphragm at very high pressure, approximately 10,000 psi. This pressure forces the diaphragm and metal into the die, thus forming the part. After the part is formed, the pressure is released and the diaphragm returns to its flat shape but the part retains its formed shape. The part is removed from the die and trimmed around the edge, followed by finish-machining just as with the cast-aluminum housing. The advantage of this process compared to the conventional method is it makes a much nicer looking part which is more uniform in thickness and, consequently, stronger.

Finally, titanium bellhousings are manufactured by the *spinning* technique. A flat blank is supported on a *mandrel* which is basically the same as a male punch used in the stamping process, but circular in shape. This means spun parts must also be circular—spun hubcaps for example. A housing is formed by spinning, or rolling the blank over

the mandrel with a wheel as the blank is rotated with the mandrel. After the part is formed, it is removed from the mandrel, trimmed and finish-machined.

Titanium is a high-performance material with over twice the strength of mild steel and about half the weight. The exact numbers are:

	Density Pounds/ft^3	Yield Strength Pounds/inch^2	Ultimate Tensile Strength Pounds/inch^2
Mild steel	490	40,000	69,000
Titanium	281	120,000	150,000

Low weight and high strength don't come cheap. Only the serious racer with a big budget will be able to afford one. One titanium housing costs about the same as two sets of radial tires for the family sedan.

BELLHOUSING FUNCTIONS

Following is a list of the functions of a bellhousing:

1. Rigidly supports the engine and transmission in fixed proximity to each other.

2. Protects the clutch from contaminants such as water, oil, dirt

and grease.

3. Supports the clutch release-lever.

4. In some cases, supports the starter motor.

The following two items apply only to *safety* bellhousings:

5. Contains the clutch and flywheel in the event of either of them failing as a result of centrifugal forces.

6. Can be used for mounting the engine and transmission.

Holds the engine and transmission together—The bellhousing rigidly supports the engine and transmission while spacing them apart to provide room for the flywheel and clutch. The rear face of the engine block and the front face of the transmission must be parallel and the input shaft of the transmission must be held in line with the engine crankshaft. If these conditions are not met, shifting may be difficult, particularly into top gear. The pilot bearing may fail and seize or ruin the transmission input shaft or the front bearing in the transmission will wear excessively and fail prematurely.

Titanium bellhousings provide what every racer is after—increased strength with reduced weight. *Photo courtesy Trick Titanium, Inc.*

Loads imposed on a bellhousing can be very high. This housing was cracked by extreme vibration when the car's driveshaft exited the car. Note the super heli-arc job (arrows).

The reason top-gear shifting would be difficult is the input shaft would be misaligned in the transmission from being forced out of position. As a result, the 3rd and 4th gear slip yoke and synchronizer ring would not line up with the top-gear dogs on the input shaft. This is particularly troublesome if you are going drag racing. As you would try to shift into top gear, the slip yoke would hang up slightly, causing a missed shift and a lost race. In a 3-speed trans the problem occurs with misalignment between 2nd and top gear.

Therefore, the transmission and engine must be located as accurately as possible. For drag racing, they should be located closer than you might think would be necessary. So, make sure your bellhousing is right on. If it's not, get it Blanchard ground if the two faces are not parallel. If the bore locating the transmission is not concentric to the engine crankshaft, the housing should be replaced. If you've purchased a new one and it's out of spec, return it for another one. In the installation chapter I tell how to align a bellhousing.

Keeps the clutch clean and dry—Now that the transmission and engine are locked together, the clutch must be enclosed to keep it clean. Unfortunately, the bellhousing holds heat in as it keeps contaminants out. There's not a whole lot that can be done about it because a contaminated clutch will not work properly, if it works at all. However, if a clutch is properly chosen and operated, heat will not be a problem. If you must vent your housing, the best place to do it is at the top rear. Just drill a few evenly spaced 1/2" holes here, but before you do, consult the rule book to see if such holes are permitted. After drilling the holes, shroud them so any oil or water running down the back of the housing from the engine will not enter but will be directed around the holes. I recommend not drilling an aluminum housing because of the danger of weakening it. If you're lucky, you have one of the few production units which is already vented. For housings equipped with a cover plate at the lower front, don't remove it for ventilating the clutch. If you do, the bellhousing then becomes a very efficient scoop for collecting dirt, oil, water, grease, rocks, chickens—or you name it. This is particularly important in the case of street or road-race cars which have to be driven in the rain on occasions.

Front-engined cars are especially vulnerable because the wakes from the front tires are directed at, or in the general direction of, the bellhousing. With the front cover off, the clutch can be drowned in water in short order, rendering the clutch useless because the water acts as a lubricant. This drops the coefficient of friction between the clutch disc, pressure plate and flywheel to a point where the clutch is incapable of transmitting engine torque. So, keep the clutch well enclosed and protected.

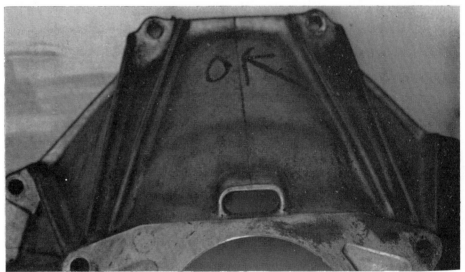

About the only good place for a housing to be vented is at the top rear. Vent is designed so water will be diverted from entering the housing.

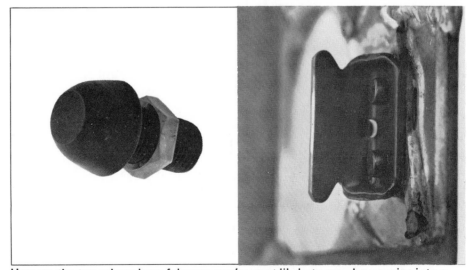

Here are the two release-lever-fulcrums you're most likely to see when peering into a bellhousing. The L bracket is the type used by Ford and Chrysler and the ball type is standard on GM cars and all safety housings.

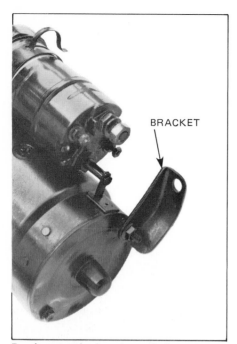

Bracket attached to the end plate of this starter attaches to the engine block. It prevents the mounting at the other end of the starter from being overstressed and failing.

You're looking at the remains of a slider clutch which separated from the flywheel of a Top Fuel dragster. Unfortunately, "explosion-proof" bellhousings are not entirely explosion-proof when a slider wants out. This floater plate cut three of the four main frame rails in half.

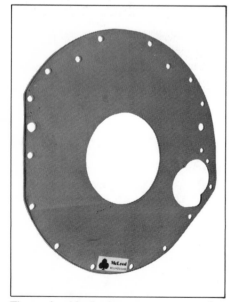

The engine block plate protects an engine from being damaged in the event of a clutch or flywheel explosion.

Supports the clutch-release lever— As I discussed in the linkage chapter, the release lever is pivoted on and retained to the lever fulcrum. It is simply a screw-in ball stud or a riveted or bolted angle bracket attached to the bellhousing. The release lever extends out of a *window* in the housing which is sealed by a rubber *boot* which slips over the lever and attaches to the housing. Another type uses a release shaft which rotates in the housing and operates the release bearing with fingers on the shaft. No boot is required for this type as it is automatically sealed by the bushing it rotates in.

The starter is usually mounted on the bellhousing, however some are mounted on the engine block. For mounting, drilled and tapped holes are provided. If your car is intended for any type of endurance racing, it is a good idea to provide some additional support for the starter by fabricating a bracket that attaches to the front end of the starter (toward the front of the car) and picks up a mounting point on the engine. The starter is relatively heavy and the combination of the overhanging weight and chassis and engine vibrations can fatigue the starter-mounting ears so they break off. I've seen this happen on a small-block Ford. At speeds exceeding 150 MPH, the starter motor can do a lot of damage as it comes out from under a car.
Protects your body—One of the biggest safety features which can be added to a car having a clutch and flywheel is a safety bellhousing. A clutch and flywheel spinning at high revs has the potential destructive force of a hand grenade. A safety bellhousing will contain them if something lets go. Granted, if you are using a high-performance-rated clutch and flywheel, they *shouldn't* explode. However, things which shouldn't happen can be counted on the missing toes which are the result of a clutch or flywheel coming apart which *shouldn't have.* Fortunately this is now a rare occurrence because of rules requiring

safety bellhousings by the various sanctioning organizations. Even though you may not be required to use a safety housing, I recommend you get one anyway because when you see the tachometer needle passing 7 grand, you know the clutch and flywheel don't have the capability to distinguish whether you're on a race track or the street. Your feet and toes should get that insecure feeling. Face it, a clutch explosion can kill you, your passenger— and even bystanders.

Protects your engine—In addition to protecting your appendages, 0.150-inch-thick engine-block plates are supplied with safety housings to protect the backside of the engine block. This plate is secured to the engine by the bellhousing and fits between the flywheel and the engine block. Who manufactures safety housings? There are presently four; Ansen Automotive Engineering, Inc.; Lakewood Industries; McLeod Industries; and Trick Titanium.

Additional protection for your engine can be gained by using hollow, soft-steel dowel pins for locating your housing rather than the conventional solid type. In the event a clutch or flywheel explodes, hollow pins will collapse when impacted rather than breaking out a section of your engine block like solid ones do. Hollow dowel pins are available from Lakewood.

Two basic styles of safety housings are available for conventional front-engined cars—single or two-piece. The advantage of the two-

In the event of a clutch or flywheel explosion, hollow dowel pins will collapse, preventing engine-block damage as can happen with solid dowels.

Because slider clutches need frequent adjustment, housings are equipped with an access plate (arrow). This permits CF weights, lever heights and static spring pressures to be adjusted without having to remove the housing.

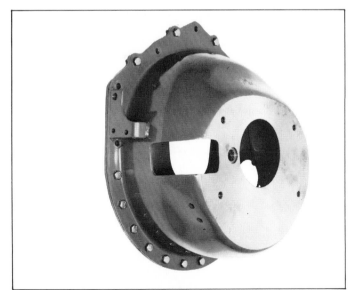

Single or two-piece bellhousings are available. The two-piece type is convenient for clutch access, but it is heavier and more expensive. *Photos courtesy Lakewood*

All SEMA-approved bellhousings must be tested in accordance with their specificiation 6-1. This flywheel exploded at 7500 RPM resulting in some housing distortion, however the housing did what it was supposed to do—it contained all the pieces. *Photos courtesy Mr. Gasket*

piece housing is your transmission doesn't have to be removed to gain access to the clutch from under your car. This can be very helpful when you have adjustable CF weights on your pressure plate. The disadvantages of the two-piece housings are they are more complex and, consequently, more expensive and heavier than one-piece housings. For cars having removable transmission tunnels, a small access cover can be used at the top of a housing for clutch inspection and adjustment. However, before you do any cutting, consult your rule book. One advantage of safety-housings is, some are universal in the sense that they accept different transmissions. For example, if you are using

This is Joe Tryson working on Grumpy Jenkin's Pro-stock engine between rounds. Note the lightened aluminum engine plate for locating the engine solidly in the chassis.

When an "explosion-proof" bellhousing is pitted against an exploding slider, this is the usual result. Anything in line with the clutch is in danger of being cut in half. Illustrated here is how housing failure begins—at the inspection window. The reason for this is two-fold. First, the housing is weakened by built-in stress risers at each corner of the window. The cover does not restore this strength. Second, the cover does not fit flush in the window, resulting in edges for exploding clutch components to "grab" as they are spinning.

This housing, for big or small-block Chevy's, can accept either a Muncie or Ford transmission. The ring makes up the difference in the bearing-retainer diameters of the two transmission—it's used with the Muncie transmission.

Dragsters, Funny-Cars, altereds and some Pro-Stockers use this type bellhousing. They can be drilled for just about any engine and transmission combination. The clutch-release linkage is very convenient to work with.

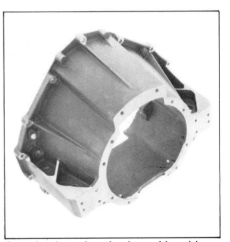

Cast-aluminum housing is used in mid-engined cars such as Formula 5000 and Can-Am cars. It's designed to set an engine as low as possible in a chassis. It can also be used as structure for the rear portion of a car.

There are all sorts of interesting things to look at in this photo of the rear section of an Indy car. The bellhousing is buried between the engine and transaxle under an array of plumbing and structure. The housing supports the engine and transaxle and also transmits the rear-suspension and wing loads to the tub, or main structure of the car. Note the window in the bellhousing for timing the engine. A pointer (arrow) and degree marks on the clutch are visible.

a Chevrolet engine, you can get a safety-housing that will enable you to use a Ford "Top-loader"—or a Muncie.

Special housings are available for fuelers, funny-cars, altereds and most other types of drag cars using anything from no transmission (direct drive), to Lencos, Clutch-flites or what have you. All you have to do is specify what you want and the maker will machine a housing to your specs. These special housings are all of the safety type, however some are available for racing purposes which are not. In some cases this is not particularly hazardous. For example, sprint cars which don't use clutches or flywheels are perfectly safe using an aluminum housing. Those which use clutches should use safety bellhousings and they are available from CAE, Halibrand, Quartermaster and ARC. In addition to sprint cars are the mid-engined USAC Championship cars and sports cars of the Formula 5000 and Can-Am variety. These cars use cast-aluminum housings specially built to accept Hewland, Z-F or Weismann transaxles and are not particularly dangerous to the driver because of the relative locations of

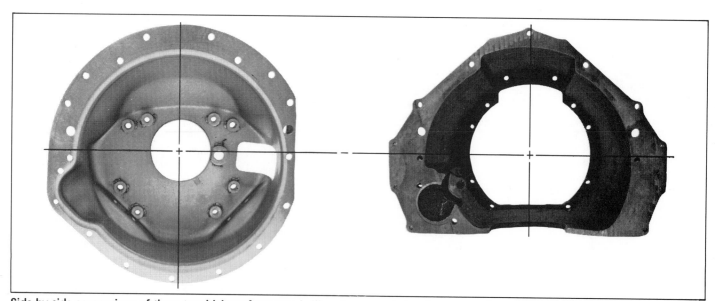

Side-by-side comparison of these two high-performance bellhousings reveals to what extent the same engine can be lowered in a chassis.

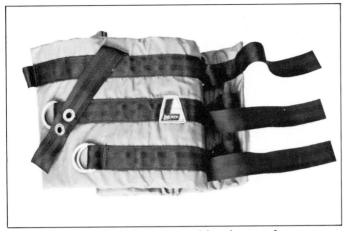

If you are running in a class not requiring the use of a safety bellhousing, it is a good idea to use a safety blanket. They are relatively inexpensive and don't weigh much.

Because safety bellhousings are made from steel, they are easy to modify. They are also very strong. This housing had its underside cut off to lower the engine and transmission in the chassis. It also uses the engine as additional structure for the forward part of the car.

the clutch and flywheel and the driver. However, there is a secondary danger of the chassis being damaged to the point where a high-speed accident could be caused from damage to the chassis in the event a flywheel or clutch did explode. Another consideration is the safety of the crews, track personnel and spectators who line the track. Therefore, if you are involved in either one of these types of racing, give strong consideration to using a *safety blanket* similar to those used to contain automatic transmissions. Admittedly the clutches and flywheels used in these types of cars are very small in diameter and thus the centrifugal loads are less than those for a production-car flywheel and clutch. And, they are manufactured from very good material with high quality. As a result, these have a very low failure rate. Everyone in racing should know it only takes once—enough said. **Useful when you need additional structure**—Finally, because safety bellhousings are manufactured from steel, it's convenient to use them for secondary purposes. For example, brackets can be easily welded on the housing for mounting the

engine and transmission or for providing additional support to other components. Some housings already have flat areas formed in them with internal nuts for mounts, or if these aren't provided, mounting brackets can be welded directly on the housing for supporting the back of the engine and the transmission. By using strong engine mounts at the front face of the engine block, the engine becomes part of the chassis structure, adding greatly to its torsional rigidity. This is important because the weakest section of any chassis is from the firewall forward. Strength gained from the engine is "free"—provided you take advantage of it correctly. As for rear-engine dragsters, especially Top Fuelers, loads going into a rear axle can twist it right out of the chassis or even bend the axle housing. As a result, additional support for the axle is essential. One simple way of doing this is to run two tension struts from the top of the center section of the axle housing forward to the bellhousing. Weld on brackets at the axle and the bellhousing for attaching the struts and the job will be finished.

Drive loads on a Top-Fuel-dragster axle are so high they have been known to twist out of their mountings. This is prevented from happening by running tension braces from the bellhousing to the top of the axle housing.

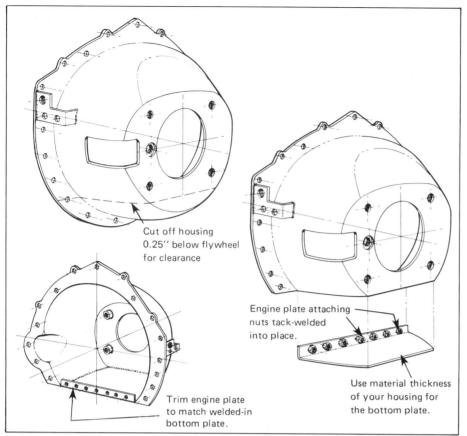

Cut off housing
0.25'' below flywheel
for clearance

Engine plate attaching
nuts tack-welded
into place.

Use material thickness
of your housing for
the bottom plate.

Trim engine plate
to match welded-in
bottom plate.

To lower the engine in your chassis, use a small-diameter clutch and flywheel and modify your safety bellhousing like this.

LOWER YOUR C.G.

If you are using a dry-sump oiling system or have a shallow bustle-type oil pan, there's one more trick you can squeeze out of your safety bellhousing. This assumes your car's performance can be improved by lowering its C.G. (center of gravity).

Use the smallest possible flywheel diameter and cut the bottom of your housing straight off at the bottom, parallel to the ground and about 1/4'' below the outer edge of the flywheel or the starter ring gear, whichever is lowest. After doing this, the housing will be severely weakened, so return it to its original strength by welding a flat steel plate of the same material thickness as your housing to the bottom.

Make sure when welding the bottom plate to your housing that you have the housing clamped to a solid flat surface, otherwise it will warp out of shape—an old engine block will do the trick. Just the same, check the housing after welding and if it warped, have it trued by Blanchard grinding.

Before welding the bottom plate into place, turn up a flange at the front for attaching the engine-block plate. Trim the block plate to match the bottom line of your newly modified housing and drill new mounting holes in the plate and the housing. Because the flange is turned up, you'll have to tack-weld nuts behind the flange due to lack of access for a wrench. If you're wondering why the flange should be turned up, it's just another 3/4''–1'' more you can lower your engine.

For complete information on how to inspect and install the bellhousing, flywheel, clutch and related hardware, refer to the clutch-installation chapter.

This is a car I designed for competition on the NASCAR Modified circuit. Joe Ruttman is tall and the car is low. The engine is to be dry-sumped and the bottom of the bellhousing trimmed to get the engine as low as possible.

Metric Chart

METRIC CUSTOMARY-UNIT EQUIVALENTS

Multiply:		by:		to get:	Multiply:		by:		to get:

LINEAR

inches	X	25.4	=	millimeters(mm)		X	0.03937	=	inches
miles	X	1.6093	=	kilometers (km)		X	0.6214	=	miles
inches	X	2.54	=	centimeters (cm)		X	0.3937	=	inches

AREA

inches^2	X	645.16	=	millimeters^2(mm^2)		X	0.00155	=	inches^2
inches^2	X	6.452	=	centimeters^2(cm^2)		X	0.155	=	inches^2

VOLUME

quarts	X	0.94635	=	liters (l)		X	1.0567	=	quarts
fluid oz	X	29.57	=	milliliters (ml)		X	0.03381	=	fluid oz

MASS

pounds (av)	X	0.4536	=	kilograms (kg)		X	2.2046	=	pounds (av)
tons (2000 lb)	X	907.18	=	kilograms (kg)		X	0.001102	=	tons (2000 lb)
tons (2000 lb)	X	0.90718	=	metric tons (t)		X	1.1023	=	tons (2000 lb)

FORCE

pounds—f(av)	X	4.448	=	newtons (N)		X	0.2248	=	pounds—f(av)
kilograms—f	X	9.807	=	newtons (N)		X	0.10197	=	kilograms—f

TEMPERATURE

Degrees Celsius (C) = 0.556 (F - 32)   Degree Fahrenheit (F) = (1.8C) + 32

°F	-40		32		98.6			212				°F
		0	40	80	120	160	00	240	280	320		
°C	-40	-20	0	20	40	60	80	100	120	140	160	°C

ENERGY OR WORK

foot-pounds	X	1.3558	=	joules (J)		X	0.7376	=	foot-pounds

FUEL ECONOMY & FUEL CONSUMPTION

miles/gal	X	0.42514	=	kilometers/liter(km/l)		X	2.3522	=	miles/gal

Note:
235.2/(mi/gal)=liters/100km
235.2/(liters/100km)=mi/gal

PRESSURE OR STRESS

inches Hg (60F)	X	3.377	=	kilopascals (kPa)		X	0.2961	=	inches Hg
pounds/sq in.	X	6.895	=	kilopascals (kPa)		X	0.145	=	pounds/sq in
pounds/sq ft	X	47.88	=	pascals (Pa)		X	0.02088	=	pounds/sq ft

POWER

horsepower	X	0.746	=	kilowatts (kW)		X	1.34	=	horsepower

TORQUE

pound-inches	X	0.11298	=	newton-meters (N-m)		X	8.851	=	pound-inches
pound-feet	X	1.3558	=	newton-meters (N-m)		X	0.7376	=	pound-feet
pound-inches	X	0.0115	=	kilogram-meters (Kg-M)		X	87	=	pound-inches
pound-feet	X	0.138	=	kilogram-meters (Kg-M)		X	7.25	=	pound-feet

VELOCITY

miles/hour	X	1.6093	=	kilometers/hour(km/h)		X	0.6214	=	miles/hour

Conversion Chart courtesy Ford Motor Company.

Chapter Nine
INSTALLATION and ADJUSTMENT

A disc can be installed one of two ways. This charred disc has less than 1000 miles of street use on it. It was installed backwards. The hub assembly must be installed facing the transmission, otherwise this is the least that can happen.

Installing a clutch can be all for nought if it isn't installed and adjusted correctly, even though it's the perfect match for the car. Every clutch manufacturer and performance shop has a collection of burnt, bent and warped pressure plates and discs—all because of incorrect installation or adjustment. For example, many discs get installed backwards. It is easy enough to do because they slide onto the splines either way. When this happens the sprung hub bottoms against the flywheel or flywheel-mounting bolts and the disc becomes instant junk. Wrong adjustment is the most common error. For instance, not enough "free play." This is a condition where there is little or no clearance between the release

bearing and the pressure-plate release levers. The result is the release bearing runs constantly and the pressure plate is partially unloaded or released, even after the pedal is fully released. The damage can range from a seized release bearing to a burned-up disc and damaged pressure plate. The clutch has a hard enough life without any extra burdens. To prevent them from happening, let's look at the right way to install and adjust a clutch.

BEFORE YOU START

Before you start this project, take inventory of all the parts and tools necessary to complete the job. How many times have you gotten into a job and been stopped because you needed this or that to

continue? Before deciding on the tools you'll need, you've got to know exactly what has to be done. First, the car has to be raised. Once this sometimes-underrated feat is accomplished, the driveline between the engine and the rear axle must be removed. Some cars will require removal of the exhaust system and the parking-brake cable. To do the job right, a complete set of tools is required. In addition to the everyday tools, a clutch-aligning tool or an old transmission input shaft, a torque wrench, a dial indicator, and a set of micrometers or vernier calipers should be on hand. These are for checking clutch housing and flywheel alignment and disc thickness. For proper lubrication, you will need some high-temperature Lubriplate or some other lithi-

Under no circumstances should you ever get under a car which isn't supported well. Jack stands like these will do the job.

Masking tape is a good way to keep U-joint needle bearings from being scattered all over the floor.

um-based grease. When it comes time for assembly, *everything must be clean.* For this, get some cleaning solvent and paint thinner or alcohol—no, not a six-pack. Now, if you are among the chosen few with a floor jack and have four jack stands, a creeper and a trouble light, you're ready.

As for parts on hand, start with the pressure plate and disc. I'm not one for buying more parts than needed, especially the way prices are. I do, however, recommend the replacement of the release bearing and pilot bearing at the same time a clutch is replaced. This is just good preventive maintenance and the cost is small considering the potential headaches and cost if they aren't replaced. If the car is used for racing only, you'll have to use your own judgement. These parts may be relatively new. At any rate, if the clutch is being replaced because it is worn out, replace the bearings.

UP IN THE AIR

The best thing to have for working under a car is a hydraulic jack and a set of four jack stands. That is, if you don't have access to a hoist. Another thing that works well is a set of ramps. Don't underrate this part of the job. When a car

falls, it tends to kill anyone under it. Under no circumstance should you ever support a car with a bumper jack. Another consideration is the positioning of the jack stands if this is what is used. It is very inconvenient to have a jack too close to your work.

DISASSEMBLY

With the car in the air, the work is ready to begin. The first thing to come out is the driveshaft.

First, mark the driveshaft and the rear-axle U-joint flange so there is a reference to reinstall it in the same position. This will prevent a possible out-of-balance condition caused by installing the driveshaft 180 degrees out of position. Once the U-bolts are disconnected, the rear of the shaft is ready to lower. Have some tape handy for wrapping around the U-joint bearing cups. This will prevent them from falling off the U-joint spider and scattering

A shop rag stuffed into the end of the transmission will help keep grease from running out all over your garage floor or driveway. Be careful not to damage the seal. The whole job is easier and cleaner if you steam clean or degrease and pressure wash the area before working on it.

There's nothing like a hydraulic jack to raise and lower your transmission. If you don't have one, get an enthusiastic buddy.

all over the floor. Replace the U-bolts in the flange so the bolts, nuts and washers won't get lost. Another handy thing is the little plastic sleeve used to ship transmissions and prevent the grease from leaking out the back around the output shaft. This slips in place of the driveshaft slip-yoke. If you can't round one up at a dealer, use a plastic bag to slip over the end of the transmission and some tape or a rubber band to secure it. It sure beats getting grease all over the floor and all over yourself.

With the driveshaft out, the next thing to do is to check to see if the exhaust pipes or the parking-brake cable will have to be removed. If you're lucky, the exhaust won't. If it does, try to get away with removing the header pipes only. As for the parking-brake cable, tie it up out of the way so you can move freely under the car.

Now for the transmission. Before it can come out, the speedo must be disconnected and the shifter will require some sort of disassembly. No matter what type of shifter is used, the boot and bezel must be removed to gain access to the shifter. If the shifter is an original-equipment Hurst as used by AMC, Chrysler or Ford, the stick can be removed by inserting a 0.015- or 0.020-inch feeler gauge along the side of the lower part of the stick and the shifter housing. This will displace the spring-steel keeper and allow the stick to be removed. Other shifters will require unbolting to be removed and the real bad ones, which are a welded assembly, require complete removal from the transmission. With the transmission clean of all the hang-ons, it is now ready for removal.

Support the rear of the engine with an extra jack stand to prevent it from dropping down when the transmission is removed. If you don't have a transmission jack, a friend or your floor jack are the best substitutes. Unbolt the transmission from the engine and the transmission mount. Support the transmission with the jack and remove the transmission crossmember. The transmission is now free to slide out. With the jack parallel to the centerline of the car, roll the jack back as the transmission slides out and lower it while balancing it on the jack. The clutch can now be seen through the back of the bellhousing. Disconnect the clutch linkage from the release lever and remove the starter motor. Now remove the bellhousing, bringing the clutch-release lever and release bearing with it. With the bellhousing off, the clutch is exposed and is ready for removal.

Two methods can be used to loosen the pressure plate. Even though you may not plan to use your old one, it is good practice to do things right and not junk a part because of poor disassembly. The first method, and the one I prefer: Progressively loosen each bolt not more than two turns at a time until the pressure ring is unloaded. Each bolt is then free to come out all the way. The second method is only good for a coil-spring-type pressure plate and not a diaphragm. It involves putting a hard object between each release lever and the cover as you loosen the cover bolts. Thick nuts will do

Spacer blocks behind the release levers in this pressure plate eliminate any chance of the cover being bent while removing or installing a pressure plate. Nuts will do the job just as well. Just slip one behind each lever before you start to loosen the pressure plate attaching bolts.

Of the several methods to remove a transmission pilot bearing this is the cleanest and easiest one. Tool is a slide hammer.

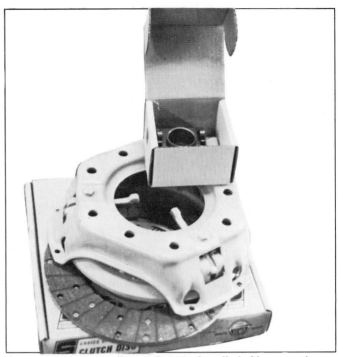

Here are the new goodies ready to be installed. Always replace the release bearing and pilot bearing when replacing your clutch.

the job. They will hold the pressure ring in the engaged position, so you can take out the attaching bolts all the way instead of taking a couple of turns at a time. As soon as the last bolt is ready to come out, be ready to lower about 20 pounds of clutch.

The last part to come out is the pilot bearing. For such a little part, it can cause problems when it comes to getting it out. Chances are when looking in the manual for your particular car, you will see special tool so-and-so. They're not required but, if you can get one, great. If not, you can still do the job just as fast. The two most common "special tools" are a *slide hammer* and a *puller*. All the slide hammer amounts to is a tool which screws into or hooks onto the back of the pilot bearing and has a heavy handle free to slide on a shaft concentric with the center of the bearing. By sliding the handle backwards, it will bottom and eventually will knock the bearing free. The puller screws

into the pilot in the same manner. The only difference is the puller uses a steady force to pull the bearing rather than an impact force. A nut on the puller is tightened and gradually pulls the bearing out of its bore in the crank. Two homemade methods employ the same basics. The first involves no more than filling the pilot-bearing bore with grease. To remove the bearing, insert either the aligning tool or the transmission input shaft in the bore and hit it with a rubber or brass mallet. Hydraulic pressure will force the bearing loose. The final method—good only for bronze or Oilite pilot bearings— uses a coarse-threaded bolt approximately 1/16-inch larger than the inside diameter of the bearing —certainly no more than 3/32-inch larger. To get the bolt started into the bearing, it must be ground with a slight taper on the first three or four threads. The bolt can then be threaded into the bearing until it bottoms on the crankshaft and pushes the bearing out. No matter

which method you use, measure and write down the depth of the bearing in the crankshaft before removing it so you will know how far the new one should go in.

Other than the normal clutch dirt, residue and highly polished friction surface, this flywheel is in good shape. When checking your flywheel, be particularly careful to look for deep grooves, hot spots and surface cracks.

If you're replacing your clutch because it gave you trouble, find out what caused the trouble. The problem with this clutch was it chattered—it wasn't worn out. Grease from the release bearing contaminated the facings and caused the chattering.

INSPECTION AND CLEANING

Now, with everything on the floor, it's time to start putting the new goodies in—but woah! This is where the first mistake is usually made. The anxiety of wanting to get your car in operation must not overcome doing the job right. This is a golden opportunity to check things out. For instance, if you are not satisfied with the way your shifter is operating, there couldn't be a better chance to clean and lubricate it, or replace it. If the car is going from street use to purely racing, maybe a light flywheel is in the picture. If you are going racing, you should have a SEMA-approved flywheel anyway in addition to a safety bellhousing. Now is the time to install them if the car is not so equipped. On the other hand, if your car is down for repair or servicing, now is the time to inspect your flywheel.

The condition of your clutch will give you a clue as to the condition of your flywheel. For example, if the facing is worn excessively and

the rivet heads are polished, chances are your flywheel is grooved. If it is it should be refaced. If the disc facing is charred due to being overheated, several bad things may have happened—hot spots, warpage or heat checking. This can mean flywheel resurfacing or replacement.

Hot spots show up as dark-blue or black spots all over a flywheel's friction surface, but don't particularly hurt anything. In fact, they are very helpful because they indicate more serious things caused by overheating such as warpage or heat checking. Therefore, if your flywheel has hot spots, carefully inspect it for these conditions.

Check your flywheel for warpage by using a good straight edge and a dial indicator. If it is warped or the friction surface is excessively worn—usually in a convex shape— remove and reface it. It should be replaced if the warpage is very bad. See page 153 for checking with a dial indicator.

Heat checking, or surface crack-

ing, is the most serious condition to look for. The cracks are caused as the friction surface of the flywheel tries to expand more than the bulk of the flywheel due to high surface temperatures. When this happens, the thin surface permanently deforms—or is compressed—because it cannot overcome the cooler portion of the flywheel which is not expanding at the same rate. As the friction surface cools, the process is reversed as it approaches the temperature of the rest of the flywheel. It now wants to be smaller than it originally was, but is resisted again by the bulk of the flywheel. Again, it loses the battle, but instead of being deformed, or stretched back into shape, the surface is torn apart in the form of small cracks.

Surface cracks on a flywheel are *stress risers*—like a scratch on a piece of glass. A stress riser is a sharp discontinuity in or on an object which causes it to be severely weakened and break when subjected to much less load than would normally be required. Once a flywheel develops surface cracks, they propagate toward the center of the flywheel and they get deeper. If you continue to use the flywheel chances are it will explode. If the cracks are discovered soon enough, a flywheel can sometimes be repaired by removing a few thousandths of an inch of material from its face. If they can't then the flywheel should be replaced.

Clean Up—Providing your old clutch gave good service and operated properly, the new clutch can be installed with reasonable assurance it will also operate satisfactorily. Before the clutch is bolted on, the flywheel and pressure plate should be cleaned with a non-petroleum-based solvent such as alcohol, turpentine, or lacquer thinner. Even better, use a fine-grit sandpaper to remove the resin binder left by the old clutch and then use the solvent. This will give the disc a clean start.

When metallic facing is used, it is very important that the pressure plate and flywheel be perfectly flat. They must also be thoroughly cleaned, particularly if they were previously used with organic facing. Resin binder from the disc impregnates the friction surfaces of the pressure plate and flywheel and acts like oil on an organic disc. Therefore, clean the two by sanding thoroughly with a fine-grit paper. In addition, the pressure plate must be matched to the disc. It must have the right amount of pressure-ring compression or the plate load will not be correct. This means the new metallic disc must have the same compressed thickness as the disc the pressure plate was designed for. For example, typical organic-faced discs have a new compressed thickness of 0.330 inches and the McLeod disc may measure as low as 0.315 inches.

Another factor to consider is plate load. Metallic facings require less plate load to obtain the same capacity due to their slightly higher friction coefficients. This is better than not having enough, but the whole thing boils down to the fact that the wisest thing to do if

you plan to use a metallic disc is to purchase a matching pressure plate from the same source. By taking this approach, you avoid the problems associated with using your new metallic disc. Just make sure the flywheel is flat and clean.

Flywheel runout—If the car is being built from the ground up and the flywheel is new or resurfaced and the bellhousing is new or the clutch didn't give good service or operate satisfactorily, some checking should be done. Start by checking the flywheel face runout by mounting a dial indicator to the rear face of the engine block and setting the dial-indicator plunger perpendicular to the face of the flywheel. Pry the flywheel in either direction so all the crankshaft end play is taken up and does not affect the runout readings. Set the indicator to read zero and rotate the crankshaft several times, noting the maximum and minimum readings of the dial indicator. To be sure crank end play doesn't affect your readings check to make sure the indicator returns to zero after each revolution of the fly-

wheel. The difference between these readings should not exceed 0.010 inch and should be less for an all-out race car. If the readings are excessive, remove the flywheel after you've marked the location of maximum and minimum readings. After removing the flywheel, check the crankshaft and flywheel-mounting surfaces for dirt or burrs. Clean both of these surfaces with a file, emery paper and cleaning solvent and reinstall the flywheel. The correct procedure for this is to fit the flywheel on the crankshaft carefully so as not to nick or dent it and compound the problems. When properly located, start all the mounting bolts and run them up to approximately a quarter turn from being snug. Check the flywheel to see if it is properly seated and snug down all the bolts in a zig-zag pattern. Finally, get out your torque wrench and tighten down all the bolts to specification in the same sequence. This will ensure proper seating of the flywheel and eliminate mounting as a cause of excessive run-out or "wobble." For bolt identification

Flywheel runout should not exceed 0.010″. To be certain crankshaft end play has no effect on your readings, the dial-indicator should return to zero after rotating the flywheel 360°.

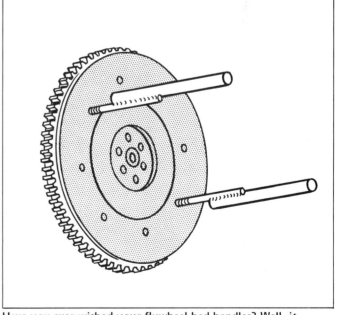

Have you ever wished your flywheel had handles? Well, it can. Just cut off the heads of a couple bolts of the same size as your pressure-plate-mounting bolts, only longer. Weld a six- or seven-inch-long round bar to each one and thread them into your flywheel as shown. *Drawing courtesy Hot Car Magazine*

and torque specifications, refer to the chart. With the flywheel back in place, you can now recheck for runout. If everything checks OK, that's one problem out of the way. If not, replace the flywheel if it is a new one, or have it resurfaced if it is your old one.

Flywheel resurfacing is best done by Blanchard grinding. The flywheel is held onto a magnetic table which rotates as do the eight grinding stones. This creates a cross-hatched pattern on the flywheel face. Resurfacing can also be done on a lathe, but this is not the best method because the cutting tool will jump over hard spots when light cuts are being taken, leaving localized high spots on the friction surface. Consequently, the finish cut must be deeper than with the grinding process, resulting in more material being removed from the flywheel than necessary.

Aluminum flywheels require a little more work to resurface. Because aluminum can't be held with a magnet, a steel *mandrel* must be bolted to the aluminum-flywheel center so the magnetic table can hold the mandrel and flywheel. An aluminum flywheel can often be repaired simply by removing the heat shield and riveting a new one in its place. However, when a

SAE Grade Number	1 or 2	5	8	Special Alloy*
Manufacturer's marks may vary. Three-line markings on heads shown below, for example, indicate SAE Grade 5.				
Capscrew Diameter (inch) and Minimum Tensile Strength (P.S.I.)	To 1/2—69,000 To 3/4—64,000 To 1—60,000	To 3/4—120,000 3/4 to 1—115,000	To 1—150,000	To 1—185,000
Bolt size and thread pitch	Torque (foot-pounds) for plated bolts with clean, dry threads.			
1/4-20	6	10	12	14
-28	7	12	15	17
5/16-18	13	20	24	29
-24	14	22	27	35
3/8-16	23	36	44	58
-24	26	40	48	69
7/16-14	37	52	63	98
-20	41	57	70	110
1/2-13	57	80	98	145
-20	64	90	110	160
9/16-12	82	120	145	200
-18	91	135	165	220
5/8-11	111	165	210	280
-18	128	200	245	310
3/4-10	200	285	335	490
-16	223	315	370	530
7/8-9	315	430	500	760
-14	340	470	550	800
1- 8	400	650	760	1130
-14	460	710	835	1210

*Torque Values shown are for high nickle-chrome alloy Bowmalloy® cap screws. Other high-alloy cap screws may not have the same values. Always use the manufacturer's specifications if they do not agree with this chart.

A bolt must be torqued properly before its optimum strength can be realized. When using lubricated threads, reduce torque values by the following amounts; 45% when using anti-seize compound, 40% when using grease or heavy oil, 30% with graphite and 25% with white lead. Increase torque values by 5% for unplated bolts. Always use manufacturer's torque specifications if they do not agree with this chart. *Torque figures courtesy Barnes Distribution, Barnes Group Inc.*

Be absolutely certain your flywheel-mounting bolts are properly torqued. More than one flywheel has separated itself from the back of a crankshaft because of a careless job. Note the screwdriver being used to keep the flywheel from turning.

This bolt has six lines indicating it is a Grade-8. Figure 8 is for those who don't know what the six little marks are for. It also has some advertising.

flywheel exhibits excessive runout, resurfacing is necessary.

When an aluminum flywheel is resurfaced, material is removed from the pressure-plate mounting surface as well as the heat shield because they must be in the same plane. Consequently, if the ground heat shield is eventually replaced, the new one will require grinding to line it up with the pressure-plate mounting surface.

Plasma-sprayed heat shields are a special case when it comes to resurfacing. Because these heat shields are so thin, they cannot be repaired by resurfacing. The heat-shield area must be counterbored so it will accept the conventional heat shield.

If a flywheel has excessive runout and its backside—side opposite the clutch—doesn't run true with the crankshaft mounting surface, it must be trued before grinding. This is necessary because the front side of a flywheel is ground parallel to the back side. To true a flywheel, it is supported in a lathe on a mandrel at the front side of the flywheel center. Material is removed from its backside. If this isn't done the runout problem *cannot* be cured by grinding.

One thing which must be checked after resurfacing any flywheel is the threaded pressure-plate mounting hole counterbore depths. This counterbore is necessary so the unthreaded shank of the mounting bolts will not interfere with the internal threads in the flywheel. Resurfacing reduces this counterbore depth by the amount removed from the flywheel. If there isn't sufficient clearance, the pressure-plate mounting bolts will run out of thread and won't pull down the pressure-plate cover solidly against the flywheel. This will result in some very serious problems if not corrected.

To be sure your flywheel has enough counterbore, try the bolts without the pressure plate. They should run all the way down by

finger tightening without binding up. This will assure you of at least 0.150-inch clearance to the first thread when your pressure plate is bolted in place. If the counterbore isn't enough, extend its depth by drilling out the threads to the proper depth. Use a drill 1/32-inch larger than the pressure-plate-mounting bolts.

Bellhousing Runout—The next item to check is the bellhousing. If it isn't properly aligned, satisfactory clutch and transmission operation will be just about impossible. Alignment can be out in two directions. It can be out of square with the crankshaft centerline, meaning the transmission input shaft will not be perpendicular to the face of the flywheel. In the other case, the rear opening of the housing can be out of concentricity with the crankshaft centerline. In other words, the center of the housing opening is not on the crank centerline. Either of these conditions can cause excessive transmission-gear and bearing wear. It can also cause the transmission to jump out of gear. Excessive wear of the pilot bearing will happen if the input shaft is not lined up with the crankshaft. The input shaft will try to rotate at engine speed whether the clutch is engaged or not. This is because the shaft is binding in the bearing. This will make shifting difficult and cause additional synchronizer wear. If the mounting face of the housing is not square to the crankshaft centerline, the clutch disc will not be parallel to the flywheel or pressure-plate faces. Two undesirable things will happen to the clutch in this situation. Additional pressure-plate travel will be required to release the disc completely as more distance is needed between the pressure ring and the flywheel. If you could view the assembly from the side, the disc would be located diagonally between the flywheel and pressure plate. Edge contact of the disc would occur on engagement and disengagement instead of full-circle engagement which happens when everything is lined up correctly.

Secondly, when the clutch is engaged and rotating, the disc facings will be forced to move back and forth, bending the disc as it rotates. This causes the disc to be loaded in a way it wasn't designed for. Failure of the hub is a possibility, especially with a solid hub.

To check bellhousing face and bore runout, the dial indicator will have to be used again. With the bore and face of the housing free of any dirt, paint or nicks which could affect indicator readings, mount the indicator on the end of the crankshaft or on the flywheel. It doesn't matter which is checked first. Say the face is checked first. Set the indicator so the plunger is perpendicular to the face and free to rotate without running into the mounting holes. Unlike checking flywheel runout, the indicator will rotate in this case. So, doing this job with the engine installed in the car, the dial can't be read as it rotates up and out of view. To solve the problem, get a small mirror. Maybe you already have one in your tool box. Just remember the image in the mirror is the reverse of actual life, so don't get the readings backward. Make sure the end play is out of the crankshaft, then set the indicator to read zero. Rotate the crank one turn and make sure the indicator returns to zero. This will show that end play didn't affect the readings. Note the locations of the maximum and minimum readings on the face. The total instrument reading—TIR— should not exceed 0.006 inch. This is the difference between the maximum and minimum readings. Now, check the bore runout. Set the indicator plunger button so it contacts the bore and is 90 degrees to the bore centerline. Rotate the crankshaft, again noting the readings. The total instrument reading should not exceed 0.010

For your transmission to operate properly, it must be in line with the crankshaft. For this condition to exist, bellhousing bore must abe concentric with the crankshaft centerline and the transmission mounting face must be perpendicular to it. Check these with a dial indicator mounted on the crankshaft or flywheel.

inch. Note the maximum and minimum locations and compare them to the face runouts. If they are both high and the maximum readings occur within 90 degrees of one another, the housing can be corrected either by cleaning and remounting or shimming. If they are more than 90 degrees apart, the housing cannot be corrected except

by machining or replacing.

If the housing is out of specification and the readings are in the same relative positions, begin by removing the housing and making sure the mounting surfaces on the housing and the engine are free from any nicks, dirt or paint. Remount the housing using the same method as with the flywheel.

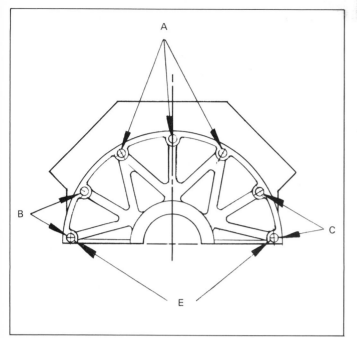

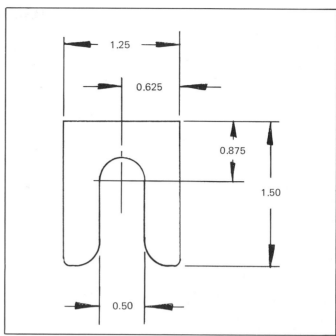

Sketch on left shows a typical bellhousing bolt pattern. To bring the housing into alignment, shim between the engine block and the housing with a shim half the thickness of the total indicated reading at the same relative position as the maximum negative reading. For example, if the housing is 0.020" out of alignment with the maximum negative reading at the top, use 0.010" thick shims at the locations indicated by A. Use the drawing on the right as reference to fabricate the necessary shims. This type shim can be installed without removing any bolts.

Start all the mounting bolts and run them up to within a quarter turn of being snug. Check the housing to see if it is properly seated and then tighten the bolts down in a zig-zag pattern. Torque the bolts to specification and recheck the runouts. If there isn't much improvement, the housing will have to be shimmed.

For aligning the housing, the shim to use is one-half as thick as the maximum indicator reading for face runout. It should be located at the same location as the maximum negative reading relative to the crankshaft. For example, if the total instrument reading was 0.020 inch at the top of the housing, a 0.010-inch shim should be placed

at the top of the housing between the engine block and the housing. This will rotate the housing, bringing it in line with the centerline of the crankshaft. You'll have to fabricate your own shims. Use the pattern shown above. Most bellhousings use seven or eight bolts. The one I've shown uses seven. No matter which one yours

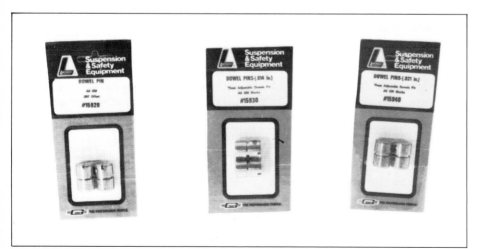

Three different offset dowel pins are available from Lakewood. Offset is apparent when comparing these two dowels turned 180° from each other. Screwdriver slot lines up with the direction of the offset.

is, the principle is the same. Refering to the sketch, if the maximum negative reading is at the bottom of the housing, place shims at the points indicated by E. If it is at the top, put the shims at A and for side-to-side, they should go at B or C. Once the shims are in place and housing bolts are torqued to spec, alignment should always be rechecked.

One final situation you may encounter is where your bellhousing bore runout is out of specification but the face runout is OK. This can easily be corrected by the use of offset dowel pins to shift your housing into position. For example, if your dial indicator shows a total indicated bore runout of 0.024", your housing will have to be shifted 0.012" toward the direction of the maximum indicate reading. Therefore, the offset required is one-half the TIR, or offset = 1/2 TIR.

To use offset dowel pins, remove the existing ones while being careful not to damage the holes in the rear face of the engine block. Clean the holes and lightly oil them before installing the new pins. Install them with the offset away from the maximum TIR. The heads of the pins are slotted in the direction of the offset. Make sure this slot is in the right direction and the slots are *parallel* to each other. Be careful not to get them 180° out of phase. After the pins are in place, install the bellhousing and recheck for bore runout. Small adjustments can be made by loosening your housing and rotating the dowel pins with a screwdriver. Lakewood offers offset dowel pins for Ford, Chrysler and GM engines.

While the car is up in the air and all apart, check the clutch linkage for wear and possible modification. If you are installing a pressure plate which has much more plate load than the one it is replacing, you should consider reinforcing or replacing the existing linkage with a stronger and more rigid setup. Refer to the linkage chapter.

Oil Leaks—If a clutch is being

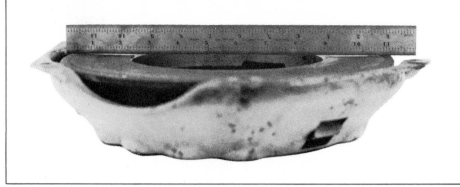

This pressure plate is suffering from having been overheated. Pressure ring is warped concave as can be seen by the gap between the ruler and the friction surface.

replaced because of oil contamination, replacing it will not solve the problem. The source of the oil must be found and corrected. If the housing is sealed, the only two sources are from the engine or the transmission. If the oil is coming from the engine, it will be from the rear main-bearing seal or the camshaft plug or an oil gallery. If it's from the transmission, it will be from the front bearing seal. Locate and fix the leak and clean all the deposited dirt and oil from inside the housing, the rear face of the engine block, the flywheel and the transmission. One bad practice is to ventilate the clutch by removing the front cover of the clutch housing or by drilling holes in it.

Pressure Plate and Disc—Checking a new pressure plate and disc is something you should never have to do. Some quick checks should still be made to head off any problems which may occur. This is particulary true if the disc is being replaced and the pressure plate is retained. Starting with the pressure plate, check the pressure ring for flatness with a good straight edge. Lay the straight edge against the friction surface of the pressure ring, looking and checking for any gaps. If the pressure ring was

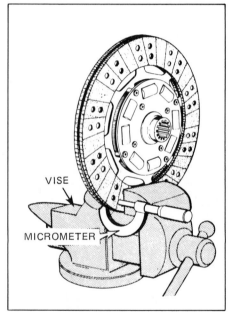

When compressing a disc to measure its thickness, be careful not to damage the facings or get them dirty. Measure as close to the clamping device as you can get so your reading will be accurate. *Drawing courtesy Schiefer*

overheated it may be warped in a *bellmouthed,* or concave shape. This will show up as a gap between the straight edge and the inside diameter of the pressure ring. If it is warped, the pressure plate should be replaced or returned to

This pressure ring has been severely overheated as evidenced by the heat-checks and chatter marks. There's no point in trying to save a pressure plate that's this bad.

Because of higher surface velocities toward the outside diameter of a clutch, facing wear is proportionately higher there. This clutch was removed after approximately 1000 miles of street use. Note the shiny worn surfaces on the pressure ring and disc.

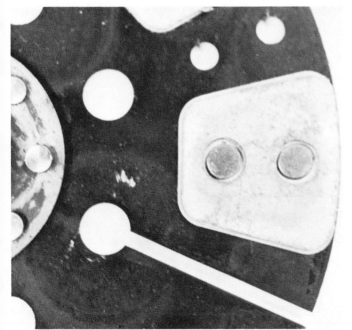

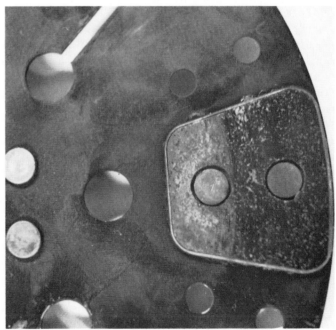

An example of surface velocity is the discoloration of a copper-ceramic button compared to the new one at left. Darker areas on the used button at right indicate higher operating temperatures.

the manufacturer for resurfacing and balancing. The same thing goes for any surface cracks. They should be removed by resurfacing. If they can't be, replace the pressure plate. The normal compressed thickness for a new disc varies between 0.310–0.320 inch. To check the thickness, compress the *marcel* spring using a vise, a C-clamp or a pair of vise grips. To prevent damage to the friction facing, do not clamp down too hard on the disc. Using a vernier caliper or some micrometers, measure the facing thickness as close to the clamping device as possible. If the thickness is not over 0.320 inch, you're in business. If a used disc measures less than 0.280 inch, it is worn out.

Worn disc with a new pressure plate—One thing which should never be done is to install a new pressure plate with an old disc. Besides not making sense, the result would be very short clutch life. The reason is, a clutch disc wears in a taper. It is thicker at the inner edge than at the outer. The reason for this is the relative *surface velocities* when the clutch is being slipped. The outer edge of the disc is traveling at a faster rate than the inner, just like on a circle track. If two cars are turning the same lap times and one has the inside line and the other the outside, the one on the outside has to be going faster. The same goes for the clutch. The outer edge travels farther, thus doing more work and wearing more. When used with a new pressure plate having a flat pressure ring, the inner edge is doing the most work because the load is not evenly distributed across the face of the disc. Clutch capacity is reduced and the clutch may slip. Because the load is concentrated on the inner edge of the disc, wear will be accelerated.

New pressure plate and disc—Like I said, checking a new clutch is something you *shouldn't* have to do. They are set up by the manufacturer, balanced and adjusted and ready to install right out of the box. Pressure plates are setup for zero balance because any other method would require making up for pressure plate out-of-balance at the flywheel. This is not practical because the same out-of-balance would have to exist on a replacement clutch and in the exact same position. So, if you ever have a pressure plate balanced, do it alone as an assembly.

If a pressure plate is ever disassembled for any reason, all the pieces must be reassembled in their same positions. To start with, the pressure ring is balanced before it ever sees the levers, springs or cover. After the assembly is completed, it is balanced by adding weights to the cover. This makes up for imbalance caused by differences in the weights of all the components making up the assembly. If everything is not reassembled the same way, chances are the pressure plate will not be in balance. Another reason for locating the springs in their same positions is many pressure plates use springs of varying loads and rates, as indicated by their colors. If they are located in other positions, load on the pressure ring will not be evenly distributed.

One quick and necessary check is the pressure-plate lever heights. This applies only to coil-spring-type pressure plates. If the lever heights are not the same—within 0.015" to 0.020" of each other—the pressure ring will not engage and disengage full-circle parallel to the face of the flywheel and disc.

To check lever heights, the clutch assembly must be mounted so the pressure ring is compressed to its engaged position. Mounting the pressure plate *and disc* to your flywheel is the handiest way of doing this. If the flywheel is not installed on the engine, the job will be easier as you can do it on the bench. In fact, it is easier just to take the flywheel off the engine and replace it than to try doing it under the car. This, of course, assumes your engine is in the car. If the pressure plate is like most new ones, it will have lever blocks installed between each lever and the cover to hold the release levers and pressure ring in their engaged positions for installation. This permits the bolts to be run down all the way prior to torquing. For a pressure plate without lever blocks, the bolts will have to be tightened no more than two turns at a time in rotation to prevent cover distortion. This

 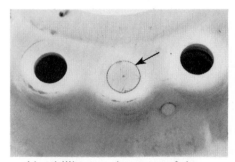

Long and Borg & Beck pressure rings are balanced by drilling out the center of the spring guides first (left photo). Pressure-plate assembly is final balanced by pressing weights into the cover (arrow).

is the same procedure used for pressure-plate removal, only in reverse order.

With the pressure plate snugged down to the flywheel—it doesn't have to be torqued all the way for checking—you can now check lever-height variation. Use a vernier caliper to measure from the clutch disc hub to each release-lever bearing contact point. If the variation between lever heights doesn't exceed 0.020" your new pressure plate is all right. If the variation exceeds this figure and you plan on doing some serious racing, replace the pressure plate. For a more accurate method of checking lever-heights and how to adjust when they are out, see page 170.

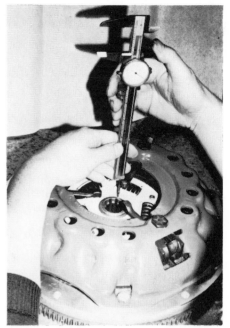

You can quickly check your new pressure plate lever heights by using your flywheel and disc to set the levers in their engaged positions. Work the levers several times to seat them in. Measure from the disc's hub up to the release-bearing-contact point of each lever to determine its height.

DISC WEAR

Clutch discs have less torque capacity when they are worn than when new. The reason is, a disc wears progressively from its outside edge to its inside edge reducing the pressure-plate-clamping load at the outside periphery where torque is produced most effectively. When a clutch is being slipped, *surface velocity* is higher toward the outside edge of a disc. Consequently it runs hotter and wears faster until the disc facings are evenly heated. Therefore, the pressure on a disc changes. It is evenly distributed across its faces when new and concentrated closer toward the center as wear stabilizes. Assuming the pressure-plate load remains the same, the mean effective radius is reduced with a subsequent reduction in torque capacity. To get a feeling of surface velocity, let's look at an actual case. If an 11.0-inch-diameter clutch with an inside diameter of 8.75 inches is slipped at 3000 RPM, surface velocity at the outer periphery is 98 MPH. At the same time, the surface velocity at the inner periphery is 78 MPH. A 20 MPH difference. This turns out to be 20-percent less, or:

Percent difference
$$= \frac{\text{Outside velocity - Inside velocity}}{\text{Outside velocity}}$$
$$\text{X } 100 = \frac{98 \text{ mph} - 78 \text{ mph}}{98 \text{ mph}}$$
$$\text{X } 100 = 20 \text{ percent difference}$$

To determine the actual slip velocities of a given clutch at any slip RPM, use this formula:

Slip velocity (MPH)
= .00297 X Diameter in inches X RPM

For the above clutch, the slip velocity at the outer edge is:

Slip velocity = .00297 X 11 inches X 3000 RPM = 98 MPH

At the inner periphery:

Slip velocity
= .00297 X 8.75 inches X 3000 RPM = 78 MPH

As a clutch wears, slip velocities remain the same for a given RPM, but the amount a disc tapers stabilizes at a point where the pressure ring and disc are evenly heated from the inside to the outside edges. This is the point at which the work done at the inside and outside peripheries are the same. If the pressure-ring and flywheel faces remain flat, extreme tapering applies only to discs using marcel springs. Heat is the major cause of facing wear. Clutch facings are heated by surface velocity and pressure. With surface velocities remaining relatively the same, the only thing which can change is pressure. As tapering takes place, the marcel spring forces the facings to open up, keeping them pressed against the pressure ring and flywheel and causing additional tapering until an equilibrium point is reached: Facings are evenly heated from the inside edge to the outside edge. For a disc not using a marcel spring, particularly one with metallic facings, facings remain nearly parallel and do not taper wear noticeably.

Final inspection involves trying the release bearing on the bearing retainer. Slip the bearing and hub assembly over the retainer on the front of the transmission and slide it back and forth, checking to see if it slides freely without any binding. If it doesn't, the retainer should be checked for nicks or dents and cleaned up with a file and some emery cloth. Recheck and do the necessary cleaning up till the bearing slides freely. This is assuming you have the right bearing.

Assembly—With everything cleaned and inspected, the parts can go back together. First to be installed is the pilot bearing. It is a bronze composition called an *Oilite bearing*. The bearing is manufactured from powdered metal and is oil-impregnated so the bearing will be

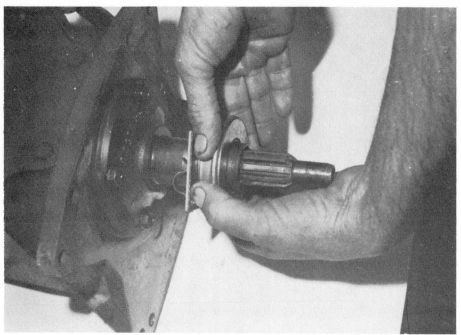

Now's the time to find out whether your new release bearing really fits.

self-lubricating. Prior to installing it, additional lubrication can be given it by soaking it in motor oil. If you prefer, the bearing can be lubricated with a few drops of oil after installation. Some bearings use a *wick* with them. It is a felt pad which is soaked with oil and is installed ahead of the bearing in the crankshaft bore. If your bearing is set up this way, soak the wick in motor oil.

You might want to consider replacing your bronze bearing with a ball bearing. The only time I would consider this necessary is if you're using a heavy full-circle metallic-faced disc/s. The weight on the transmission input shaft and, subsequently, the pilot bearing may be more than the Oilite can handle. In this case, measure the ID and OD of your Oilite bearing and match it up with a ball bearing. Sometimes the dimensions of water pump, power-steering pump, or alternator bearings are the same and can be used as a direct replacement. If

MOROSO offers this needle bearing as a direct replacement for the stock big- or small-block Chevy pilot bearing.

If you're replacing your bronze pilot bearing with a ball or needle bearing, make sure it is sealed. This will keep the grease in the bearing and prevent it from getting on your clutch.

Something is being done right in this picture. The disc-to-transmission input-shaft-spline fit is being checked by sliding the disc back and forth on the shaft. Something wrong is being done. The facings are being touched. Keep your fingers off the facings! Note also that the disc is positioned as it would be when installed on the transmission input shaft—with the hub assembly away from the flywheel.

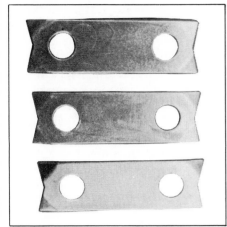

A positive way to retain flywheel bolts is with lock straps. One tab by each bolt can be bent to fit a bolt-head flat, ensuring the bolt won't come loose.

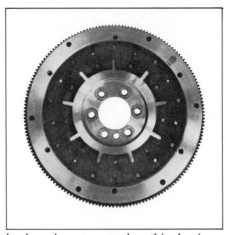

Lock washers were used on this aluminum flywheel, resulting in deep scoring. Use flat washers or lock straps under the bolts when mounting an aluminum flywheel.

I prefer not to use lock washers at all and this is the reason why. Besides not locking any more, imagine what a little piece of washer could do in a transmission, rear axle or an engine.

not, you'll have to check some industrial suppliers who carry large stocks of bearings. If you don't have any luck using this approach, then the job becomes a major one. Find the smallest bearing which matches the ID of your Oilite-bearing and bore out the end of your crank to accept the new ball-bearing. This procedure is nothing new, but you'll have to do it when your engine is torn down because the crank will have to be done in a lathe so the job will be accurate. Make sure you get a sealed bearing, otherwise the grease will fly out of the bearing and contaminate the clutch and the bearing will fail.

Now for installing the bearing. Coat the crankshaft pilot bearing bore with a light film of grease to assist in installing the bearing. If you are using the Oilite bearing with a wick, put the wick in first ahead of the bearing. Line the bearing up with the crank bore and tap the bearing into place. Use a brass hammer and a thick-walled tube or pipe which fits the outer race in the case of the ball bearing. This is important. NEVER use the inner race to drive a ball or needle bearing into a bore or you will ruin the bearing. As for an Oilite bearing, be careful not to distort its bore. It can be ruined just as easily. When driving the bearing into place, be

careful not to let the bearing cock in the bore as you start. Once it is started straight, it should go the rest of the way. Therefore, if it cocks, stop, straighten it out and start over. With the bearing in place, check the bearing bore for any damage. Make sure the input shaft "nose" fits all the way into the bearing and turns without binding. Here's where a spare input shaft can be helpful. You are now ready for the pressure plate and disc.

Flywheel installation—As soon as you're sure you have a good flywheel, the next step is to proceed with installing it. As discussed on page 152, you do not reinstall a grey-cast-iron flywheel if you will be using it on anything other than a stock engine. The first thing you should have before installing the flywheel is a new set of bolts—minimum Grade 8. You'll also need spring lockwashers and some red number 242 Loctite®. Or to be doubly sure buy lockstraps.

If you are installing an aluminum flywheel, *don't use lockwashers.* They will gall the aluminum. You'll have to use flat washers and Loctite® for retention or lockstraps can replace the flat washers and Loctite®. Lockstraps will guarantee the retention of the bolts and eliminate any possibility of

them coming loose as a result of engine vibration. Lockstraps can be used just as effectively with steel flywheels.

Before mounting the flywheel, make sure the mounting surfaces on the flywheel and the crankshaft are free from any dirt and burrs which may cock the flywheel when it is mounted, causing excessive runout. Remember, when handling the flywheel you should always take great care not to get any grease or oil on the clutch friction surface. With the flywheel in place, torque the bolts in a zig-zag pattern to the specifications on page 154 or according to the manufacturer's specifications. If the specifications disagree, always use the manufacturer's. After the flywheel is mounted, recheck runout with a dial indicator to make sure everything's OK. If you are using lockstraps, bend one tab against a flat on each bolt head.

Just before you're ready to install the clutch, clean the face of the flywheel with a non-petroleum-based solvent such as alcohol, turpentine or lacquer thinner. Now, with a clean flywheel, you're ready for the clutch.

Now is a good time to say it again. Take all the precautions you can to keep grease off the disc facings and the pressure plate and

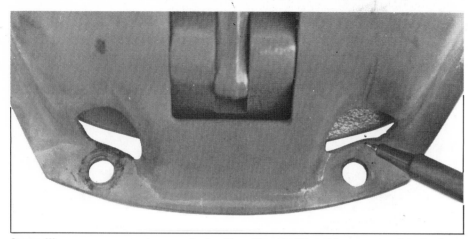

Seems like you can never do enough checking. When bolting this pressure plate to the flywheel it was discovered one bolt wouldn't start. The problem turned out to be a bent cover. The pressure plate was damaged in transit between the manufacturing plant and the speedshop counter.

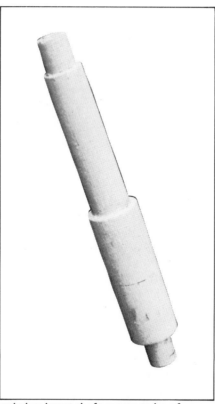

Two types of clutch-alignment tools. The transmission-input shaft ceases to be of any use in its primary role, what with a few missing teeth, but it makes a very good alignment tool. The other is a universal tool made from wood. Consequently, it is very light and doesn't add much weight to your tool box. The only problem is it can't be used for installing a multi-disc clutch as the disc splines must be in line with each other. In this case, you'll need a splined ''dummy'' shaft.

flywheel friction surfaces. When handling the clutch disc, avoid getting any oil or grease on the facings. Handle the disc like you would your favorite record—by the edge. A greasy fingerprint may be all it takes to ruin the job by causing the clutch to slip, grab or chatter after you get it all back together and in operation. Your hands must be *absolutely clean* with no trace of oil or grease on them when you handle a clutch disc. Don't put it on the floor or on a workbench surface. Put it on a clean piece of newspaper to make sure the disc does not get contaminated. Once you've had to redo a clutch job because of not paying attention to what I'm saying—then you'll fully understand what I've been talking about—and why.

In addition to the pressure plate and disc, have some new grade-8 bolts and lockwashers ready to use and the red Loctite®. The bolts and washers should've been included with the new clutch and the Loctite® doubles the retention of the bolts. Coat bolt threads with Loctite® and have the washers on them ready to use. Lift the pressure plate and disc into place and start three bolts to hold the assembly while the alignment tool— an old transmission input shaft is perfect for the job—can be placed in the disc and pilot bearing to hold the assembly in alignment. If the pressure plate has the lever blocks in place, the bolts can be run down. If not, the bolts will have to be taken down no more than two turns at a time in sequence to prevent cover distortion. Don't forget to remove the lever blocks if they are used. They will loosen up and fall out as you tighten your pressure plate down. Some people seem to think it's not necessary, but I don't like extraneous pieces flying around in any mechanical device. After the bolts are snugged down, the aligning tool can be removed and the bolts torqued to specification.

With the clutch in place, you're

With the pressure plate tightened down you can remove the alignment tool. Also, remove the release-lever spacer blocks as they loosen up.

You're looking at a transmission sitting on a chest. This is the hard way to install a transmission and the easy way to damage a disc.

now ready for the bellhousing. If you have the two-piece type, then leave the bottom half off until you've adjusted your clutch linkage. Regardless of the type of housing you have, you must still install the clutch-release lever in the housing. Use high-temperature Lubriplate to lubricate the bore of the release-bearing hub. It will have a groove inside the bore for this purpose. Fill the groove with Lubriplate, but be careful and don't overdo it. Next lubricate the lever pivot lightly and the lever-to-bearing-hub wear points. Install the lever-and-bearing assembly in the bellhousing using the spring clips, wave washers or whatever is used to retain your release lever to the lever pivot. Be careful not to bend the retainers. Make sure the rubber boot covering the release lever is installed securely in place to keep any oil, water or road dirt from entering the bellhousing. If you have the one-piece housing, install it to the engine block loosely. If you shimmed the housing for alignment, install the shims in their proper locations. The easiest way to remember where they went is to mark the housing with a grease pencil indicating the number and location of the shims at the bolt holes.

With everything in place, run the bolts down and torque them to specification.

The transmission is next. Be careful when installing it because you can easily bend the clutch disc. Then there will be trouble. To avoid this, make sure the transmission is well supported when it is being put in place. As in removing the transmission, it's best to have a friend helping. One who can lift, in addition to a floor jack. Before lifting the transmission, put it in first gear. This will let you turn the input shaft from the output end so it will engage the clutch-disc splines. With everything ready to go, lift the transmission into place, lining it up with the center of the clutch disc. Move it forward into the center of the release bearing, being careful not to force it off the release lever, and on into the clutch disc. When the transmission contacts the clutch disc, the input shaft will engage the splines and slide home if you're one out of a million. If you're like the rest of us, you'll have to do a little jockeying. With the transmission supported on the jack, hold the transmission against the clutch disc splines while turning the transmission output shaft. This will rotate the input shaft until it engages with the disc.

Slide the transmission forward, being careful to keep it supported all the time. If you let the transmission drop, the disc will bend immediately and you'll have to buy a new disc. Attach the transmission crossmember into place and bolt it up while holding the transmission up with the jack. Once the crossmember is secured, the jackstand supporting the engine and the jack under the transmission can be removed. You'll now have more room to maneuver under the car.

With the transmission in place, all the other parts can be put back. Remember to replace the driveshaft according to the index marks you made at the rear-axle companion flange. Reinstall the clutch linkage, the parking-brake cable and the exhaust system if it was removed. Don't set the car on the ground yet. The next critical step has to be done with the car in the air.

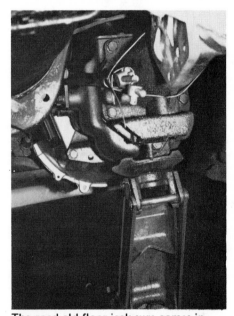

The good old floor jack sure comes in handy when it's time to slide the transmission back in. Note the shift rods tied out of the way. If your shifter can't be installed on the transmission, a little tip is in order. Adjust the shift rods while the transmission is out of the car—you must have the shifter bolted to the transmission. Remove the shifter so you can install the transmission and reinstall it after the transmission is in place. If it needs any more adjustment, it won't be much.

Here's what can happen to a clutch when it isn't adjusted properly. The badly worn release levers indicate there wasn't enough free play in the clutch linkage. As a result, the clutch slipped due to the lack of full engagement, overheating the pressure ring and ripping the facing off the disc.

Clutch Adjustment—The major cause of premature clutch failure is wrong adjustment. The pity of it all is it's the easiest, but the least understood thing to do. If not done correctly, the results may be anything from a burned-up disc to worn-out transmission synchronizers. Proper adjustment guarantees full engagement and disengagement at any engine RPM. Before getting into the actual adjustment, some basic terms must be understood.

The two major objectives when adjusting a clutch is to obtain full engagement when the clutch pedal is fully returned and full release when the pedal is fully depressed. Sounds like double talk, but that's the way it is. To obtain full release, there must be clearance between the pressure plate or flywheel and the disc to prevent the disc from dragging when the pedal is pushed to the floor or stop. This helps to ensure clean shifts and helps to prevent undue loads on the transmission synchros. The clearance, called *air gap*, is measured with a feeler gauge. The amount is determined by the type pressure plate used. Airgaps are specified in chart on page 168. Sketches on next page describe how pressure-plate/release-bearing and pedal travels relate. At the pedal, *air gap* is defined

as *pedal reserve*. *Pedal reserve* is the amount of travel between minimum clutch release and full pedal travel. Full travel is when the clutch bottoms against the floor or a pedal stop. All-out race setups should incorporate an *adjustable* pedal stop.

With the car still on jacks, start the engine and warm it up while engaging and disengaging the clutch to get it warm and to wear some of the *fuzz* off of the disc. The clutch must be warm to be adjusted. Fuzz on an organic-faced disc is little particles of cotton, asbestos and copper fibers sticking up and closing pressure-plate and flywheel clearances. Shut the engine off. The first adjustment to be made is *air gap.* If you have a two-piece bellhousing, you're in luck. If you don't, you have two choices. One is to drill a hole at the bottom of the housing directly under the disc and pressure-ring surfaces so a feeler gauge will fit through for measuring air gap. To adjust for proper air gap, you'll need someone in the car to depress the clutch pedal. Start by fully engaging the clutch and then depress the pedal to the floor. With the proper feeler gauge, check the clearance between the pressure ring and the disc. As the pressure plate is disengaged,

the pressure ring pulls back from the disc. The disc remains in contact with the flywheel and opens up if it has a marcel spring. All the clearance is on the pressure-plate side as a result. Adjust the clutch linkage at the pushrod for the proper clearance. Before tightening the jam nut down on the adjusting pushrod, cycle the clutch pedal full travel at least 20 times. This will take any slop or clearances up so the air gap can be measured again. Check and readjust if necessary. Lock the jam nut while being careful not to disturb the adjustment. You can now button up the underside of the bellhousing and set the car on the ground.

The other method involves adjusting the clutch just past the point of preventing the transmission gears from clashing when entering reverse gear. This works because reverse is an unsynchronized gear. Therefore, with the clutch fully engaged, the engine running and the transmission in neutral, bring the engine up to the RPM you plan to do your shifting at, disengage the clutch and slip the transmission into reverse. If no clash results, shorten up on the air gap by shortening the clutch pushrod until you get a little clash then go back the other

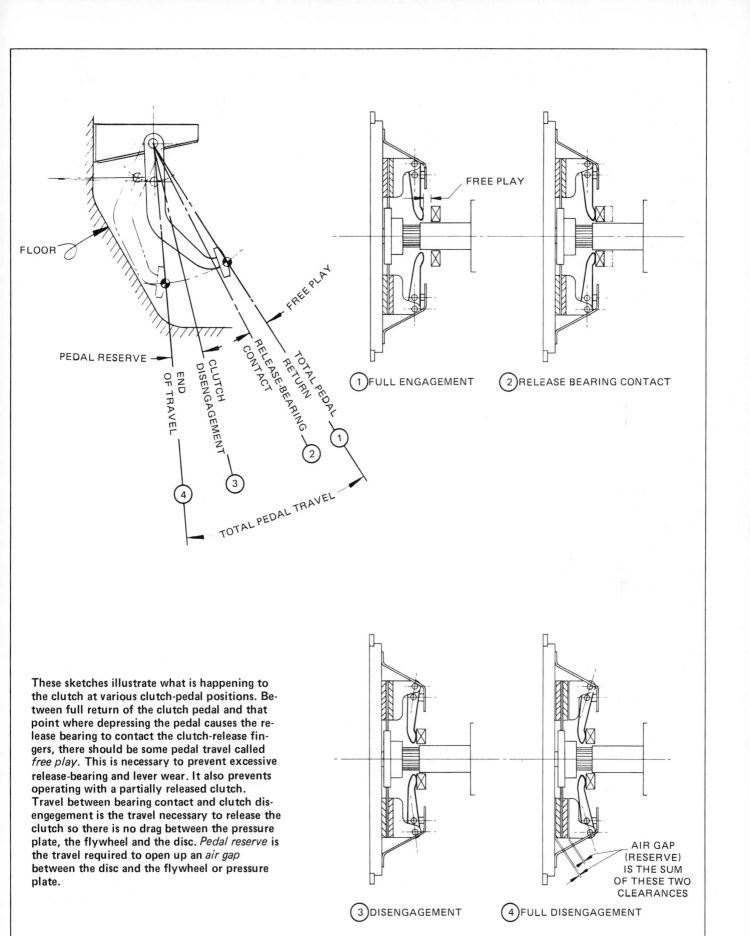

FLOOR

PEDAL RESERVE

END OF TRAVEL

CLUTCH DISENGAGEMENT

RELEASE-BEARING CONTACT

TOTAL PEDAL RETURN

FREE PLAY

④

③

②

①

TOTAL PEDAL TRAVEL

FREE PLAY

① FULL ENGAGEMENT

② RELEASE BEARING CONTACT

These sketches illustrate what is happening to the clutch at various clutch-pedal positions. Between full return of the clutch pedal and that point where depressing the pedal causes the release bearing to contact the clutch-release fingers, there should be some pedal travel called *free play.* This is necessary to prevent excessive release-bearing and lever wear. It also prevents operating with a partially released clutch. Travel between bearing contact and clutch disengegement is the travel necessary to release the clutch so there is no drag between the pressure plate, the flywheel and the disc. *Pedal reserve* is the travel required to open up an *air gap* between the disc and the flywheel or pressure plate.

AIR GAP (RESERVE) IS THE SUM OF THESE TWO CLEARANCES

③ DISENGAGEMENT

④ FULL DISENGAGEMENT

Type Pressure Plate	Air Gap (inches)
Diaphragm	0.030—0.040
Borg & Beck	0.040—0.050
Long	0.050—0.060
Long/Borg & Beck	0.050—0.060

To get sufficient clutch release, use this chart to determine the proper amount of clearance for the type of pressure plate used. For racing, use the high side of the clearances shown for the Borg & Beck and Long. Stay at the low range for the diaphragm. Avoid excessive clearances, especially with the diaphragm. Permanent damage to the Belleville spring may result if adjusted for more than the specified clearance.

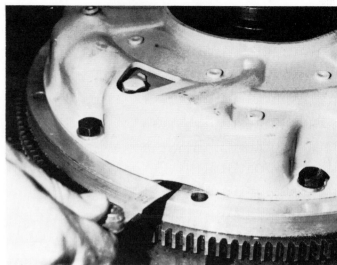

This clutch is in the released position on a clutch machine just as it would be in a car. With a hole drilled in the bottom of your bellhousing, measure the air gap with a feeler gauge.

way a slight amount to get the proper clearance. Remember, EXCESS DISENGAGEMENT clearance can damage a pressure plate, particularly a diaphragm pressure plate. If the spring is forced past the travel for which it was designed, an overload or overstress will result, ruining the spring. If a coil-spring-type pressure plate is excessively traveled, the springs may bottom. This won't damage the springs, but may bend the cover and ruin the pressure plate. Take care in this department!

Free play is the distance the clutch pedal travels, measured at the foot pad, after the release bearing breaks contact with the pressure-plate levers and moves to the at-rest or full-return position. Free play is necessary for complete engagement of the clutch as well as for long release-lever and bearing life. The minimum for this distance is 3/4 inch. I prefer limiting *free play* to a maximum of one inch for high-performance applications. It is best to limit free play to a minimum because the less travel means faster clutch disengagement for shifting. Less travel also means less linkage wear.

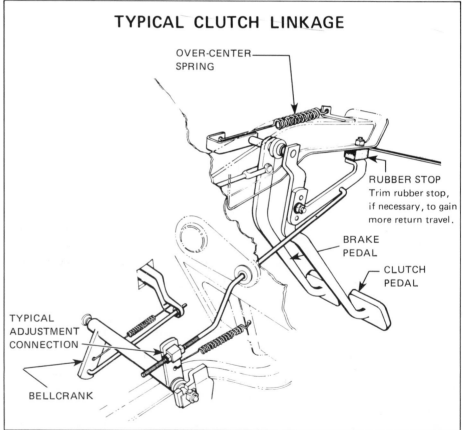

TYPICAL CLUTCH LINKAGE

OVER-CENTER SPRING

RUBBER STOP Trim rubber stop, if necessary, to gain more return travel.

BRAKE PEDAL

CLUTCH PEDAL

TYPICAL ADJUSTMENT CONNECTION

BELLCRANK

If you need more or less travel at the return position of your pedal, this can be done by shimming or trimming the rubber pedal stop. Shimming reduces travel—while trimming increases it. *Drawing courtesy Schiefer*

Prior to any pedal adjustments, *free play* is established at the time the *air gap* is set. For instance, if a production car is fitted with a clutch requiring additional pedal travel for complete clutch operation, there will not be enough *free play* left over after the air gap is adjusted. On the other hand, if the clutch requires less travel, free play will be excessive. There are two ways to handle this situation. The first, and probably the easiest, is to modify the pedal-return stop. To gain additional free play requires trimming the pedal-return stop. Because the stops are rubber a knife can be put to good use. Trim a little at a time until the desired free play is gained. To reduce pedal travel and free play, the rubber stop must be shimmed. Most rubber stops are mounted with studs. These can easily be shimmed using washers. Other types use Christmas-tree type ends which push into a square or round hole. This is great for production, but bad when it comes to modify, so replace this type with one using a stud. After any adjustments are made, drive the car around the block, starting and stopping the car to warm up the clutch. Adjustments may change after everything is warmed up so, check to make sure. For a complete explanation of clutch linkages and how they operate, see the chapter on linkages.

If your car is going to be used for drag racing, one little trick you can do to extend the life of your organic-faced clutch disc is to remove it the first opportunity you get. When your engine or transmission is down for repairs, remove the disc if it has had several runs on it. Have it glass-beaded. This process removes the excess resin binder which came to the surface as a result of being heated. It also removes any other surface residue. At the same time, clean the friction surfaces of the flywheel and pressure plate with fine-grit sandpaper and non-oil-based solvent. The result

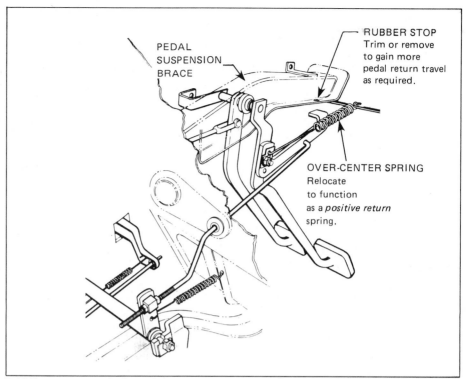

Schiefer recommends that when using their Rev-Lok® pressure plate (diaphragm) the over-center spring should be relocated to act as a return spring. This can only be done with a tension-type spring as shown. Drawing on previous page shows linkage in stock configuration. *Drawing courtesy Schiefer*

will be a better-operating and longer-lasting clutch. No matter what a car is to be used for, periodic checks of clutch clearances should be made. You can feel this change take place during the first few miles of operation of a new clutch but, as the clutch gets older, these changes take place more slowly. Therefore, don't trust your feel. A feeler gauge and ruler are more accurate.

Over-Center Spring—Schiefer recommends making an additional change to the clutch pedal linkage when using their Rev-Lok® diaphragm pressure plate. Schiefer is largely responsible for introducing this type pressure plate to the high-performance field. The change is relocating the *over-center* spring—the spring used to assist in operating the clutch. When the clutch pedal is at full return, the spring is located so it actually holds the pedal in the returned position and

requires additional force while taking up the free play travel. At or near the point where the release bearing makes contact with the pressure plate release levers, the spring goes *over center*. It now subtracts from the pedal force required to operate the clutch rather than adding to it. The problem is, a pressure plate must not only clamp the disc, it must also return the clutch pedal at the same time. Generally, the problem will not be encountered with a car originally equipped with a diaphragm pressure plate because they are not equipped with over-center springs. If a diaphragm pressure plate replaces a Borg & Beck or Long, the over-center spring should be removed. There are two reasons why: First, the spring is not required for pedal assist due to low forces required to operate the diaphragm pressure plate in the first place. Secondly,

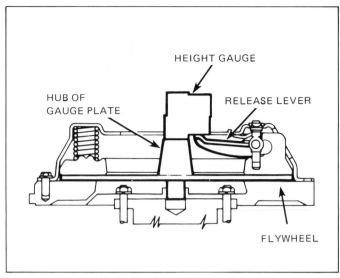

A more accurate method of checking lever heights is to use a gauge plate rather than a clutch disc. Center the machined lands under the release levers and use the gauge as shown. If you can't get access to a gauge plate, make one using a 3/8"-thick, 10"-diameter plate and have it ground to the specified thickness of the discs you will be using—about 0.325" thick. Rather than measuring to the hub, measure to the disc. *Photo and drawing courtesy AMC*

the over-center spring may cause the pressure plate to hang up during high-RPM operation. Schiefer suggests going even further by relocating the spring so it will act as a return spring rather as an assist spring. This can only be done if it is a *tension* spring.

Adjusting lever heights—If you are brave of heart and wish to attempt adjusting pressure-plate lever heights, you will need a special tool. It must simulate the disc thickness the pressure plate was designed for and provide a flat surface to measure lever heights from. New-car dealers have such a tool for their service use. It's called a *clutch gauge plate*. Accompanying this tool is a *lever-height gauge* to measure lever height from the gauge plate. The thing is, you'll have a difficult time even finding anyone who has one. Just the same, the gauge plate is used to simulate the disc. It has

three machined *lands* on each side of a cast aluminum disc. These accurately simulate the thickness of the clutch disc. In the center of the gauge is a center hub with a machined surface to check lever heights from, using a *lever-height gauge*.

A *lever-height gauge* is a flat piece of metal offset on four sides for measuring lever heights of four specific clutches. If you've switched pressure-plate styles, chances are you'll have to fabricate your own gauge. In this case, make up your own gauge out of a piece of .060" flat steel stock fitting it to one lever. It can then be used to check *relative* heights of the other levers. If you want to try different lever heights, make the offsets on your custom-made gauge accordingly. With four sides on your gauge, you'll be able to check levers in four different positions.

For checking lever heights with

these tools, the plate is centered on the flywheel off the car and on the bench. The pressure plate is then centered over the gauge plate and flywheel with the gauge plate located so the lands are located under the release levers. This reduces any inaccuracies due to pressure-ring and cover deflections. The pressure plate is then bolted to the flywheel and the gauge set on top of the machined hub. Each of the three levers should be at the same height. If one is low, it will show up as a gap between the lever and the gauge. A high lever will not let the gauge pass over it. If the release levers are a *little* too high or low, this can be compensated for in the linkage adjustment. The problem is having them uneven. If this condition exists, the levers should be evened up. For example, if one or two levers of a Borg & Beck pressure plate are too low, they should be raised. The opposite is

A more sophisticated tool for working on pressure plates is Stan Carlson's clutch machine. Here it is being used to check the lever heights of a Borg & Beck pressure plate. First, the pressure plate is placed over the gauge plate and centered. A three-pointed clamp pulls the pressure plate down into its engaged position where it is clamped with six clamps around the edge of the cover. Lever heights are checked using a gauge which fits over the center post of the machine.

true with the Long style. The higher lever/s should be lowered to match the low lever/s.

Another tool used to check lever heights is called a clutch machine. This tool is not only used to check lever heights, it is also used for the assembly and disassembly of pressure plates. One such machine is manufactured by Carlson Machine Products of Santa Ana, California. Carlson's machine is made up of a surface plate, an interchangeable gauge plate, a center post for operating the release levers and clamps for holding the pressure plate in the engaged position. It also has a gauge for measuring

lever heights. Rather than using pressure-plate mounting bolts to compress the pressure plate, a clamp mounted on the center post of the machine pulls down on the back of the pressure plate and compresses the pressure ring into the engaged position. How the center post is operated depends on which machine is used. The portable model is raised and lowered with screw threads. Production machines use air cylinders. With the pressure plate pulled down into position, lever heights can be checked or the pressure plate can be disassembled.

Lever heights are adjusted for

different reasons. The major one is to make all the lever heights the same and to bring them into factory specification. Another reason, particularly with the Long, is to change the centrifugal assist of the lever. The higher a Long style lever is, the more centrifugal assist it will provide. This is true even though it doesn't have any centrifugal weights. For an illustration of this effect, see the graph on page 172.

To adjust lever heights of a Long or Borg & Beck pressure plate, the pressure ring must first be compressed to a position which will unload the levers. Because

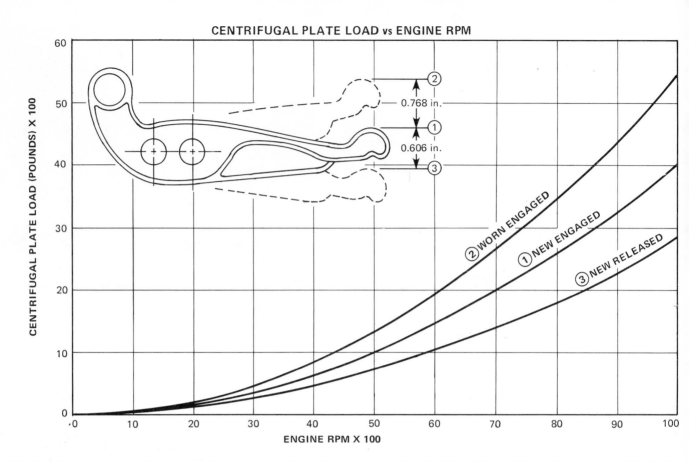

CENTRIFUGAL PLATE LOAD vs ENGINE RPM

CENTRIFUGAL PLATE LOAD (POUNDS) X 100

② WORN ENGAGED
① NEW ENGAGED
③ NEW RELEASED

0.768 in.
0.606 in.

ENGINE RPM X 100

Centrifugal assist on a Long-style pressure plate is greatly affected by its lever angle or height. This can be seen in the graph. The higher or closer to the cover a lever is, whether due to disc wear or adjustment, the more centrifugal assist it provides. Graph illustrates the change in centrifugal assist from a lever in the engaged position, both with a new and worn disc, and when it is in the released position.

Rather than using lock washers, the eye-bolt-attaching nuts are staked into place. Each eye bolt has two grooves in it for locking the nut by staking (arrow).

lever heights must be accurately measured after being adjusted, a clutch machine or gauge plate and flywheel might as well be used. If you don't have either one of these, a flywheel, three 1" x 2" metal strips which simulate the thickness of the proper disc and a height gauge will do the job. The Borg & Beck pressure plate does not require disassembly to adjust lever heights. The Long does unless you happen to have an ultra-high-performance setup which can be adjusted without requiring a teardown similar to the method used with the standard Borg &

Beck.

Borg & Beck—If you will remember, the release-lever eyebolts used in the Borg & Beck style pressure-plate extend up through the cover and are secured by nuts on the outside of the pressure-plate assembly. To raise the levers, turn the nuts clockwise. Turn the nuts counter-clockwise to lower them. After the levers are adjusted to the correct heights, operate them several times to make sure they are "seated in" and recheck. When the levers are stabilized at the right heights, *stake* the nuts into position with the eyebolts using a dull centerpunch. Staking prevents the nuts from turning and changing the lever adjustments.

Long—If you have an adjustable Long-style pressure plate, use the same procedure as with the Borg & Beck. If not, the pressure plate will have to be partially or completely disassembled, depending on whether the levers need to be raised or lowered. If a lever is too high, it can be shimmed down without removing the lever or yoke from the pressure-plate assembly. The shim can be slipped in between the yoke and cover and bolted back in place without removing the cover. If a lever is to be raised, the yoke must be milled at its cover-mounting surface. This requires removing the cover from the assembly so you can remove the yoke from the lever. Before doing this, you must first determine how much the lever must be shimmed or milled to get the desired lever movement. This particularly applies to milling because it is difficult to put the metal back. It could be shimmed, but this would be the amateur's approach.

To determine how much a lever must be shimmed, first you have to measure it. It will have to be removed from the pressure-plate assembly for this. Measure between the yoke and pressure-ring pivot points and the release-bearing-contact point. These dimensions give you the necessary information to determine how much milling or shimming will be required. For example, a lever with a distance of 0.547 inch between pressure-ring and yoke pivot points and 3.125 inches between the pressure ring pivot and the release-bearing-contact point, the amount the lever yoke must be milled to adjust the lever 0.20 inches higher is:

$$X = A\frac{S}{L} = 0.20\ \frac{0.547}{3.125} = .035 \text{ inches}$$

If the lever were to be lowered by the same amount, the required shim should also be 0.035 inch. A simpler method of determining the amount to add or subtract from the

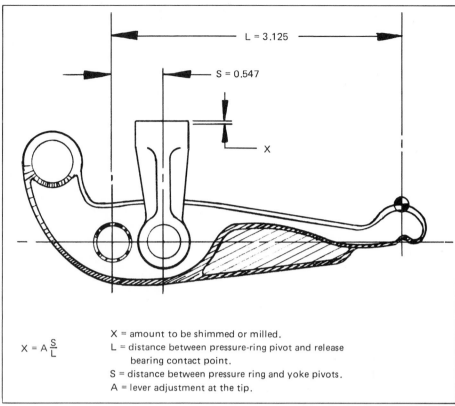

X = amount to be shimmed or milled.
L = distance between pressure-ring pivot and release bearing contact point.
S = distance between pressure ring and yoke pivots.
A = lever adjustment at the tip.

$$X = A\frac{S}{L}$$

The geometry of the release levers must be considered prior to attempting any shimming or milling of the lever yoke, particularly milling. The amount a lever height will change is directly related to the pivot points and the length of the lever and the amount that is added to or removed from the lever yoke at the cover.

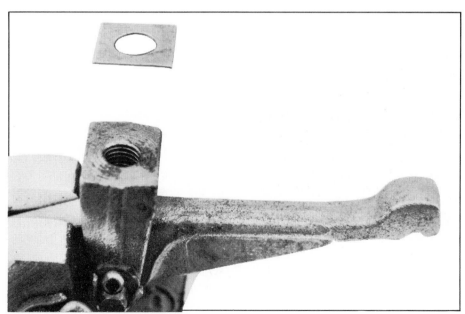

Shimming a Long lever reduces the lever height and centrifugal assist.

Surrounding conditions can have great effect on clutch operation. For example, clutch hydraulic lines and master cylinder must be shielded from heat, which is problem with front-engine, turbo car such as Trans-Am Porsche. Otherwise, clutch malfunction or failure may result.

lever is to shim the yoke down a certain amount. A flat washer with a known thickness will do the job. Make sure it seats inside the cover. For example, if 0.125-inch washer gives a 0.71-inch reduction in lever height, then the above ratio checks out because 0.547 divided by 3.125 equals 0.175 and 0.125 divided by 0.71 also equals 0.175. This automatically gives you another way to do it, and I might add, probably a better way. The important thing is to see how the two relate. Using the other method is done by the following:

Amount to be shimmed or milled
= Desired lever travel(0.20 inches)

$$X \frac{\text{Test shim thickness (0.125 in.)}}{\text{Lever movement (0.71 in.)}}$$

= 0.035 inches

A quick-and-dirty method of adjusting Long lever heights is to bend the levers. I'm not particularly keen on this method, however it is a standard procedure as recommended by Borg-Warner, one of the oldest and largest manufacturers of clutch assemblies. To determine how much bending you'll have to do, you'll still have to clamp the pressure plate down in its engaged position using one of the methods I've described. Now, for bending don't use heat. Just get a tool which is strong and will give you enough leverage, such as a pipe, so you can do the job without heat or roughing up the tip of the lever where it contacts the release bearing.

As for how close lever heights should be to each other, I've asked

this question of several *very* qualified people and have gotten some variation in their answers. The general consensus is a 0.015" variation is acceptable, especially when you consider the fact that there will always be some deflection in the cover to compensate. For clutches using marcel-sprung discs, the variation can even go higher, up to 0.020" without any ill effects. Therefore, when you are matching lever heights, work with these figures, 0.015" variation when using discs without marcels and 0.020" with marcels.

After adjustments are made using either method, always work the levers several times to seat the pressure-plate assembly so you will get accurate readings when rechecking lever heights.

Chapter Ten
THE SLIDER CLUTCH

Here is a slider clutch receiving final balance as an assembly. Material is removed from the floater plates (arrow) for balance in this step. When reassembling a slider, make sure all the components go together in the same order and direction to maintain balance.

The theory on which the slider clutch is based is basic—reduce static pressure-plate load and increase centrifugal assist so a clutch will slip until a predetermined RPM is reached under the full torque input of a given engine. The reason for this is simple. *Less* static plate load adjusted into a slider means *less* initial engine torque or shock load transfered to the driving tires on launch. This prevents two things from happening, the tires spinning or the engine bogging. Reduced static load (spring pressure) means centrifugal assist must be increased by adding lever counterweights and/or increasing lever angle.

NUMBER OF DISCS AND DIAMETER?

Before I get into setting up a slider, let's take a look at the size of clutch you should be using. If you are running a Top Fuel or Funny Car, you should be using a three-disc 10- or 11-inch slider. If yours is a Pro Comp car, a two- or three-disc, 10- or 11-inch unit is best. A dual-disc 10- or 11-inch clutch works best for Competition Eliminator. Eleven-inch sliders require a little less plate load and wear slightly better than a 10-inch unit, but a 10-inch clutch is better for engine response because of less rotary inertia.

When considering just the torque capacity formula, fewer discs could be used in most cases, particularly when considering the amount of plate load available from a slider pressure plate. For example, a single disc could be used in a B-Dragster running in Competition Eliminator class, however the problem is one of the *heat-absorption capacity*, or heat sink—*not torque capacity*. If there isn't enough mass and surface area to absorb and dissipate the heat generated during slipping, warpage or excessive wear will result. For example, a typical Pro Comp car gets an average of 60 runs from a three-disc clutch,

Here are the three things you have to work with when setting up a Long-style slider clutch: lever counterweight, static spring pressure and lever angle.

Conventional high-temperature lubricants can't handle the temperatures developed in a slider clutch. Here's something that can, high-temperature anti-seize compound.

but only 40 if two discs are used. I could get into thermodynamics at this point, however it's beyond the scope of this book. Besides, what I've said has been proved in the best laboratory in the world, the drag strip.

THE SLIDER'S "BRAIN"

Initial torque transmitted to the driving tires, rate of torque build-up and ultimate lockup is dependent on the proportion of static spring pressure to centrifugal assist adjusted into a pressure plate. For instance, say you want clutch lock-up at 7000 RPM and your engine is developing 1200 foot-pounds of torque at this point. What this means is if you are using an 11-inch three-disc clutch, you'll need 3150 pounds minimum plate load at 7000 RPM (see following graphs). Torque transmitted by each disc will be 1200 ÷ 3 = 400 foot-pounds because the curves are for single discs. Now, if you are using a Long-style pressure plate with 83-gram levers and 700 pounds static plate load is what you want to try first, resulting in 270 foot-pounds of torque capacity, you'll need an additional 930 foot-pounds of capacity for lockup. This has to come from centrifugal assist. Each

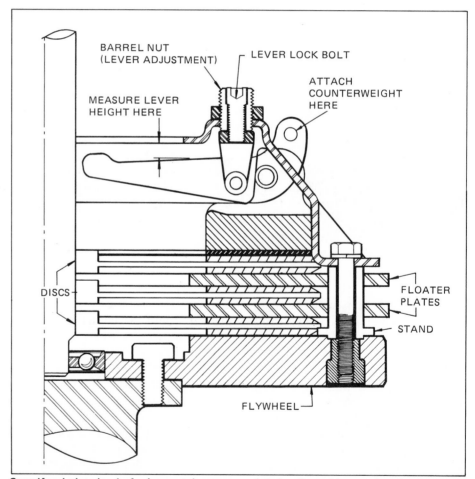

Centrifugal plate load of a Long-style pressure plate is adjusted by varying the amount of weight at the end of each lever or by adjusting lever height/angle with the barrel nut. *Drawing courtesy Schiefer*

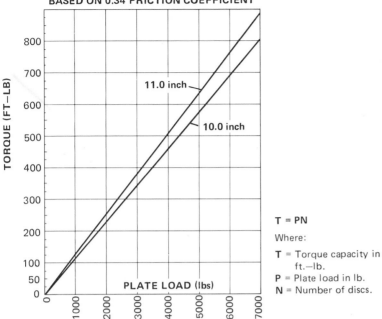

SINGLE-DISC TORQUE CAPACITY vs PRESSURE PLATE LOAD
SINTERED IRON AGAINST STEEL
BASED ON 0.34 FRICTION COEFFICIENT

$T = PN$

Where:

T = Torque capacity in ft.—lb.
P = Plate load in lb.
N = Number of discs.

Torque-capacity versus plate-load graph for 10- and 11-inch clutches with facing widths which are 20% the overall diameter of the discs. Use the formula $T = P \times N$ for multi-disc clutches.

Static plate load is increased by rotating the spring-adjusting screws counter clockwise. Limit spring compression to 3-1/2 turns to prevent coil bind. *Photo courtesy Schiefer*

disc will have to transmit an additional 310 foot-pounds of torque, requiring 2440 pounds of centrifugal assist at 7000 RPM. 7000 RPM and 2440 pounds meet at approximately 33 grams with levers at 8°. Add 33 grams to each lever. Now, if you discover everything with this setup works well except the car could be launched a little harder, adjust in some additional static load. To prevent the clutch from locking up sooner, remove counterweight according to the CF assist and capacity curves used to arrive at the original setup.

Static spring pressure adjustment— Two types of pressure plates are used for slider clutches, the Long and the Crowerglide. They vary mostly in the way static load is handled. Also, centrifugal assist of the Crowerglide builds up at a much faster rate than the conventional Long. This is necessary because the Crowerglide is de-

signed so the springs *subtract* static load from centrifugal load whereas the Long *adds* static load. The result is the Crowerglide has a slightly longer time delay, but has a smoother torque build-up. This suits it to very high-powered cars which depend on dynamic weight transfer to re-distribute the car's weight to the rear tires for traction. The prime example of this type car is the Funny Car. If the tires were shock loaded like a Top Fueler's, they would immediately "go up in smoke."

Let's look at how static spring pressures are adjusted. Using the Hays slider as an example, four static springs with the same rate (385 lb/in.), but different free heights are available. Consequently, their compression from free height to maximum installed height are different, resulting in loads of 60 pounds, 100 pounds, 117 pounds and 140 pounds each. Total minimum plate load will be the spring load multiplied by the number of springs used—six or nine. If you have a choice as to how many springs to use, use nine. Doing this will evenly load the pressure ring and promotes better pressure-ring cooling as the springs help in dissipating heat. Say you're using nine of the shortest springs. Total minimum static plate load of 9 springs X 60-lb/spring = 540 pounds. If that's too much, you'll have to pull out three springs for a 360-pound static plate load. Having a pitch of 16 thd/in., one turn of the adjuster with a 385-lb/in. spring results in an increase in plate load per spring of 385-lb/in. ÷ 16 thd/in. = 24 pounds. A nine-spring pressure plate will have a static plate load increase of 215 pounds if all springs are adjusted evenly as they should be. The resultant static plate load now equals 216 pounds + 360 pounds = 576 pounds.

Static spring adjusters should not be tightened down more than 4 turns—3-1/2 turns to be safe. The reason for this is the springs will be compressed too close to their solid heights, preventing full clutch release as the levers try to compress them even farther for disengagement.

Now, when adjusting a Crowerglide, keep in mind that as the adjusting nuts are tightened (turned clockwise), pressure plate load is *reduced.* In fact, the maximum static pressure-plate load of a Crowerglide is zero—it goes down from there. Centrifugal assist must overcome this *negative* load before the clutch can transfer any torque.

With six springs having a rate of 1143-lb/in., one turn of the adjusting nut which has a pitch of 24-thd/in. results in a static plate load change of 6-springs X 1143-lb/in. ÷ 24-thd/in. = 285 pounds of retracting, or *negative* force. The maximum number of turns the adjusting nuts can be tightened after initial contact with the springs is 3. Any more and the result is just the opposite of the Long, the springs will go solid before the pressure ring fully engages the discs, thereby preventing full engagement.

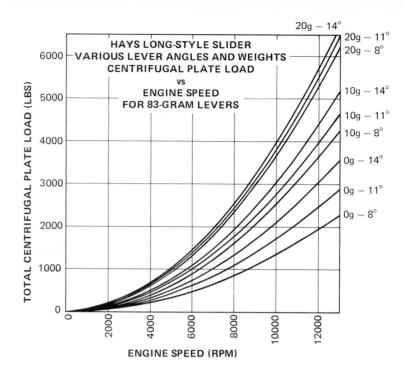

Curve shows how CF weight increases centrifugal assist. Note how the 20-gram curves are much closer together than the 0- and 10-gram curves. *Data courtesy Hays*

Lever height/angle is increased by rotating barrel nut counter clockwise after loosening center locking bolt. Levers should be run at the same angles. To prevent lever bind and excessive lever-pivot wear, restrict lever angle to 14° maximum. *Photo courtesy Schiefer*

Therefore, to determine total spring load regardless of whether it is a Crowerglide or Long pressure plate, use the formula:

Total static spring load in pounds

$$= NK \left(H - h + \frac{n}{p} \right)$$

Where:

N = Total number of springs.
K = Spring rate in lb/in.
H = Free height of spring in inches.
h = Maximum installed spring height in inches.
n = Number of turns of adjusting screw/nut.
p = Pitch of adjusting screw/nut in thd/in.

Release-lever adjustment—Conventional Long slider release levers have two adjustments, counterweights and angles. The amount of counterweighting determines how much centrifugal assist the levers will provide and lever angle determines how effective the counterweights will be. This is to say, as lever angle is increased, so is the centrifugal assist of a lever. Another

important point comes up. As can be seen from above graph, as weight is increased, centrifugal assist is less sensitive to lever-angle changes. Reading up from 6000 RPM to the 0-gram curves, there is approximately 280-pounds difference in static assist between a lever set at 8° and one at 14°. Now look at the 20-gram curves. There's only 120-pounds difference between 8° and 14° at 6000 RPM. What this means is, as the discs wear and the levers assume a lower angle in the pressure plate, there will be less change in the operation of the clutch with one using more CF assist. On the other hand, it means lever-angle adjustments will have less effect.

A word of caution about lever angle: As it is increased, the levers are put in an increasing bind. When the levers are rotated higher, the cover must flex to compensate for the levers trying to bend their yokes toward the pressure-ring drive lugs Remember, you are dealing with a slider pressure plate which is stronger than a

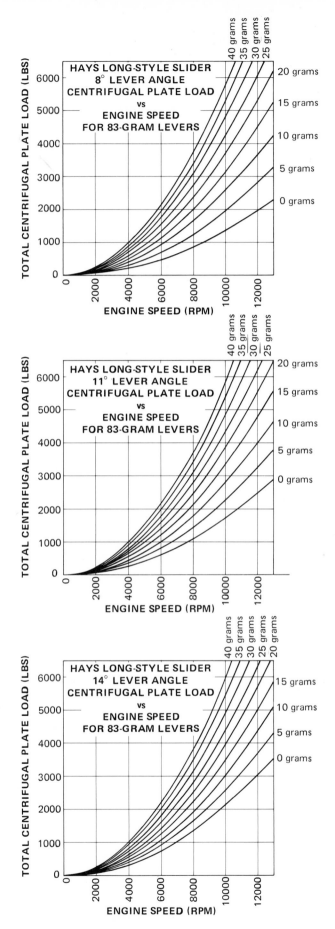

Remember, when using these curves to determine plate load, you must add static plate load to obtain total pressure-plate load. *Data courtesy Hays*

conventional high-performance unit. Consequently, the cover won't comply as well, causing lever bind and excessive pin and bushing wear. So, keep your levers adjusted to a moderate angle—6°–12° is a good range. Otherwise, your clutch may be unpredictable and the lever pins and bushings will wear excessively.

Another thing to be aware of. *Lever height is not lever angle.* Although lever height is a factor in determining lever angle, it isn't the only factor—it is a combination of lever height and the distance between the pressure ring and the cover. You can get into trouble without knowing what's happening if you just set heights. For example, by using lever height only to compensate for disc wear, lever angle will gradually increase causing a subsequent increase in centrifugal assist. This causes premature lockup depending on the amount of CF weight you are using.

Determine lever angles using graph on page 180. It takes into account lever height and pressure-ring-to-cover distance. Measure the two dimensions and subtract them and read angle directly from the graph.

As for lever angle and the Crowerglide, there is no such animal except for the distance the levers must move the pressure ring into engagement with the clutch pack (the discs and floater plates). The more this distance becomes, the more distance, or angle the levers must rotate. What happens is the stall springs are compressed more, causing the stall speed to increase or the springs to bind, restricting full engagement. To prevent this from happening, maintain an air gap of 0.040"–0.045" by pulling shims (earlier model) or adjusting the drive stands accordingly. Finally, remember when using the torque-capacity and centrifugal-assist curves, subtract static plate load from centrifugal assist rather than adding it as is done with the Long-style sliders.

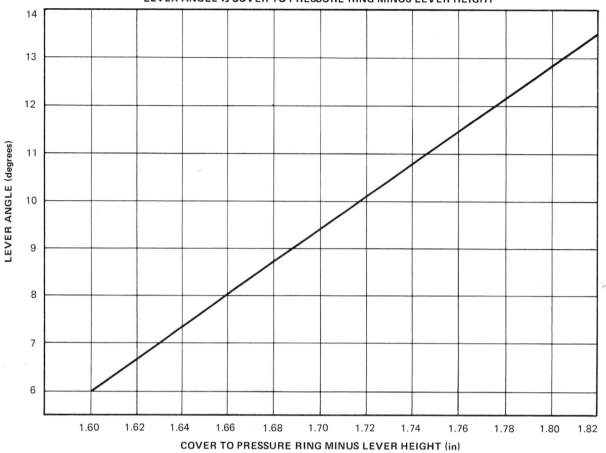

HAYS LONG-STYLE SLIDER
LEVER ANGLE vs COVER TO PRESSURE RING MINUS LEVER HEIGHT

LEVER ANGLE (degrees)

COVER TO PRESSURE RING MINUS LEVER HEIGHT (in)

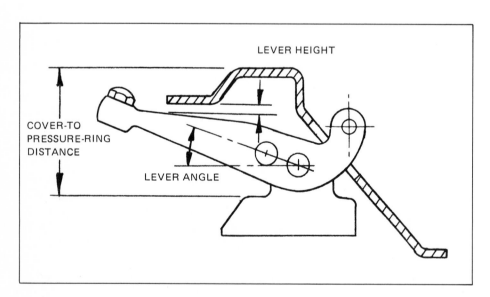

LEVER HEIGHT

COVER-TO PRESSURE-RING DISTANCE

LEVER ANGLE

This curve ties in lever angle to the relationship between lever height and pressure-ring-to-cover distance for a Hays pressure plate. The concept holds true for any Long-style pressure plate as shown by the sketch. *Data courtesy Hays*

Use these two curves to determine total plate load at various engine speeds for a Crowerglide clutch. Remember static plate load subtracts from centrifugal plate load.

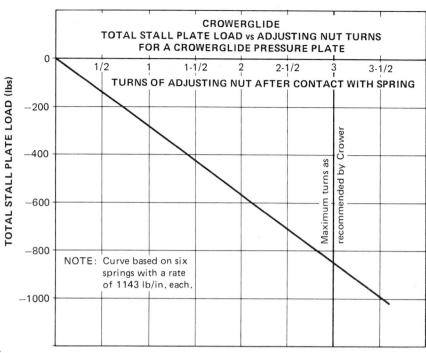

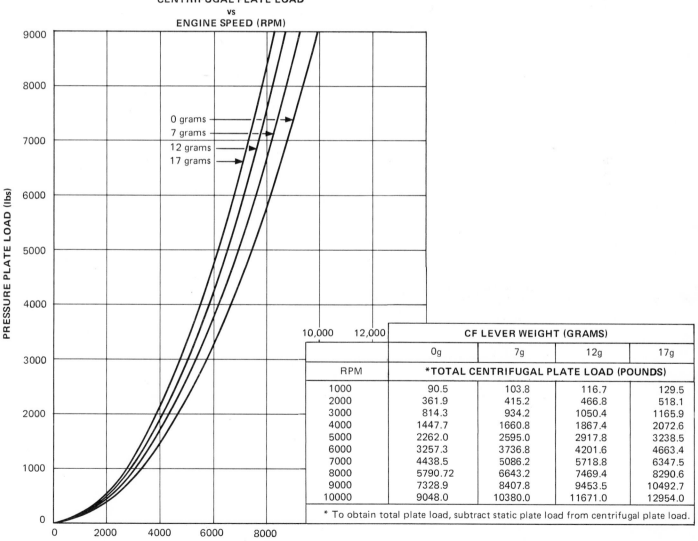

	CF LEVER WEIGHT (GRAMS)			
	0g	7g	12g	17g
RPM	*TOTAL CENTRIFUGAL PLATE LOAD (POUNDS)			
1000	90.5	103.8	116.7	129.5
2000	361.9	415.2	466.8	518.1
3000	814.3	934.2	1050.4	1165.9
4000	1447.7	1660.8	1867.4	2072.6
5000	2262.0	2595.0	2917.8	3238.5
6000	3257.3	3736.8	4201.6	4663.4
7000	4438.5	5086.2	5718.8	6347.5
8000	5790.72	6643.2	7469.4	8290.6
9000	7328.9	8407.8	9453.5	10492.7
10000	9048.0	10380.0	11671.0	12954.0

* To obtain total plate load, subtract static plate load from centrifugal plate load.

Suppliers

BELLHOUSINGS

Ansen Enterprises, Inc.
8924 Bellanca Ave.
Los Angeles, CA 90045

Lakewood Industries
4566 Spring Road
Cleveland, OH 44131

McLeod Industries
1125 N. Armando
Anaheim, CA 92806

Trick Titanium, Inc.
321 Elmwood
Troy, MI 48084

BLANKETS, SAFETY

Bob's Safety Equipment, Inc.
1301 East Goerge St.
Hazel Park, MI 48030

Diest Safety Equipment
641 Sonora Ave.
Glendale, CA 91201

Lakewood Industries
4566 Spring Road
Cleveland, OH 44131

Simpson Safety Equipment, Inc.
22630 South Normandie Ave.
Torrance, CA 90502

CLUTCHES & FLYWHEELS

Borg Warner Automotive
  Parts Division
11045 Gage Ave.
Franklin Park, IL 60131

Crower Cams and
  Equipment Company
3333 Main Street
Chula Vista, CA 92011

Crown Manufacturing Company
137 W. 157 St.
Gardena, CA 90248

Direct Connection
Chrysler Corp
CIMS 423-13-06
Detroit, MI 48288

Ford Motorsport
Ford Motor Co.-SVO
17000 Southfield Rd.
Allen Park, MI 48101

Hays Clutch Division
Mr. Gasket Company
4566 Spring Road
Cleveland, OH 44131

Hoosier Racing Tires
65465 U.S. 31
Lakeville, IN 46536

Hurst Performance, Inc.
50 West Street Road
Warminster, PA 18974

McLeod Industries
1125 N. Armando
Anaheim, CA 92806

Midway Industries, Inc.
15116 Adams St.
Midway City, CA 92655

Quarter Master Industries, Inc.
185 Lively Blvd.
Elk Grove Village, IL 60007

RAM Automotive
201 Business Park Dr.
Columbia, SC 29203

RRS Engineering, Inc.
137 Oregon Street
El Segundo, CA 90245

Sachs Automotive Products
909 Croker Rd.
Westlake, OH 44145

Scott Performance Industries
166 S. Irwindale
Azusa, CA 91702

Sweet Manufacturing Inc.
126 South 14th Street
Schoolcraft, MI 49087

10,000 RPM
22624 S. Normandie
Torrance, CA 90502

Tilton Engineering Inc.
P. O. Box 1787
886 McMurray Rd & Easy St.
Buellton, CA 93427

Troutman Ltd.
3198L Airport Loop Drive
Costa Mesa, CA 92626

Unit Service Exchange Company
3173 E. 66th St.
Cleveland, OH 44127

Weber Performance
2985 E. Blue Star
Anaheim, CA 92806

Zoom
Rt. 5 Dovesville Hwy.
Darlington, SC 29352

CLUTCH MACHINES

Carlson Machine Products
1987 Ritchey Street
Santa Ana, CA 92705

CLUTCH TOOLS

Carlson Machine Products
1987 Ritchey Street
Santa Ana, CA 92705

Kent Moore Corp.
28635 Mound Rd.
Warren, MI 48092

Owatonna Tool Company
Eisenhower Drive
Owatonna, MN 55060

FIREWALL SUPPORTS

Hays Clutch Division
Mr. Gasket Company
4566 Spring Road
Cleveland, OH 44131

Rocket Racing Products
3501 Union Pacific Ave.
Los Angeles, CA 90023

Speed Research & Development, Inc.
147 Pennsylvania Ave.
Malvern, PA 19355

Qaurtermaster Industries, Inc.
185 Lively Blvd.
Elk Grove Village, IL 60007

LINKAGES, HYDRAULIC

Ansen Enterprises, Inc.
8924 Bellanca Ave.
Los Angeles, CA 90045

Citation Engineering
Rt. 2
Zionville, IN 46077

Hurst Performance, Inc.
50 West Street Road
Warminster, PA 18974

Lucas Industries North America Inc.
Systems Group
Girling Brake & Hydraulic
5500 New King Street
Troy, MI 48084

Neal Products
5231 Cushman Place
San Diego, CA 92110

LINKAGES, MECHANICAL

Hays Clutch Division
Mr. Gasket Company
4566 Spring Road
Cleveland, OH 44131

McLeod Industries
1125 N. Armando
Anaheim, CA 92806

Trick Titanium, Inc.
321 Elmwood
Troy, MI 48084

MOTOR MOUNTS

Moroso Performance Sales
80 Carter Drive
Guilford, CT 06437

Mr. Gasket Company
4566 Spring Road
Cleveland, OH 44131

Rocket Racing Products
3501 Union Pacific Ave.
Los Angeles, CA 90023

RELEASE BEARINGS

Borg Warner Automotive
Parts Division
11045 Gage Ave.
Franklin Park, IL 60131

Hays Clutch Division
Mr. Gasket Company
4566 Spring Road
Cleveland, OH 44131

McLeod Industries
1125 Armando
Anaheim, CA 92641

Midway Industries, Inc.
15116 Adams St.
Midway City, CA 92655

RAM Automotive
201 Business Park Dr.
Columbia, SC 29203

Rocket Racing Products
3501 Union Pacific Ave.
Los Angeles, CA 90023

Weber Performance
2985 E. Blue Star
Anaheim, CA 92806

Zoom
Rt. 5 Dovesville Hwy.
Darlington, SC 29352

Index

Index